WORKS IN
PROGRESS

Martha Saxton, Editor
Andrea Starr, Associate Editor
Joel Snyder, Art Director

WORKS IN PROGRESS

NUMBER FIVE

Book trade distribution by
Doubleday & Company, Inc.

The Literary Guild of America, Inc.
New York, N.Y.

WORKS IN PROGRESS
is published in the United States
by The Literary Guild of America, Inc.
277 Park Ave., New York, New York 10017

Library of Congress Catalogue Card Number:
76–115968

CONTENTS

EDITOR'S NOTE

For *Works in Progress* #5 we continue to assemble a wide range of material in an effort to demonstrate the kinds of things that are being written and published. We include a one-act television play by Lorraine Hansberry. Barbara Kevles has written a moving documentation of a women's takeover of a New York publishing house in which she explains what her arrest meant to her life. We offer the letters between an editor and author, revealing their care, professional and personal, for each other. In addition to excerpts from the novels of four first novelists and seven established writers, there is a selection from a book by Yehudi Menuhin introducing the violin, two short stories, three poems and an interview with the poet Ted Hughes. And from the manuscripts of the late Oscar Lewis we have taken part of a study of a Puerto Rican woman.

The fiction this time is resoundingly diverse. Of the first novelists represented, Thomas Sanchez has written a study of four generations of Washo Indians; George Davis looks at the war in Vietnam from a black point of view; Barry Hannah writes about growing up in the South; and Theodore Weesner describes the life of a young boy in reform school. Paul Smith's *Annie* is a heartbreaking account of a fifteen-year-old girl's efforts to keep from succumbing to the Irish poverty to which she was born. In *Sound Money Kill* Sol Yurick begins an experiment in writing and deduction; he attempts to solve the Clutter murder case using the Marxist dialectic. Alan Scholefield has written an overwhelmingly bittersweet account of a young man growing up

9

in South Africa. L. Woiwode pieces together the ambiguous relations between a midwestern father and his son. *The Quarter Turn* is an extraordinary piece by Lore Segal in which she reflects on the fears and defenses of a woman writer in various stages of her career. Frederick Barthelme has an indescribable and refulgent imagination which he displays in his latest novel, *Ten Bears*. And finally, there is a tender encounter set in the bleak Scandinavian landscape by the late distinguished Tarjei Vesaas.

LORRAINE HANSBERRY

Lorraine Hansberry's best-known work is probably *A Raisin in the Sun,* for which she won the New York Drama Critics Circle Award in 1959. Her other plays include *Les Blancs, The Sign in Sidney Brustein's Window* and *To Be Young, Gifted and Black,* which is currently on its fourth national road tour. *What Use Are Flowers?* was first conceived as a fantasy for television. It was written in 1961 and will appear in a collection of Ms. Hansberry's work which Random House, Inc. will publish.

WHAT USE ARE FLOWERS?

> "Lullaby baby
> What's rustling there?
> Neighbor's child's in Poland
> Mine's who knows where."
>
> —Bertolt Brecht,
> *Mother Courage*

CHARACTERS

> An elderly and scholarly hermit.

> A party of children of about nine or ten years old.

The scene is a vast rocky plain near a great forest.

SCENE 1

> A plain somewhere in the world; darkness and wind. The HERMIT appears from left, surveys the area as best he can in the darkness, shuffles to an outcropping of rock at right, and crawls up and into a crevice and goes to sleep. As he sleeps, the light comes up slowly and the CHILDREN appear, on their knees, in stark silence, at several different points left and right and upstage. They are stalking a small creature which has led them to the place. The most arresting thing, aside from their appearance, is their utter silence, as not one of them is beyond the age of ten. The old man sleeps on in the crevice. The light is that of dawn.

Presently, the children pause, as instinctively still as the animal; one of them rises with a rock in hand and lets it fly; then, as one, the children rise and run, now screaming, to the quarry, which has been successfully stoned, and violently fall to fighting one another over it. They must really seem to *fight* one another; there should be nothing about the action to suggest the mere game of children. And, moreover, those who are strongest triumph, those who are most frail or slow are also, noticeably, the thinnest.

Among the more savage of the group is a small blonde girl. But she is wiry and tough and skillful in the fighting and expert in biting. She achieves her share as do one or two others. The others glower and whimper like unfed puppies watching them consume the raw meat.

At the sound of their noise the old man is roused and sits up rubbing his mouth and his beard and his eyes. He shifts his position to see out of the cave. He does this at the point at which the children are still actively fighting. He cannot altogether make out what they are fighting about. That is, he cannot see that they *eat* it.

HERMIT (Dryly but loudly): Well, I see you haven't changed,' to say the least. *Animals!* Down unto the fourth and fifth generation of you, that's what. (Grumbling) Well, what did I expect, what indeed did I expect?

> (HE starts to prepare to leave his shelter, getting his bundle and crude walking stick in order.
>
> The CHILDREN, for their part, when they become aware of the voice, freeze in astonishment.
>
> The OLD MAN, himself dressed only in the residue of manufactured garb and animal skin, tries to start down from the rocks which were easier ascended, even in the dark, than *descended* at his age. He feels about for a foothold—at the moment nonplused by the children, or their appearance, which is that of naked beasts with very long hair.
>
> As the OLD MAN descends grumbling aloud, one of the BOYS stoops, apprehensively, for yet another defensive rock; the OTHERS are taut—ready for flight.)

Why the devil don't you give an elderly gentleman assistance? I see that your manners haven't changed either. And that part is just as well: the only thing you ever did with manners was hide your greater crimes. How very, very significant, how very significant indeed that the very first thing that I should see upon my return is the sight of little hooligans abusing a creature of nature! With the blessings of your elders, I am sure, I am sure!

(HE halts and gestures to one of
them in particular who is closest to
where he is gingerly trying to climb
down)

(Shaking his stick)

You, I am talking to you, my little open-mouthed
friend.

(The CHILDREN merely continue
to stare, open-mouthed)

Ah, you don't like that, do you!

(HE then gives a surprisingly
sprightly jump, for his years, and
clears the incline neatly—but then tot-
ters a second when he has reached
level ground to obtain balance)

There we are! What do you think of that!

(Breathing heavily from the exertion)

And now if you undisciplined little monsters will be
kind enough to give me direction to the city, I shall
make myself absent from your admirable company.

(THEY stare)

You there—

(Indicating yet another)

With the eyeballs: which way to the city?

(Holding the courtesy deliberately)

Please. I should like, with your cooperation, to reach,
if you will forgive the reference, some outpost of "civilization" by nightfall. What is the nearest town? I no

longer recall these points, apparently, and have got myself utterly lost.

> (The CHILDREN stand fixed, staring)

Do you hear?

> (HE makes a half step toward one who immediately steps back)

What you need, my little zombie, is a well-placed and repetitive touch of the cane. But I suppose that anything as admirable as that is still forbidden.

> (HE looks around at all of them, then;)

Well, close your mouths and go away, little uglies, if you won't be helpful. I am sure your doting parents are anxious for you, for some ungodly reason. Why are you all got up like that anyway? Is it Halloween? Dear Lord, don't tell me I've come back just in time for *that!* Well, I wonder then if you might interrupt your mute joke long enough to tell an old man one thing. If there were any way that I might persuade you quite what it would mean to me, I do not think you would tease me any more. You see, I should very much like to know—

> (Deep pause)

what *time* it is. You think that's silly, don't you; yes, I rather thought you would. That a chap might go off and hide himself in the woods for twenty years and then come out and ask, "What time is it?"

> (HE laughs)

But you see, one of the reasons I left is because I could no longer stand the dominion of time in the lives of men and the things that they did with it and to it and,

indeed, that they let it do to them. And so, to escape
time, I threw my watch away. I even made a ceremony
of it. I was on a train over a bridge—and I held it out
the door and dropped it. Quite like—

(HE is gesturing, remembering)

this. But do you know the very first thing I absolutely
had a compulsion to know once I got into the forest?
I wanted to know what time it was. Clearly I had no
appointments to keep—but I longed to know the hour
of the day. There is, of course, no such thing as an
hour, it is merely something that men have labeled so
—but I longed to have that label at my command again.
I never did achieve that. Ultimately I gave up seconds,
minutes, and hours; ah, but I kept up with days! I
made a rock calendar at once. It was a problem too:
the wild animals would knock over the rocks. Finally,
I gave up and made a game—a game, ha!—of keeping
up with the days in my head. It got to be a matter of
rejoicing that the seasons came when I knew they
should.

(Looking down)

Or, at least, that's how it was for the first fifteen years.
Because, naturally, I lost track. I accumulated a back-
log of slipped days which, apparently, ran into months
because, one year, quite suddenly it began to snow
when I expected the trees to bud; somewhere I had
mislaid a warm autumn for a chilly spring. . . . I almost died that year; I had lost a season. Consequently,
among other things, I no longer know how old I am. I
was fifty-eight when I went into the woods. And now
I am either seventy-eight or perhaps more than eighty
years old. I imagine that I must be the first adult you
have ever met who did not know his age. That is why
I have come out of the woods; I am afraid men invent
time*pieces;* they do not invent time. We may give time

17

its dimensions and meaning, we may make it worthless or important or absurd or crucial. But, ultimately, I am afraid it has a value of its own. It is time for me to die, and I have come out to see what men have been doing, and now that I am back, more than anything else just now, you see, I should very much like to know —what time it is.

(The CHILDREN stare)

Ahh. . . .

(Stiffening and shaking his finger at them)

But you must not for one second take that to mean that I *regret* my hermitage or do in any wise whatsoever return repentantly to the society of men. I return in contempt!

(More quietly)

And, if one must tell everything—*curiosity*. Not love! Not once, not once in all those years did I *long* for human company. Not once!

(HE flicks his fingers at them in a sweeping gesture, settles himself on the ground and spreads a small cloth)

Get along then; go ahead: shoo! I am going to have my breakfast and I prefer privacy. I've gotten used to it.

(HE first looks to the setting out of his food and then up again to see them still standing; apparently transfixed with him)

I am quite serious about it and will become stern with

you any moment now! The diversion is OVER; toddle along. To your—

(Nastily)

Mummies and Daddies. Who presumably want you.

(THEY stand)

Do you *not* understand the language merely because it is literately spoken? I don't wonder—recalling the level of study. Indeed, indeed. Shall I employ sign signals?

(Gesturing impromptu hand signals)

GO A—WAY! *Andale!* SCRAM!

(THEY stand and HE is angry)

You might as well know that you do not frighten me. I shall eat my breakfast and be content whether you stay or go. And when you recover your tongues, I will accept your directions. I must confess I do not remember this plain at all. I could have sworn that the forest continued for many miles more. But then my memory has to cover a long span of time. You might as well know that you little folk are the very first human souls that I have seen in twenty-odd years. Well, what do you think of that!

(HE points to the woods, roaring proudly)

I've been in there, in the forest: for twenty-odd years. Deep, deep in the forest. I am, or was until this morning, a hermit.

(Showing off, stroking his beard)

Eh, what do you think of that? Just like the sort in books.

(To another child)

What is your name? You look like a pupil of mine. But I suppose he would be a little older by now. I am Charles Lewis Lawson. I was an English teacher until I went away.

> (HE lifts out a handful of food from his bundle—begins to place it on his cloth; as swiftly the CHILDREN throw themselves upon him and the scraps of food. In the scramble he is knocked over. Those who get some, wolf it down and the OLD MAN gets himself righted in time to see one of them gulp down the last morsel. HE reaches out tentatively to the child as if, in outrage, to recover it, but the child gnashes his teeth—quite like a cur. OTHERS pick up his bundle and empty it and paw about in the articles in a cruelly savage search for more food. The OLD MAN turns from one to the other frantically)

Animals! . . . Animals! . . . I'm an old man! Don't you know anything!

> (The CHILDREN fall back a short distance away from him and now lounge about, still watching him)

Oh, all that I have missed, all that I have undoubtedly missed!—

> (Bitterly)

in the society of men!

(HE gathers up his things angrily)

Well, why don't you laugh? Go ahead. Go ahead. Go ahead! It is a great game to beat up an old man and take his food from him, is it not?

(In a curious rage about it)

I can see that nothing at all has changed. Damn you! And damn your fathers!

(HE sinks down and pouts rather like a child himself)

Why did I come out; why, why, why . . . !

(The CHILDREN sit and watch him and do not move. Then, presently)

Well, are you all still with me? You must be looking for your grandfather. Or Santa Claus. Well, I am neither!

(HE gathers up his things again and stamps off right; the CHILDREN sink down where they are and freeze as the lights come down and then up again. The OLD MAN comes on from left, having gone in a circle on the plain. The CHILDREN are stretched out where HE left them, asleep. THEY rouse)

Oh, there you are. I was hoping I would find you again. Certainly haven't been able to find anyone else, or the city, or anything else. Just this interminable plain. I came back because I must have directions to the city. You must end this little joke of yours and talk to me. I will admit it: I am impressed that you can hold your tongues so long. Well, I will have to stay with you until you tire of it. Or, until your parents come for you.

> (HE is mopping his brow and smiling at them. THEY look back at him and say nothing. HE looks at each one separately)

Listen, I happen to know that you are not, whatever else, mute, because I heard you screaming *yesterday* morning.

> (HE neatly arranges a pile of dry twigs and dead leaves, and begins to twirl a flint. HE works hard at it and, presently, as the first thin stream of smoke arises, the children, silently, lean forward, pop-eyed)

Pretty neat, eh? You get good at it if you stay in the forest long enough. But I will tell you the truth though. There was not one time that I ever made a fire like this when I did not fancy myself an Indian scout on television. My word, television! I suppose the images walk right into the living room by now and have supper with you.

> (High sarcasm)

Oh, all that I have undoubtedly missed!

> (Gesturing to a little boy nearest him)

Don't think that's funny, eh? What dry parents you must have, the lot of you. Speaking of your parents, where the devil are they? To tell you the truth, I was rather hoping that they might give me a lift when they come to get you. Ah, there we are.

> (HE gives a good hard rub at this point and a small lick of flame rises.

The largest of the BOYS jumps to his
feet and shouts VAROOM! and the
CHILDREN hit the dirt, face down,
and try to bury their heads under their
arms. The OLD MAN looks up from
the fire, notes them and then gestures:)

Bang, bang! I've got you. Rat-tat-tat-tat!

(One of the tinier ones raises his
head)

You there, step here, since you are the least dead of
the cowboys. I need a bellows and you will do nicely.

(The CHILD does not move)

Now, listen—come here. *Kommen sie hier! Venga!*—well,
I don't remember Arabic.

(With total exasperation, HE goes
back to the fire, fixing a string of wild
fowl he has caught on a skewer across
the flame and then sitting back comfortably to wait. The little bit of meat
sends up its bouquet; the CHILD
sniffs and goes closer. The OTHERS
lift their heads slowly. It is an unfamiliar smell. Then, like beasts of
prey, they stealthily shift to stalking
positions and start to close in on the
OLD MAN—who mugs back at them,
draws his "sixshooters" and stares
them down as in a game)

Once upon a time there were seven little—ugly, unwashed, uncombed and unmannered little children—

(The CHILDREN throw themselves

23

on his birds and tear them to pieces
and devour them raw, precisely as
they did his breakfast the day before.
The OLD MAN rises, horrified, his
eyes wide, looking from child to child)

Why . . . you're not playing . . . you *are* wild!

(HE regards them for a long time
and then reaches out abruptly and
pulls one of them to him)

Are you lost children? What has happened to you?

(HE inspects the child's elbows and
kneecaps which are hard calluses)

Dear God! Calluses. You really don't understand a word
I am saying, do you?

(Experimentally, but swiftly, expecting nothing)

Mother—*Mutter—Madre—Mater—venga—Bambino.*

(HE is looking closely at the child
and smoothing the hair back from the
face so that he can see the eyes for
any sign of recognition)

No—words don't mean a thing to you, do they? Dear,
dear God. . . . What I have found?

(Hardly audible)

You poor babies! Here—

(HE pulls out a pocket knife)

Lad—what's this?

(The BOY looks but does not touch.
The OLD MAN opens and flips it

into the earth; then retrieves it and
lays it flat on his palm. The BOY
clutches for it)

No, not *blade* first, lad!

(Closing and pocketing it, HE sits
back on his heels, stunned, looking
around at them)

You eat raw meat, don't know fire and are unfamiliar
with the simplest implement of civilization. And you are
prelingual.

(HE stands up slowly, as if to con-
sult the universe about his impending
sense of what has happened)

What have they done . . . ?

(Slowly turning about; his voice rising in its own eccentric hysteria, crossing down center to the audience)

What have you finally done!

(In a rage, tearing at his beard; beating his thighs with his fists)

(Screaming)

What have you done!

(As the lights come down, the OLD
MAN assumes the anguished stance
of the classical prophets; only he does
not charge a deity. He charges us)

BLACKOUT

SCENE 2

> Many weeks later. Several rather serviceable lean-tos have been fashioned, and at far right, a tiny garden is crudely fenced off. The CHILDREN, who have been crudely combed, the least bit, so that it is hardly discernible, sit cross-legged in a semicircle; the Master, in the stance of his old profession, stands in front of them.

HERMIT: Before we go any further at all, I must distribute names. I can do that, you see, because in this present situation I am God and you must have names. Ah, you are wondering, "Why?" Well, it is because I will keep you from having to remember who you *really* are as you get older. Let's see, quickly now, you are hereby: John, Thomas, Clarence, Robert, Horace, William. You may be Charlie and you are henceforth Alexander.

> (To ALEXANDER)

But may I caution you at the outset to avoid all temptations toward any adjective to follow it.

> (Indicating little girl)

And you—you shall be Lily.

> (Gruffly)

Now, down the list:

> (HE holds up items or gestures actions)

CHILDREN: Food.
HERMIT (Holding up the knife)

CHILDREN: Knife.
HERMIT (Holding up crude earthenware pot)
CHILDREN: Pot.
HERMIT (Gesturing with his cheek on his hands; his eyes closed)
CHILDREN: Sleep.
HERMIT (Gesture)
CHILDREN: Drink.
HERMIT (Gesture)
CHILDREN: Lift.
HERMIT (Action)
CHILDREN: Eat.

> (HE has not had *such* a good time for twenty-odd years—which is not yet, however, in his own awareness.

> HE speaks fluently to them regardless of their only understanding a handful of words. When HE wishes them to do or understand something explicitly, HE speaks slowly and with abundant gesture)

HERMIT: Very good. So much for today's academic lessons. Time now for the vocational section. And all I can say is that primitive though my knowledge of technical skills may be—you had better be bloody grateful that I have at least some. In my world, certain men prided themselves on *not* knowing the things I am attempting to teach you.

> (HE looks at them)

So, I shall do the best I can, do you hear me?

> (Under his breath)

And when you learn to understand what the deuce I am talking about most of the time, you will also under-

27

stand that you have just had a profound apology for ignorance, disguised as a boast. I was indeed a true member of the tribe!

(Loudly)

Now let me see—ceramics. If only we had a manual. Does one bake the clay before or *after* it's dry? You see, there is a point at which the *clay* must be put into—a kiln—which is not a word I shall even try to teach you! That is, it must be put into the fire and baked. But, in any case—Remember yesterday we gathered clay at the river bank?

(Holding up a handful of clay)

Repeat it: CLAY.
CHILDREN: Clay.
HERMIT: Very good. Clay. And I did this to it

(Holds up clay pot again)

and sat it in the sun. SUN.

(HE points)

And now, see, it is hard. And now it is possible for one to carry not only one object—but several. Now the process

(HE makes as if he is fashioning the pot again)

is called: WORK. Say it.
CHILDREN: WORK.
HERMIT: And with clay and work, you can make all you need of these. So that you can USE it.

(HE gestures putting objects in and out of the pot)

This, I will admit, is something of an abstract concept,

but it is a vital one and you will have to master it quickly. Use, use. . . .

> (The CHILDREN are silent; it is too abstract. And HE goes through it again. Then, CHARLIE raises his hand)

You got it, Charlie? Good boy: come and show me what to *USE* something means.

> (CHARLIE gets up and picks up the pot and puts things in it and carries them back to where he sat and takes them out and looks at the teacher who nods, yes, and CHARLIE puts them back in the pot and takes it back to the teacher)

HERMIT: Very good, Charlie!

> (To the class)

Charlie has *used* the pot.

> (HE takes out his knife and whittles a twig)

I am USING the KNIFE.

> (HE looks at them doubtfully)

It is such a vital verb, you must master it. Well, on with the weaving.

> (HE sits down and crosses his legs contentedly and picks up, as do the CHILDREN, the beginnings of the baskets they are making)

Cross one over, bring the other through, then—

DIMOUT

> As the lights come up this time: stone implements, baskets, and hoes as well as drying meats are in evidence. The MASTER and the CHILDREN come on far right; they are rather more frolicsome than we would have supposed they could be. And, for the first time, the LITTLE GIRL is the only one with long hair. The BOYS have been barbered and are dressed in foliage or animal skins now.

HERMIT (Pausing at the garden): By heaven, those are most attractive radishes, Thomas. Very good! Come along now, time for class.

> (The CHILDREN moan)

How quickly you learn! Come along, or you'll get a caning.

> (THEY obey and take the positions of the prior scene)

Well now, you've made such admirable progress that I think you are actually ready to graduate to an area of knowledge which, sadly enough, all things considered, used to be known as "the humanities." And, in that connection, Charlie and I have prepared a surprise for you. A surprise is something that you do not know is coming and, in life, most surprises are quite unpleasant—but every now and then, there are those which are pleasant indeed and they generally have to do with another abstraction which you have already experienced but do not know how to call by name as you didn't know how to call one another by name until I taught you. Now the name of this abstraction which you cannot call by name, but which you have already experienced

> (Touching one of them)

by your nose, your eyes, and way, deep inside you, is called: *beauty*. Say it.

CHILDREN (Shouting out of habit): BEAUTY.

HERMIT: My word, you needn't shout it. Beauty is just as well acknowledged softly as loudly. Say it like this, so the word itself is beautiful.

> (Sweetly, lifting his head back and gesturing)

Beau—ty.

CHILDREN (In dead earnest mimicry): Beau—ty.

HERMIT: Again.

CHILDREN (They repeat it): Beau—ty.

HERMIT: Lovely. You see, your very voices have this abstraction in them. Now, to proceed: Here is our dear and useful friend the pot again. Which, as we have learned, *works* for us, when we have worked to make it. Now, we have also learned that we can *use* it to carry all sorts of things; the berries we have picked; the water we wish to carry somewhere—but, also,

> (HE lifts up a tiny and lovely little bouquet of wild flowers)

we may use it simply to hold that which we ENJOY, remember that word?—because

> (HE puts the flowers into the pot)

they have BEAUTY. Like the flowers which are almost as beautiful as our little Lily, which is why we have named her after them.

> (LILY promptly preens herself before the BOYS)

William—?

WILLIAM (Loudly): USE?

HERMIT: What *use* are flowers? Well, there were, in the old days, certain perfectly tasteless individuals who insisted on making wine out of them. But that was not a use. It was a violation. Ah, but the uses of flowers are infinite: one may smell them

(HE lifts them around to the noses)

one may touch their petals and feel heaven

(HE puts fingers on them)

or one may write quite charming verses about them. Now do not ask me what verses are; when you have become proficient in language you shall discover that no power on earth will be able to stop you from composing them, I am afraid. Now, on to the surprise; I think that it will be the most satisfying thing that I will be able to teach you. Later Charlie will demonstrate another part.

(HE begins to sing, horribly)

Alas, my love, you-oo do-oo me wro-ong
To ca-ast me out discourteously
When I have lovéd you so long
Delighting in your company.

Greensleeves was my delight
And Greensleeves was all my joy
Greensleeves was my song of songs
And who but my La-ay-dy Greensleeves.

(The CHILDREN first giggle at the curious sound, but, presently, hush and listen, caught in the phenomenon of the human voice lifted in song)

HERMIT: Well, that is what is called a melody; it belongs to a great body of pleasure which is called—music. That particular melody was old even when I was born and has great purity, a purity which should not be greatly disturbed. I know you little rascals; as fast as you learn things—you improve on them. In any case, there are other forms of music which are beautiful because they *are* embellished to make what are called harmonies. Now we may make harmonies with our voices when we sing together. For which purpose, I am going to teach you the words to the next melody that you are going to hear. That is—as soon as I can recall them well enough to translate them. The original text was in what was called the German language —and I simply have no energy left to teach the declensions. However, there is another noble aspect to this business of music: one can make it on instruments other than the human voice. All right—Charlie. . . .

> (CHARLIE steps forward as nervous as a performer has ever been and for the first time reveals a reed instrument which is a crude but competent flute. He lifts it to his lips and haltingly plays the first measures of Beethoven's Ninth, the chorale; the MASTER strives to lead him in this but, after a bit of it and the CHILDREN'S faces watching the miracle, HE must turn from them and weep freely, still waving his hand to the music)

HERMIT: Yes, yes, keep to the tempo now, Charlie. . . .

> (Stamping his foot a bit at the primary martial passage)

Yes, yes, Charlie, that's damn good Beethoven, boy!

Damn good—

>DIMOUT

>After which Beethoven's assertion continues on the primitive flute.

SCENE 4

>In the between-scene darkness, CHARLIE's halting, poor music slowly has its notes drawn out as if we are experiencing that evolution which is the learning process, under a microscope, and then the notes become more controlled, more perfectly rendered than before, more fully resembling the Hymn to Joy as we know it, the tempo, addressed to the spirit of man: martial, certain, aspirational.

>Then, Schiller's* flash of ecstacy shouted in the darkness, against the simple playing of the pipe, in English, by the OLD MAN:

HERMIT: "Joy thou source of light immortal"

>(The CHILDREN repeat in already practiced and effective unison, singing:)

CHILDREN: "Joy thou source of light immortal"
HERMIT: "Daughter of Elysium!"
CHILDREN: "Daughter of Elysium!"

>(The lights come up. The CHILDREN are arranged in that stiff self-

---

* Louis Untermeyer's translation.

(conscious grouping which is the style
and posture of all choruses, with the
MASTER beating time before them.
They sing it with thrust and vigor,
and what we should be forced to
thrillingly feel is childhood's assumption of the inevitability of its statement and lyric. The MASTER stands
facing upstage, waving his arms in
accurate tempo and lacking only
flowing black robes)

CHORALE (CHILDREN and HERMIT):
"Touched with fire, to the portal
Of thy radiant shrine we come.
Thy pure magic frees all others
Held in Custom's rigid rings;
Men throughout the world are brothers
In the haven of thy wings."
HERMIT: Yes, yes, very good, children. That will do
for now. Uh, Charlie. I should very much like to talk
with you.

(The group disperses and various ones
settle down to different onstage activities. The MASTER ushers CHARLIE
into his lean-to, with oddly deliberate
social mannerisms all of a sudden)

Have a seat, won't you?

(This lean-to is not, of course, what
man or child can stand up in fully,
and the "seats" may be well-placed
flat rocks)

Would you care for some water?

(The BOY signifies "no" with his head
and looks at the MASTER curiously)

HERMIT (Shoving a mug of water at him): No, you must say yes, Charlie.

(Passing some grapes)

Because we are not pupil and master just now—we are friends and—

(Settling down on the rock after forcing CHARLIE to sit on the other and
accept the water and grapes)

what we are doing now—

(Taking a grape himself and smack-
ing over it elaborately)

is socializing. And, you see, since this is *my* home, it is my obligation to make you feel welcome and even to entertain you and give you refreshments. And, under the last codes that I recall, it was more graceful to ac-cept than not. But, I will admit that such rules fre-quently reversed themselves.

CHARLIE: How—you—?

HERMIT: Socialize? Exactly like this. We sit and we look at one another and eventually begin to tell one another perfectly outlandish stories, you see. It was a kind of ritual. But I shall have to teach you quite what a joke is. The last one I recall—well—oh yes, why does a chicken cross the road? That is to say, why does the wild guinea hen that we eat, you know, why does it run across the path? You are supposed to say: "I don't know, sir."

CHARLIE: Why?

HERMIT: Because if you don't say that, I shan't have an altogether logical reason to give you the answer and it was the answers, I gather, which were purportedly the point of these quite extraordinary exercises of the human mind.

CHARLIE (Stiffly): I-don't-know-sir.
HERMIT: Well, a chicken crosses the road to get to the other side.

> (THEY stare at one another)

Now you do this, lad.

> (Holding his stomach like jolly old St. Nick in order to instruct)

"Ho, ho, ho, ho!"
CHARLIE (Frowning mightily and imitating with exactitude): Ho, ho, ho, ho!
HERMIT: Show your teeth rather more, I think. And throw back your head. Yes, very good. That will do.

> (Looking down at his hands with sudden seriousness)

Look here, there's another reason for our little get-together this afternoon. And it has to do with something fairly serious. And this really is the proper setting, because what we are having here is a sort of cocktail party, you see, which is where most really important matters were generally decided. Under circumstances quite like this—I mean with people chatting amicably and drinking things. Be that as it may. I want to try to discuss something rather serious and rather difficult with you—and, well, the fact of the matter is that I don't really, to tell the absolute truth, know how to go about it.

> (Blurting suddenly)

Not that I didn't know one hell of a lot about women myself, you see! But, with the young, we traditionally preferred to make an awkward process out of it. And I don't seem to know how to reverse the custom.

> (The CHILD simply stares at him)

What I am trying to say is: do you know why I did
not cut *Lily's* hair?

> (As quickly realizing the futility of
> that approach)

Oh, no, no—! Listen, let us approach it this way: you
are a leader, Charlie, and there are some things which
. . . you poor fellow, I shall have to hope that you take
responsibility when I will—have gone away.
CHARLIE (Jumping up): Go? Where?
HERMIT (Quietly): That will have to be a different
lesson one day soon. But we still have time, and for
the moment—this other matter is more imperative—so
that when I do go away. . . . What it has to do with
is

> (Looking at the LITTLE BOY with
> serious eyes)

the survival of—

> (His lips fall with the weight of the
> impossibility of trying to suggest to a
> ten-year-old that the organization of
> the perpetuation of the human race
> could possibly be his responsibility.
>
> Throughout the prior scene the fol-
> lowing has been occurring outside at
> right: of two BOYS making pottery,
> one has proven more an artist than
> another and thus the first has simply
> reached out and claimed one or two
> pots of the other fellow's and the
> other fellow has retaliated by yanking
> them back, for which he is socked,
> which launches a grim, stark and sav-
> age fight with one bashing the other's

head until it is red with blood and the other as passionately trying to choke all life out of the first. Again, there must be no comic aspect or playfulness in it. It is the fight of savages who mean to maim or destroy. The air is filled with a counterpoint of primeval, dreadful grunts.

As THEY tussle, THEY crash a lean-to here and some pots there. As it is not yet spectacle or sport in *their* society, the CHILDREN do not pay the fighters the least bit of attention, but merely move out of their way when they roll their way and go on with whatever they are doing.

Hearing a crash finally, the HERMIT looks out to see what is happening)

HERMIT (Seeing and screaming at them):
Animals . . . !

(HE runs to them and tries to tear them apart, they snarl and tear at him viciously in their eagerness to get at one another again)

Animals, I say! . . . Will you never change!

(Now HE is also being covered with the blood of one of them as HE is flung about trying to tear them apart, screaming all the while, working himself into a hysteria not unlike that at the end of Scene 1, when he realized man's crime afresh)

Even in your wretchedness . . . are you still at it!

39

(ONE of them flings him to the ground)

Go ahead! Sink back into your primeval sloth and stupor! Destroy yourselves! You do not deserve to survive!

(The CHILDREN who are fighting do not hear him but continue tearing away at one another. The OTHERS simply stare at the screaming OLD MAN with a quizzical expression on their faces)

HERMIT (Getting up almost in delirium, rolling and falling in trying to get on his feet): Forget everything I have taught you—!

(HE rises and stamps on the pots, violently tears some baskets to pieces and generally goes mad as the boys fight on, pantingly, wearily but savagely still)

I RENOUNCE YOU AGAIN! . . . YOU AND YOUR PASSIONS! . . . MAY YOU PERISH THEN . . . YOU AND ALL YOUR SEED . . . FOREVER FROM THIS PLANET. . . .

(HE goes reelingly toward the woods. The fight continues)

BLACKOUT

SCENE 5

A few hours later.

Blue lights at rise. The CHILDREN sit in a stiffly arranged group at right.

With apprehension. The OLD MAN
is flat upon his back in his lean-to;
one hand is upon his stomach, another
trails to the floor. HE is sick.

At right, each child hands CHARLIE
a flower and he crosses from them
left, to the lean-to of the MASTER.

CHARLIE: Flowers.
HERMIT: If you got hungry enough you'd kill me and
eat me. Go away, Charlie. I've had enough. Of men of
whatever shape or age.
CHARLIE: Sing . . . ?
HERMIT: I do not want flowers, music, or poetry. Not
even Beethoven and Schiller. . . . You want to know
why, don't you; well, because I hate you. You are human, therefore you are repulsive. All of you. But *you*
in particular. Now, *that* is what is known as an insult
and, in the face of them, people generally go away.
. . . Ah, so you don't like insults then? It only proves
that you are a more common type than I had supposed.
So go away, Charlie, I have decided to die and I prefer to die alone, after all. Ah, you still don't know what
that is, do you? Well: you just stand there and watch!

(HE turns his face gruffly away and
CHARLIE with the flowers comes
closer and peers down at him in-
tently as if a lesson, like all others, is
to be rendered pronto. The OLD
MAN turns to see the earnest face
above his own and shouts)

GET OUT OF HERE!

(Primitive or not, CHARLIE is hurt
by the tone and starts to back out as
a hurt child must)

41

Charlie. . . .

> (The BOY halts; but the OLD MAN
> does not look directly at him)

When it does happen—

> (Slowly, seriously)

and it will be soon now . . . not tonight . . . but soon
enough. I will get cold and stiff and still and it will
seem strange to you that . . . I ever moved at all. It
will seem then, boy, that I was . . . a miracle . . .
but it will happen. Because I am old and sick and worn
out—

> (A hoarse rasp)

—and mortal. But what you have to know is this: When
it happens you will all stand for a long time with your
mouths hanging open with wonder. That's all right, boy,
it's an awesome thing; it is in the nature of men to take
life for granted. Only the *absence* of life will seem to
you the miracle, the greatest miracle—and by the time
you understand that it should be the other way
around . . . well, it will probably be too late, it won't
matter then.

CHARLIE: Hen cross road.

HERMIT (Smiling the least bit): No, it really isn't a
joke. Some men, in my time, spent whole lifetimes
writing books trying to prove that it was. But it isn't.
The thing that you have to know, when mine is over,
and I have grown stiff and quiet for a while—I shall
begin to exude a horrid odor and what you must all
do is to dig the deepest hole that you possibly can and
put me in it. It doesn't matter which way and I don't
have to be wrapped in anything . . . I shall be glad
enough to merge, atom for atom, with the earth again,
and that is all there is to it.

CHARLIE: All?

HERMIT: All. Ah, I know you are wondering, how will I get out? I—won't. I will stay there forever. For always. For eternity.

(Shouting irritably)

Well, you've seen other things die! The birds, the fish we eat. They don't come back, do they! The wood we burn, it doesn't come back! Nothing comes back!

(Looking at CHARLIE's puzzled eyes)

You are thinking that I am not a bird or a fish or a piece of wood. All right, I am not—

(Raising up on his elbow, screaming feverishly)

I cannot solve the question of immortality for you, Charlie! Just accept what I tell you. I will have been and will be no more!—That . . .

(Lowering himself down again)

is all we ever knew about it. And I know you don't like it. Thy name is man and thou art therefore the greatest arrogance in the universe. . . . Well—

(With a gesture of dismissal of this question)

put a stone over my head when you have buried me and come and spend hours there pretending to have dialogues with me and you will feel better. It won't mean a thing to me, but you will feel better.

(Then, more softly)

The truth of it is that you really are going to miss me, Charlie. All of you. You will discover an abstraction that we never got to because there wasn't time. Affection. And, for some of you, something worse than that even, something more curious, more mysterious, that I shouldn't have been able to explain if there had been time. Some of you—*you* for instance, because we have been closest—will feel it; it will make you feel as if you are being wrenched apart. It is called "grief" and it is born of love.

That's what I was really trying to tell you about this morning, Charlie. Love. But you see it wasn't a very respectable sort of business in my time; as a matter of fact we tried any number of ways to get rid of it altogether.

CHARLIE: What use?

HERMIT: *Use* it? How to *use* love? Well, we never found that out either. Mostly it got in the way of important things. And, for all I know, they did get rid of it altogether. . . .

> (Sitting up again with great determination)

Now, look here, Charlie!—Do you—do you like Lily?

> (CHARLIE shrugs)

Well, you will. Agh! The problem is that you *all* will. You can't imagine how glad I am that I shall be out of here before all of that confusion erupts. Dear Heaven! But that's beside the point, the point is—

> (Once again lost in the Victorianism of his world)

Well, listen, let's put it this way, boy: you've got to take rather good care of Lily. What I mean is, if there should be a time when, well, when there just isn't enough food . . . for all of you—well, Charlie, you've got to see to it that Lily isn't the one who goes without . . . it mustn't ever be Lily as long as there are three of you. . . . Yes, I know I taught you to share; but you can't have permanent rules about things. The only rules that count are those which will let the race—

> (HE halts once again; weighs this thought and its persistence and deciding afresh)

—let the race continue.
I'm avoiding a good part of the thing about Lily, Charlie. Mainly because I can't help myself . . . I promised myself, when I first realized your situation here, that I would tell you only the truth, or as much of it as I have ever known. . . . Only the truth, including the fact that there certainly IS a Santa Claus, the truth —and here I can't even get into it about little girls. . . . Well, let's have a go at it this way:

Lily is different, you see. That is to say that, someday perhaps, when one of you is feeling—well, as I am feeling now, that is to say—sick . . . Lily is the one who will make it tolerable by bringing you an extraordinary cup of tea and looking at you in a way that will be . . . different from the way the others—hang it, this is impossible!

Basically, you see, Charlie; you are right, the thing I saw in your eyes before when I was explaining death. I am nothing more and nothing less than a bundle of mortality; an old package of passions and prejudices, of frightful fears and reasonings and a conscience; and deep in my heart I long for immortality as much as you do already without even understanding it. We all did, and cursed one another for it. And renounced one another for it. That is why I went into the woods, you see, I was outraged with mankind because it was as imperfect, as garrulous, as cruel as I.

> (Turning and looking at him)

But tell me something, Charlie, I've puzzled out a lot about you. . . . I know that you were prelingual when I found you; you must have been perhaps five or less when—it—happened as you seem to be about nine or ten now. Can't really tell; with your diet you might be much older. But let us suppose that you are ten. . . . The thing is, it seems strange to me that you've not seen human death before. I assumed at first that there have been more of you; some who died around you. But you don't know human death. Why were there so few of you—

> (Raising up, and enunciating care-
> fully as when HE really means for
> them to understand him)

How did you get here . . . ?

> (CHARLIE begins a narrative in flow-
> ing articulate gesture)

. . . Yes, Charlie—

> (Studying a gesture which sweeps
> from one place to another)

why, you were brought here! Yes, go on—

> (As a stone rolls so did that vehicle)

In a thing that moved! Yes, yes!

> (Great blades of grass grew here on
> that day; high like this)

Yes, there were many trees then! I understand, boy, go on!

> (The outline of the human figure)

You were brought here by one like you—

(No, by the head)

like *me!*

(Yes, by the head; the BOY picks up
a flower: the lily)

—ah, by one like Lily, only big. A woman . . .

(Understanding on his own)

of course: a nursery school teacher or attendant brought
you here to the perimeter of danger . . .

(CHARLIE goes to him and reenacts
the only kiss of his memory)

and kissed each of you . . .

(The sweeping gesture from one
place to another again)

—and went away. . . . And then—and then—?

(A circle of the arms collapses)

I see—"The sun fell down." Yes, I see. And some—great
woman—who had probably gone back for more had tried
to guarantee the human race. She voluntarily went back.

(Throwing back his head in anguish)

Dear God: what a strange tribe they were! Lunatics
and heroes all.
CHARLIE: *Heroes?*
HERMIT: A hero was a fool. . . . No, come here,
Charlie.

(HE draws the boy to him)

How ashamed we were of our heroes always. That one,
like Lily, who brought you here, she was like the song
I taught you. . . . Do not ever be ashamed of what you
feel when you think of her or it.

Listen, Charlie, I've not tried to weigh you down with a lot of moral teachings; for one thing there hasn't been time. And so much of what I would have tried to tell you about all of that would have been absurd and obstructive, and you will get into your own habits in time about that. But look here, fellow, about that woman, well, for reasons that we never did agree on, the vast majority of humankind, over the centuries, became committed to the notion that, well, this particular unpremeditated experiment of the cosmos which was the human race—well—that it ought go on . . . it was a defiant notion; and only something as fine, as arrogant as man could have dreamed it up. Only man could have dreamed of triumph over this reckless universe. But the truth is, we didn't quite know how. In the beginning, you see, we had such a little to work with and we never quite believed our poets when they told us that, in the main, we were doing the best we could. We demanded more of ourselves than that; for above all else, boy, man was valiant, really—

(An admission)

quite splendid you know. Ah, the things he perceived! You will be like them—heroes, all of you, merely to *get on* as long as you do.

> (THOMAS enters with a thing; a crude wheel with little clay scoops attached to its spokes)

Hello, Thomas. . . . Now what is that, boy—

> (THOMAS brings it and puts it on his stomach)

Well, it's fetching, child, but what is it?
Look, Charlie, Thomas had made something. . . . Now the question is—what has Thomas made?

48

> (HE turns the thing about, utterly
> confounded. THOMAS races out and
> then back again and, mutely, pours
> water from a pot into the topmost
> scoop so that its weight forces the
> wheel to turn and scoop up more
> water)

Yes . . . Yes!

> (Drawing THOMAS to him)

I understand, boy . . . you have found the wheel as
simply as all this! Creation, what ignites this flame!

> (Smoothing THOMAS'S hair about
> his face with adulation)

I should have christened thee "Leonardo," Thomas!

> (In a rage of jealousy CHARLIE
> promptly smashes the invention)

Ah, Charlie, Charlie! You can't understand, can you,
that it is something for all of you. . . . Thomas saw a
problem and invented something to solve it. It's all right
to be jealous, in fact it's a fine thing; it means that
you have placed value on something and that is fine.
But you must *use* your jealousy, Charlie. You must
help Thomas to build a big one like this and then you
won't have to waste all that time carrying water and
can do something else, sit around and sing if you like,
in the time that you used to spend carrying water before Thomas thought of this. Of all the things you must
learn, this is the most difficult and that from which you
most will profit.

But the truth is, I don't think you will learn it. The
truth is, children, that I don't think you will survive
at all. I have been engaging in a timeless vanity of man

pretending with you that it was possible. . . . Pretending that you wild little things could conceivably raise Egypt again; bring forth great China, ha! *you* little things! You little blind and brilliant organisms once again claim the equations of Copernicus and Newton; ha! the perceptions of Shakespeare and Einstein! Pretending that I could hand to you the residue, badly learned and hardly retained, of—five thousand years of glory!

(Turning away)

—on which I turned my back with all the petulance of our kind. . . .

(Turning back and shouting)

Why, you don't even know what steam will do yet! We didn't even get to steam! Steam, Thomas! a force that would make your wheel turn with revolutions undreamed of in your primitive soul! Mere simple heated water . . . you don't know it.

That foolish, foolish woman! That silly sentimental female! Why did she leave you here to torment me in my last absurd hours? It's all finished with you, the lot of you! Your little adventure among the stars is all over! Your brief and stupid episode will end now! The universe will have peace now. . . .

(Falling back; spent)

(CHARLIE holds out the lily. The OLD MAN lifts his head)

Use . . . what *use?* Charlie, the uses of flowers were infinite. . . .

(HE lies still)

(The children do not notice that HE

has left them and come one after the
other and cluster about the wreck of
THOMAS'S wheel which he, squatting before it in the dirt, is patiently
reconstructing)

CURTAIN

L. WOIWODE

L. Woiwode, originally from North Dakota, now lives in Wisconsin. He is a poet and author of the remarkable novel, *What I'm Going to Do, I Think,* which received the William Faulkner Award for 1969. The following selection is from his novel in progress, *Beyond the Bedroom Wall,* which Farrar, Straus & Giroux, Inc. will publish.

FATHERS AND SONS

"What's the time?" asked the girl with the small hands.

"What's the difference?"

"Who cares?"

"What's news?" somebody said.

"Dig it," said Neil.

There were five of them at the table. Jackie, the girl with the small hands, sat next to Vi, the folksinger, and Neil and Charles sat across the table from the girls. Happy, who never smiled, was at the end of the table, near the steps, fiddling with a light meter from his camera case. The five of them had been showing up together at Armando's, a coffeehouse on MacDougal, for the last couple of weeks, and though they seldom had money to make a purchase, the proprietor of the coffeehouse, Chip, a dark, burly man with a deadpan sense of humor, was not high-handed toward them and had asked them to do him a favor: "Sit at that table at the window and attract the tourists. Smile. Look stoned. They expect to see freaks in a coffeehouse."

So they displaced the pair of middle-aged chess players who'd been at the window table most of the summer, so intent on their game they looked like chessmen themselves.

This afternoon, however, when the five of them walked into Armando's after returning from a rooftop where they'd poked down a joint apiece (all but Hap), they were so obviously high and unable to contain it that Chip, looking annoyed and somewhat concerned—did he actually care about them?—told them to take a table in the back room. It was down three steps from the main part of the restaurant and was dimly lit, long and large, with a low ceiling covered with tin and three windows along the summit of one of its cement walls, and they had it nearly to themselves: a drifter who occasionally waited tables was sleeping across four chairs in the corner, and somebody else was at the rear, in shadow, tuning up a twelve-string guitar.

"God, do I feel awful," Vi said. "Tones even sound off."

"What's the time?" Jackie asked.

Her hands had always seemed small to Charles but now, with his senses bending under the effects of first-class Panamanian Red, they looked unnaturally small, miniature, grotesque, like two sudden and inexplicable deformities she was exhibiting on the tabletop. And when the five of them were on the roof (they tried the entries of walkups in the neighborhood and when they found a door that opened they went up five flights, and then up the sixth and onto the roof to smoke; it was impossible for a cop on the beat to catch you at that level, unless he sneaked up for a cigarette himself, in which case you were sitting behind the raised doorway he would have to come through and could throw everything overboard)—when they were smoking on the roof, Neil, who was passing the joint to Charles, whispered, "Dig Jackie's teeny hands. Freaky."

Her hands pranced around her face as she talked, turning on their wrists, patting her hair, performing near her mouth, posing on her chin. She had large prominent teeth, and her fleshy upper lip curved up from them in such an attractive, sensual way that whenever Charles could forget about her hands and focus there, he had an instant erection.

"Freaky."

Neil was from Miami. He was eighteen, a private in the army, stationed at Fort Dix—"Military Reservation is right," he said. He sported a skimpy juvenile moustache that the army permitted him to grow. Every Friday he received a weekend pass ("My master sergeant's gay," he explained), and appeared in the Village by dinnertime wearing a multicolored Mexican pullover with a brown karate belt around it ("I earned that"), a leather headband, and a gold ring in his right ear, and attended the weekend acting classes at the David Neuman Studio. Charles, who was taking the same classes, met him there, through Neuman in a way; when students disagreed with Neuman, a cruel and demanding man, he sent them onstage and had them perform an improvisation while he mocked their unnaturalness or technique for the rest of the class—he was a flawless mimic—and Neil and Charles were appearing there so often, sometimes together, that it was only natural for them to talk. Neil sold Charles a nickel bag of grass so heavily laced with oregano that all it gave Charles was a headache, and Neil had been promising to make it up to Charles ever since. He'd introduced Charles to Vi and Jackie and Hap and this was the third time Charles had been with the group. He'd lived in New York for only two months, after dropping out of college in his last year, and he felt much older than the others.

"The hands, the hands," Neil said, and nudged him, and Charles, who was passing the joint to Vi, took it from Neil and drew on it, his lips hissing as he carburated the smoke, filling his lungs until they felt raw, and then, as he stepped down on the toke with his rib cage and diaphragm, he turned to Jackie and saw that her wide brown eyes, moist and dilated from her high, were fixed on his eyes, and that smoke was escaping from her mouth and rising through her stare.

God, Charles thought, she's only sixteen.

Jackie came up to him and stood three inches away, her upper lip curving into Charles's high, and whispered, "Jesus. Was that beautiful."

"What's that?" The words came out in two squeaks from Charles's constricted throat.

"The way you knocked down that toke," she said. Her eyes defocused and then she held Charles again with her stare. "It's the most beautiful thing I've ever seen."

Neil, who was sitting against a ventilator, turned and lay face down and slapped the roof, laughing, and cried, "Love at first sight! Love at first sight!"

On the way back to the coffeehouse, as they came to a long metal grate set into the sidewalk next to a building, Charles turned to Jackie and said, "You see those little bars? Those are little steps. They're all uphill." And then he started climbing them. Jackie followed, holding onto his belt, and they walked uphill for so long, straining, leaning forward, holding onto the side of the building for leverage, that the others became dazed and went on ahead, and when Charles finally reached the top of the grate, the summit, it was only natural for him to take Jackie in his arms (enormous, pillowlike breasts), and kiss the mouth he admired. A policeman rapped on Charles's back with his bat. "Hey," he said. "You two kids been using dope?"

"Yup," Charles said.

"Are you high?"

"High as a kite." Kites?

"Go on, get out of here. You kids make me sick."

"But, sir, we're high as two kites on the Fourth of July. Don't you want to arrest us?" Charles said. Because Neil had told him you couldn't be arrested if you were merely high and not in possession. Was that true? Jackie, who was pale amber, took his arm in hers like a school chum and as she led him off, she said, "Don't do that again. It takes some balls, I know, but don't ever do that again."

"What's the time?" Jackie asked now.

"Come off it."

"Who cares?"

"Plenty of time for you, baby," Neil said.

"Why do you—" Charles began, and was interrupted by a delayed, involuntary laugh. "Why do you want to know?"

"The parents."

Jackie came to the Village every morning in faded levis and a wide-striped boatneck sweater, and every evening around six, somebody, a male body, had to accompany her home on the subway because she was afraid of "perverts" and "the coloreds," and yesterday Charles had been elected for the task and after an hour-long ride found himself in a neighborhood of highrises with lush gardens and parks surrounding them— the Bronx—and as he joined Jackie in the elevator of one of the newest and most ostentatious buildings, he noticed that a single button, *Penthouse*, was lit. Her father was a movie producer, her mother a television actress, Charles learned as they rode up, and neither of her parents got home until eight or nine, and then the doors clattered back, Jackie gave Charles a peck on the cheek, ran over the thick carpeting to the door of the penthouse, put her key into its lock, and the rest of her life was sealed off by the closing elevator doors.

Charles blinked and his head jerked back—Jackie was across the table from him—and he suddenly felt a need for a solid surface. He leaned against the wall behind him, but his center of equilibrium stayed where his head had been, and the three shafts of rectangular sunlight he was staring at, slanting from the high windows down to the floor, were so substantial in the dim room they were buttresses supporting the wall, as Charles now supported the wall behind him. Neil had his right elbow on the tabletop and his forearm up, in the arm-wrestling position, and although there was no other arm on the table he was grunting and straining and trying to make a press—his face was crimson, beads of sweat popped out on his forehead—and Charles realized that the invisible arm Neil was taking on was the world.

"I gotta know the time," Jackie said. "If they found out where I was they'd break my neck. Ma used to live in the Village. Besides, it just feels so strange this afternoon—being so early, I mean. I mean, being early in the day. Isn't it? I can't explain. I never get stoned before three o'clock."

Neil tried so hard not to laugh that a spray of mist, triangle-shaped, appeared in front of his lips; it began to disperse, fine streamers falling down from it, and then it faded and drifted through the shaft of sunlight Charles was staring at as he tried to contain himself. He couldn't look at Jackie or Neil, who were laughing in the tightly constrained, the nearly silent, hysterical laughter of people so stoned they can't be sure of the attention they're attracting to themselves. Charles was giddy, was giggling—it was the first time in his life he'd been so high—and their laughter was like rising water beneath his giddiness, lifting it higher and higher until he realized he was sliding up the shaft of sunlight, *up*

it, not down, defying the laws of God and nature, riding
their laughter up the buttress of sunlight and out the
window.

"Hey," Hap said. "Did you all see that broad?"

Their faces turned suddenly passive and solemn and
their heads, in unison, swiveled toward the doorway
behind Hap.

"No, no," Hap said. "Not here, not now. Jeez, you
guys must all be stoned." His close-clipped hair rested
so far back on his head he looked perpetually startled
and his face was running with perspiration; with al-
ternate thumbs he kept clearing his eyebrows, and then
flicking the thumbs clean. "No, I mean that broad I
was talking to outside, the blond, the bombshell, the
tall one. She must have been six feet three. And did
you see those knockers on her? She was some kind of
high-class dish."

"That's a hell of a way to talk about a woman," Vi
said. Her voice was low and throaty, green-blue with
accusation.

"Zooks!" Neil said. "You're bringin' me down with
your love banter. I'll have to release the fabled bird
from his nest." Neil hooked his thumbs together and
began waving his outstretched hands like wings. "Up,
Bird of Paradise," he said in a reverent voice. "*Up,*
seeker after truth, big fella. Eeee! Eeee!" The bird's
wings beat faster and lifted Neil's outstretched arms
toward the ceiling. "Up there, big fella. High! High!"
Neil was drawn out of his seat and the wings started
slapping against the tin ceiling. "Eeeeeee! *Eee! Eee!
Eee!*"

And everybody was smiling the Mona Lisa of the
stoned again except Hap, who never smoked or took
any sort of dope. He stared at them with his startled
look ("He'll want testimonials later," Neil said), encased in a pair of Tyrolean lederhosen, whose embroidered braces formed a brightly colored H over his

T-shirt. He was older than they, thirty or thirty-five—
though he looked ageless, between eighteen and forty—
a photographer who could usually be found near Washington Square in his leather shorts and knee socks, with
a gadget bag and three or four cameras hanging from
him, and he was also a pusher, a well-known Village
pusher, and the cameras and bag were convenient
for making deliveries. Hap was earnest about everything he did—like following them around to gauge the
quality of his latest shipment, wearing the happy H so
you'd know him whether you were too stoned to see or
hadn't met him in your life—and it was the earnestness,
it seemed, that made him constantly sweat.

"I said that's a hell of a way to talk about a woman,"
Vi repeated, louder.

"What do you know?" Hap said.

"I know you bass-ackwards, buddy," Vi said.

"Bull!" Hap turned away from her. He was always
approaching young, long-legged, large-breasted girls,
his swarthy oval face glistening with perspiration, and
saying, after a few minutes of everyday talk, "Hey, you
want to pose for a couple nudies? I got dope." It was
amazing the comers he had, and Vi was one, an ex. She
sang in a beat-up basement coffeehouse on MacDougal,
one of the coffeehouses that seemed to be changing
hands every month and with each change acquiring a
new name and a different shade of bright paint to the
level of the sidewalk—where burnt and unpalatable es-
presso was served for a dollar a cup and a hat was
passed for the performers. Lately Vi had been sleeping
there and she was beginning to look haggard and
middle-aged, though she was only in her twenties; her
black hair was oily and thin, pulled into a tight bun at
the back of her head, there were violet stains of fatigue
beneath her eyes, and she'd begun wearing matronly
skirts below her knees and homemade blouses of cotton
and calico. She was from the Midwest, like Charles, and

she exaggerated her accent (Charles was already putting on the accent of New York) even though she'd traveled all over the country, playing dates in different cities. In Miami, she'd met Neil.

"Oh, Jeez, do I feel awful," she said. "This grass of yours is fallin' apart inside of me, Hap."

"That's you, not the stuff. It's first-class, ask your friends."

"Hey," Jackie said, and leaned toward Charles, pressing her breasts into the tabletop until the tips were flattened into two round areas the size of saucers ("Dig it," Neil whispered), which made her hands, lying in front of them, shrink even more. "Hey, have you ever been to the Top of the Sixes?"

"The only place I've ever been," Charles said, "is right here."

Her hands began gesturing around her face, leaping in the air as though being jerked by strings, and Charles sensed that someone had once told her that her tiny hands were attractive. "It's really a neat place," she said. "I go there with my parents all the time. They say, 'Where do you want to go this weekend?' And I say, 'The Top of the Sixes,' and we go there and get our table by the window and look down at the Park while we eat, at all the lights and the taxis moving around down there, and I always order butterfly steak. It's beautiful, thin as paper, and it evaporates up your nose. And I have wine. They let me have all the wine I want from their bottle and it really sends me up, looking down on the Park like that. I want to go there with you and sit at our table and look right at you while we eat. Would you like that?"

"You bet," Charles said.

"Do you have a suit?"

"One and a half."

"Because you have to wear one there."

"Of course."

"I'll pay," she said.

"Be my guest," Charles said.

"Neil," Vi said, "will you watch me in case I get really sick?"

"Right, baby," he said.

"Will you take care of me like the last time?"

"Right, baby."

"Because I'm goin' over that line, Neil. I'm headed for it right now."

"I gotcha, baby," Neil said. He was drumming on the tabletop and his right leg, balanced on his toes, was beating in a frantic rhythm that made the table wobble. Neil leaned close to Charles and whispered, "She's on coke, been on it a year. Bad shit." His leg kept beating.

"Do you know how to handle headwaiters?" Jackie asked Charles.

"Any kind of waiter," he said.

"Because Ma called the one at the Top of the Sixes a finicky old bitch."

"Nothing to it," Charles said.

"Boy," Hap said, pointing his light meter around. "Boy, is this shadow nice."

"Oooo-*whee*, Hap!" Neil said. "You're telling *me?*"

"I used to have such pep," Vi said. "I ain't got no more pep."

The table began to wobble even more and Charles saw that both of Neil's legs were beating now and that he was pressing his outstretched fingers on the table-top in patterns, as though chording on a piano. Neil leaned his ear close to his hands to listen. His face was boyish, and with his skimpy moustache, which he some-times darkened with mascara, he reminded Charles of the young RAF aces of the First World War. He had the same feverish bravado in his eyes, with the same tentativeness behind it, and when he laughed his eyes

went out of focus and filled with a look that was homicidal and crazed.

"Oh, Jeez," Vi said. "If this keeps up, my head's
going to shrink into nothing and fall off like a little
ball."

"A great ball," Neil said. "A *great* ball, baby."

"I caught that," Hap said.

"Tell me, baby," Neil said to Vi. "Lay it out where I
can see."

Vi looked at Neil, her green eyes glazed but direct
and considering. "You know what coke does to your
insides?" she said. "It eats them. I can feel every cell
in my fucking body."

"That's it," Neil said.

"Every cell has a set of teeth along one side, sharp
teeth, and they're eating the side that's left. Try
and imagine that, Neil. Look in my eyes and think of
that. A row of teeth along each side like alligator teeth."

"A crock," Neil said.

"What?"

"A crocodile. He's the color of your eyes. He's in your
belly."

"Ah!" Vi cried, and covered her face.

"Why don't you lay off?" Hap said.

"Lay off her?" Neil asked.

"No, no. Why doesn't she lay off that crap?"

"What we're into here," Neil said, "is shock therapy.
You dig it, Hap?"

"Shit."

"You want a charge?"

Vi leaned back in her chair and stared at Neil, her
eyes tired-looking and more deep-set. "It don't help
any," she said. "Just makes me feel sicker."

"So why don't you lay off it?" Hap said.

Vi moved her eyes to Hap and they turned as cold,
with Neil's suggestion behind them, as the eyes of a
reptile. "Sit on your thumb," she said.

"Have you ever had butterfly steak?" Jackie asked.

"Not to my knowledge," Charles said.

"Would you like some?"

"Wings and all."

"Hey, Hap," Neil said. "Why don't you join us here? Why don't you come on up? Use that first-class stuff of yours. Don't bother running outside. Just eat an ounce right here. Put it in a bowl like cornflakes. Eat it up. A bowl, waiter! Or pop one of your"—Neil picked up a camera of Hap's and looked at its lens cap—"pop one of your handy Nikon tabs."

"Hands off, asshole," Hap said, and grabbed the camera from him.

"Hey, *hey*," Neil said, "Ize jes' funnin' ya, Hap. Hee hee hee."

Charles felt a wave of violence radiate from Neil and turned to him. Neil's legs were still. In spite of his boyish face and moustache, he was rough-looking, trim and muscular, with concave cheeks granular from acne, a long scar through his right eyebrow, and fight scars around his mouth. The ends of his front teeth were broken off ("Karate," he said), and when he smiled or laughed he bit his upper lip to keep them concealed.

"Really, Hap," he said. "Why don't you ever use the good weed? Or a bit of that nice Hershey Bar you wrap up in tinfoil for me? Huh? Or in real life are you actually—my goodneth!—a closet dope-freak?"

Hap cleared the sweat from his eyebrows. "Hell, I ain't going to mess my life up with that crap. I got enough problems the way it is. I'd flip out for good, I'd end up in Bellevue, that's what'd happen. Besides, if my old man found out, he'd kill me. He's in City—anyway, he's got an important job."

"Doesn't he ever wonder where you get the money for your classy clothes?" Neil asked.

"Lay off," Hap said. "I'll burn you."

The table began to wobble and shake even more and Charles saw that Neil's upper body was jiving in spasms as he tried to contain a laugh. "Hey," he said. "Hoo boy, oh, Jesus; hey, dig what I'm into. I'm from Hollywood, Florida, right? Right." He spread apart the thumb and forefinger of each hand and unfurled a marquee. "Hollywood, Florida, movie capital of the world! Stars! Glamor! Flashy cars! Go go go go go-go girls! *Dog races.* No, no, I can't," he said. "Buck up, boy! Where was I? Aha, thought you lost me, huh? Mother. My mother, God bless her, a lovely woman—my mother, a big lady, could be a Sumo wrestler—*my mother* works in a freight shipping office. Hobnobs with the truck drivers, a real pal to them—vroom! vroom! Diesel coming through! You know what Daddy does? Daddy's a typist. He works in the county courthouse typing up county records, tickety tackety tappety rippity. Daddy's the *fastest typist they have.* And when he comes home, how does he relax? He plays the piano. Right, right, gets the aching pinkies in there and tickles the old Mozart and George Gersh. Plinkety plunkety plinkety hum. In my virgin days, I used to think, hey Dads, old poopsie, you got a problem, hum? Because he was also having kids over every weekend—greasers in tight pants and Hawaiian shirts who ran around saying *Whee!* He played the piano for them in his gold threads, his special suit. The concert pianist worked himself into a frenzy! And when I was eleven I woke up in the middle of the night and there was old Dads beside the bed with a jug in his hand, looking like he was about to job me. Whee! I took off and didn't come back for a week. 'Why'd you miss so much school?' Teach wanted to know. 'Oh, well, you know Daddy, he—'"

Neil was laughing so hard he'd begun to cough and his cheeks were wet with tears. "Inhale! Exhale! Inhale! Exhale!" he said, and then he signaled that he couldn't go on and lay his head down on the table, on his crossed arms, and his back arched and leaped beneath his shirt.

"Oh, Jeez," Vi said. "Oh, Jeez, Neil."

"Beautiful," Jackie said. "Beautiful."

The man at the rear of the room, who wore a black cowboy hat with the brim pulled low over his face, moved his chair into the shaft of sunlight farthest from Charles, settled the twelve-string guitar in his lap, in his hands, and began to play, quietly and politely at first, and then with growing force and inventiveness as he began to approve of his tuning.

"Oh, shit," Vi said. An iridescence appeared in the violet depressions beneath her eyes and spilled over, and iridescence ran in lines down her cheeks. "Oh, shit, can that man play some bad-ass blues."

She covered her face and put her elbows on the table.

Charles leaned back against the wall. He felt dizzy, displaced, and his eyes were flipping as they did on a moving subway; he had to concentrate to hold them on one aspect. He fixed on the chin showing beneath the brim of the black hat. Then on the hand fretting the strings, the fingers spreading, barring, standing high, stretching and returning to former chords, moving autonomously, of their own passion, over the strings, in a realm unrelated to the black-hatted man or his instrument. The music, a separate phenomenon, came from the hole in the center of the guitar and across the length of the room, where only empty chairs were standing, in widening waves of sound, silver in color, and struck the front of Charles's body. He felt his chest part, his ribs lift, and a cavern expand to admit the sound, exposing a region where his heart glowed red and rode along the silver current of music, skipping up or sliding down the smaller steps, rising to a higher level, sweeping along to a crest that left him breathless, and then dropping into the deep driving plaint of the blues refrain until death drew so near it became a part of his body—the liquid blackness enveloping his heart.

Charles thought of his father. He'd missed his father lately more than he'd missed him in his life. Charles would wake in his rented room in New York in the early morning, at seven or seven-thirty, hours before he usually woke, and find himself thinking of his father, and the day would lie ahead like a blank vista with no shape or color or hope of surprise, so he'd fall back into bed and sleep until noon. And when Charles woke, his mind would be filled with images and dream fragments of Illinois and of how his father changed after the death of Charles's mother. His father lost twenty pounds within a few weeks and his face became immobile and gray. For a year his father never spoke unless it was absolutely necessary and then he spoke in only the most minimal of phrases. His father was so restless he could hardly sit and yet he sat in front of the television for entire evenings on end, looking as though he'd chained himself to his chair, and the worst sort of melodrama had the power to move him so uncontrollably he'd have to leave the room. His father showed no desire to go back to teaching, his real profession, and worked for his brother as a mixer and hodcarrier on a plastering crew. "Oh, if your mother were here," his father would say to the air, and then his eyes would glaze and he'd go off on a wordless reminiscence. Or he'd say, "Oh, I suppose much of my ambition was for her."

His father wrote to Father Schimmelpfenning, his closest friend in Hyatt, the village in North Dakota that Charles's family had moved from the year before, and told the priest that he was going out of his mind for familiar company, and two young men whom his father had taught in Hyatt and who had graduated from high school since, appeared at the house in Illinois. His father persuaded his brother to give them jobs, and beds were moved into the garage—into the basement in the winter—and the former students roomed and boarded at the house for free. For four summers his father returned to North Dakota and hired himself out as a laborer on a farm. He met a widow who lived near Rugby and began to write to her every week from Illinois. He finally returned to teaching but he was no longer meticulous about his appearance, as he'd once been, and he wore work clothes to school, or mismatched jackets and slacks, or no tie, with his collar open and a stained T-shirt showing beneath. And now Charles realized that there was a period in his life that he'd completely closed off: his father took a year's leave of absence from his job in Illinois and went back to Hyatt to teach, and Charles and his sisters, Marie and Susan, went back with him.

His father was a hero, nearly a legend in Hyatt, because the last year he'd taught there he'd taken a basketball team to the state tournament (there were only nine males in the high school at the time) and they'd won third place. The school board wanted his father to coach again but his father said that he'd rather let that final record, nearly perfect, stand. Marie and Susan stayed with a couple in Hyatt who had children their ages and Charles and his father rented a small run-down house near the high school. Charles was a freshman and the familiar village was oppressive and constricting to him; he had changed, his friends had changed, he hadn't thought he'd ever see them again and now he didn't know whether he wanted to, and he stayed home often from school, feeling too lethargic and burdened to move. He became interested in music and began to play the baritone. He wrote long letters to his brother in Illinois. He read books and magazines until his eyes refused to focus. In the beginning he and his father went to New Rockford during the weekends and had dinner together and went to a movie or went bowling, in order to get away from Hyatt, but with the first cold weather the car wouldn't start and it sat beside the road in front of their house until the drifting snow covered its roof.

There was one bedroom in the house, with one bed, a double bed, and Charles and his father slept together in it. A single heater for heat, a cookstove in the tiny kitchen, where his father prepared all of their meals— And now Charles realized that the hour he was waking in New York was the hour when he and his father used to wake in North Dakota and have breakfast together. . . . A marshy area behind the house, a woodlot in the back yard: his father splitting wood, his forearms and back muscles bulging beneath his shirt, striking the splitting wedge so hard one time it shot through the chunk of elm and stood upright in the chopping block.

His father at the cookstove, staring ahead, his eyes blank and distant, rolling a walnut between his fingers and palm and then the sound like a gunshot as he cracked it with his bare hand. The silent meals in the tiny kitchen. The vacant, drawn-out days when Charles stayed home from school. Sitting in bed and playing his baritone to the empty rooms. The dampness of the bedclothes, the dampness of the furniture and rugs, and the corrosive feeling of dampness that rose from the floors of the old house. Wandering from room to room as though on an endless search for a missing essential. Wearing pajamas for the first time since childhood because he slept with his father—flannel pajamas that made him feel like a baby and that he left on all day. His wandering form reflected in the golden bell of the baritone. The unformed pastiness of his face in the mirror. The glory and the terror of erupting with semen—what to do with it?

And then, at school, the persistent embarrassment of having his father for a teacher—that new, unalterable relationship. Staring at the floor when his father lectured or read. Never lifting his eyes from the desk when he was asked a question. Rattling off the answer to his father with irritation. Averting his eyes when he passed his father in the halls. Why did it make Charles feel he was betraying his father? In the winter, at a basketball game in a neighboring village, one of the few basketball games his father didn't attend, Charles and three of his friends got some money together and gave it to a senior who could pass for twenty-one, and he bought a bottle of whiskey and a bottle of sweet wine. They drank both bottles in a car, quickly, during the half of the basketball game, and went back into the warm auditorium. One of Charles's friends, a freshman, passed out and vomited over the bleachers and had to be carried from the building. It was discovered that he was drunk, not ill, and the next day the sheriff arrived at the high school in Hyatt and everybody who'd been drinking was summoned into the office of Charles's father. He was the superintendent. The sheriff called them dopes and knuckleheads and said that he could throw them all in jail. Charles stared at the floor, feeling his father's eyes on him, and then he heard the sheriff say that he would put them on probation if they had a long talk with their parents and their minister. The three who were Catholic went to see Father Schimmelpfenning; the priest stepped into the confessional and when it was Charles's turn, he drew aside the velvet curtain and knelt in darkness, praying for anonymity, and then the slide at his face shot back and Father Schimmelpfenning said, "Charles, Charles, Charles. I don't believe you'll ever know how much you've hurt your father."

Now, in New York, with the press of people moving past in the street, Charles would see a face or a certain feature—a forehead, an eye, a mouth—that reminded him of his father, and there would be a catch in his stride and then he'd slow down, feeling that his father had seen him but had continued on, and sometimes Charles would even stop in the street and turn to see.

"Hey, what's the *time?*" Jackie asked.

"Seven-thirty," Charles said, and felt the guitar music swell in his chest.

"Seven-thirty?" Jackie's hands stopped in mid-air and all the color left her lips. "Oh, Jesus," she whispered, and stood. "Oh, holy Jesus." She grabbed her purse and ran up the steps.

"Is it?" Vi asked.

"Hell, it's lucky if it's four," Hap said.

Jackie reappeared, walking stiffly down the steps, her face ashen, and came over to the table. "You bastard," she said to Charles. "You just wrecked my high. You just wrecked my head and my whole goddamn day. You dirty lying bastard!" She turned away and ran up the steps.

"No Top of the Sixies for you, poopsie," Neil said, and fluttered his hands in front of Charles's face.

"Don't," Charles said, and pushed the hands away.

"Why'd you do that?" Vi asked. "She can't help it she's that way. She's just a kid."

"I didn't mean to." Charles was frightened. The four of them had set up this scene to trap him, to victimize him, and now they were closing in. He felt his high shift, assume an anchorlike shape between his lungs, and he believed the high was leaving so he'd be able to defend himself but it returned with a more powerful surge and locked around him in a new form, with wires and claws that he couldn't escape: terror.

"Oh, God," Vi said. "I didn't mean it that way. I'm sorry. I didn't mean to— Oh shit," she said. "Isn't this a lovely day?"

"Do you know where she is?" Charles asked.

"How should I know?"

Charles slid out from the table, surprised that he

could perform the action so simply, and went up the steps and was startled by the brightness of the other room, by his distorted face sliding over the shining urns, by the colorfully clad bodies shifting along his periphery like hooks that would remove his vision. There was a hand on his shoulder.

"Chuckie," Neil said. "Friend. I'm supposed to meet a broad here later but if she doesn't show could I sleep at your place?"

Charles stared back at him, unsure of what he'd asked.

"Hey, hey, poopsie," Neil said. "Don't worry, no sex. I'm wearing the rag." He laughed, biting his upper lip, and his eyes went out of focus. "*May* I stay at your place?" he said. Now his eyes were apprehensive, tentative and questioning, and he looked as though he could be easily hurt.

"Sure."

"It'll probably be late if she doesn't show and I can't hook up somewhere else."

"That's OK."

"Thanks," Neil said, and punched Charles's shoulder, and with the slight blow Charles felt that his personality had been shifted into a different setting, while his body, wherever that was, remained in the old one. He was still high.

"Later," Neil said.

"Right," Charles said, and went out the door. The air outside was hot and damp, tropical to him, and the row of buildings across the street, painted in alternating garish shades, reminded him of something from his past —the primary-colored cardboard houses he used to set in rows beneath the Christmas tree to represent a village; or a childhood book with gaudy, oversimplified drawings of Hometown, Everywhere. In his present state he couldn't place the image.

He went down MacDougal, away from the Square toward Bleecker, crossed Bleecker, and turned east on it. Every face that passed him seemed to know that he'd hurt Jackie and was out looking for her. People smiled. He felt his body giving off such an obvious, vulnerable aura—from the back of his neck and his buttocks, from the way his arms and legs were moving —that everybody on the street, everybody looking down from their apartment windows, could spot him as a mark and move in. A crowd of students was approaching and he couldn't bear to face them. He stopped at a storefront and looked in the window. The building was being remade into yet another coffeehouse; burlap and construction materials lay on the floor, along with round-topped tables turned upside down. There were wooden platforms at several levels, and around the edges of the platforms, running from the floor to eight feet into the air, were lengths of colored pipe—orange, blue, white, red—that had been fitted together randomly, in patterns that were right-angled and grotesque and matched exactly the disorder in Charles's mind. He'd been led to this window to look at himself. Jesus God.

His eyes adjusted and he saw the reflection of a man's face beside him—a distinguished, fine-lipped Irish face, with the querulous and insinuating look of a detective. The face, which was also looking in the window, turned to study Charles several times, and then moved closer.

"Could you give me a quarter or fifty cents?"

Charles turned. The man was about forty-five, with sandy-colored hair combed back from a high forehead, pale eyes, and a day's growth of copper stubble.

"I haven't got fifty cents," Charles said.

"Are we still on speaking terms?" the man asked.

"I don't know you."

"No, you probably don't. I've lived in the neighborhood longer than you've been in this world and you probably don't even remember me. I saw—" His direct

73

gaze suddenly veiled over and turned inward, as though he'd lost his train of thought. He was wearing a new, button-down shirt with the creases from the shirt cardboard still showing in it, and expensive-looking tapered pants. "Does this place cost much?" he asked.

"It's not open. It's new."

"I know it is, I know it is. I've lived in this neighborhood all my life and I've never seen it. Sure. Teddy Cummins and I were altar boys over at St. Anthony's for Father McKeough—that's how far back I go. Do you serve there now?"

"I'm not from here."

"Sure you are. Don't you remember?"

Was this one of the alkies that Charles gave money? He often gave alkies or bums the last quarter he was carrying.

"I saw you just the other day," the man said. "You're a painter. You were carrying one of those—" With his hands he outlined several shapes in the air and from the precision of his gestures it was obvious that he wasn't drunk (although Charles could smell sweet wine on his breath), but he also wasn't drawing anything definite. "What do you call those?"

"An easel?"

"No, no, no. It's all covered up with something. It's real big. You were carrying the whole big deal."

"A canvas?"

"No, no, no. You painters have a special name for it."

"I'm not a painter and I don't think I was ever carrying anything like that around here."

"Then it was one of your friends. They all look like you, your friends. How's your daddy?"

"What?"

"Your daddy. I haven't seen him for a long time, either. How is he?"

"I don't know."

"You don't know! Doesn't he live right there on Sullivan Street?"

"He lives in Illinois."

"Well, naturally. But I like to come back once in a while and look the old place over and he should, too. Tell him. Now I'm going down to the Bowery." He stared down the street and his eyes, shaded by overhanging golden eyebrows that glinted in the sunlight, filled with a tentative, homeward look that was familiar to Charles. He wasn't sure he didn't know this man, though he was positive he'd never met him, and he felt the terror start in him again.

"Down to the Bowery," the man repeated. "The Bowery."

"You live there?"

"*Me?*" His voice was filled with disdain. "Hell, no, I hate the place. I can't stand it. I just like to come back and— You don't remember your daddy, huh? Well, damn you, you should! Wasn't he there when you wanted him? Wasn't he?"

"I guess."

"You damn betcha he was. You were little then, right?"

"Right."

"Sure. Now I remember. And then the next thing I knew you were carrying that what-you-may-call it around. What was that thing you were carrying around, that artist's thing?"

"I'm not an artist."

"Then it was three years ago I saw you carrying that and I haven't seen you since, have I, Michael?"

"I think—"

"You're right, it wasn't just the other day, it was three years ago. Now I remember."

He stared beyond Charles's shoulder with bewilderment. He seemed uncertain, for the first time, of the person he was speaking to or the location where they stood, and then his eyes altered, as if he'd seen through to a moment too horrible to comprehend, and then his eyes emptied of all expression, became blank, and he turned and walked away from Charles.

BARRY HANNAH

Barry Hannah was born in 1942 in Meridian, Mississippi. Educated at Mississippi College and the University of Arkansas, he presently teaches at Clemson University. This excerpt, *Green Netherlands,* is a portion of his first novel, *Geronimo Rex,* which The Viking Press, Inc. will publish in early 1972.

GERONIMO REX
Green Netherlands

There are these rolling lumps of turf, with the forest looking deep and sappy and real shade on the road and big rocks lying mossy off the roadbank, all of which at one time belonged to the Sink brothers, who were the paper mill barons of Dream of Pines. They called it Pierre Hills, and put two mansions out there on this premium property. The sign saying Pierre Hills on a turnoff from the highway would make you think it was a subdivision under development, or something like that. But it isn't. There were only the two Sink mansions—which were just big and New Orleans style in a fat way—nestling in all that luscious gloom of oaks and hickories. And none of the other hundreds of acres of Pierre Hills was for sale. Eat your heart out, landluster. The Sink boys had it for their own park, after tearing down every pine tree of beauty back in Dream of Pines for lumber and paper pulp. Dream of Pines was a smelly heap a mile east of Pierre Hills. By the time my old man moved us into our house between

the Sink mansions, however, the Sink brothers and the
rest of their friends managing the mills had stoked up
such a glut of wood in the mill production that Pierre
Hills itself breathed a slight fart of the industrialized
woodlands.

So when we got into it, Pierre Hills was not the exclusive rolling green it used to be. Still, it was a great
privilege for the old man to get to buy in and put a
house out there. He always thought the Sinks had been
kind to him. He paid so much for the land, my mother
left him for a month in protest and stayed with her
mother in Vicksburg, Mississippi. Apparently he shot
about nearly everything from two good years at the
mattress factory he owned. He was third-richest man
in town, after the Sinks. When my mother came back,
he had the house he meant to build just starting. He
and she fell down in the truck ruts and embraced, the
afternoon she came back. It's shadowed enough to do
that in Pierre Hills. My mother is a fading egg-white
brunette I can understand a man could miss after a
month. And at heart, she's wild for any kind of project
—any kind of definitely plotted adventure. So I suppose
it happened. Love bending back the trees, and luggage
from Vicksburg being kicked everywhere. I can see the
beauty. They were in between their big old shingled
house in Dream of Pines and the huge country home
of square gray stone we finally had in Pierre Hills. I
always thought of it as the bottom half of a small English fort. My mother had a miscarriage, her last baby,
when we were two months in the place. I remember
everybody saying—I was six—that it was an awfully late
and dangerous time to lose a baby. The Sink boys never
sent condolences or anything. This came up. My aunt
was sitting in the kitchen and mentioning this while
my mother was at the hospital. My old man didn't really
allow anything to be said against the Sink brothers. He
always had a blind admiration for anybody holding

monstrous wealth; he thought it took an unearthly talent to become rich beyond rich. He loved the state of New York because it was so incomprehensibly rich. He loved paying homage to it, and I guess that's why we took all the New York magazines and newspapers. They filled up the house, and nobody read anything in them beyond the gaudiest headlines. I think he *enjoyed* paying through the ear for the land his house is on. And, by the way he acted, I got the idea we were owning this land in Pierre Hills on probation. No misbehaving or loose talk, or we were off.

The old man had a Buick. He liked to wheel it up our brick drive, which was bordered by a dense cane patch. He was one of these magazine handsomes who was turning gray in the hair at forty-five; the gray strands were flames from a hot and ancient mental life, or so he thought. His mental life was always the great fake of the household. He's had three years at L.S.U., makes sixty thousand a year, has the name of a bayou poet—Ode Elann Monroe—and has read a book or two over above what he was assigned as a sophomore. So he's a snob, and goes about faking an abundant mental life—he always had this special kind of wrenched and evaporated tiredness when he came home from the factory. "Show me a bed, Donna" (my mother), "the old head's been working overtime today," he sighs—and he's demanding Quiet Hours outside after supper in his study. His study, where, if my guess is right, he sits scrutinizing his latest hangnail and writing his own name over and over in different scripts until he bores himself into a coma. About midnight, he charges out of the study, ignoring Mother and me watching the national anthem on the television, every insipid show of which (TV was brand-new to us then) he adored better than breath, but denied himself for the mental life, and he is bashing the walls of the hall making toward his bed and sleep, so frightened by the dull drafts of

79

his own thoughts that it's truly sad. He always thought a college man like himself was entitled to life on a higher plane, and always endured the horror of knowing that his thoughts in the study were no different than the ones he had during the day when he added a random sum on the to-the-good book. I found his name, written in different, sometimes perversely ornate, scripts on the top of variously sized and colored notepads, on the desk of his study in the mornings. Perhaps he wanted to do an essay, or a poem, or an epitaph. I don't know what he wanted to write on the blank lines. I remember once he was intending to write a letter to the editor of a New York paper, but never finished a copy he thought presentable enough. God knows, I'm on his side in this hustle about the mental life. I've *inherited* a major bit of the farce from him, by what I can tell. And both of us jump into sleep like it was a magic absolver—of an unbearably dull mental life. Both of us, I would imagine, yearn too for the body of a woman, knowing from the first touch of sex to sex, it's all a black dream going into sleep.

I'm second-grader Harriman Monroe. My mind is full of little else but notes on the atrocities of World War II. I saw them all in photographs in a book compiled by a national magazine. It was on some playmate's daddy's shelf. Then I'm eight, third-grade, and have in part understood what I saw. I'm not even smart enough to be horrified yet.

The Sink brothers had two peafowl that came trespassing in our cane patch alongside the driveway. It did my old man no end of good to see the birds prissing around on his land. He wanted to be such neighborly chums with the Sink brothers. North of us was Sid, and south of us, Ollie. The peafowl also had two quaint names which I refuse to remember. The female was a whore, and the male lived on her, and was jealous of anything that moved. They went in the deeps of the cane and loved it up, and in between times, laid an inch-high carpet of green droppings back in the romantic, cavey places, and the cock ran me out when I tried to get in there to play, not knowing all the swell places were already floored with dung. A peacock, by the way, will drill your ass if he knows the odds are anything near equal. He got me a couple of times I won't forget.

Then one day I got in the cane when they were gone, went back to the deeps, where the Jap snipers should've been sitting ideally in the high crotches and just ready to be potted by my air rifle. I hit a dip and slid off into that peafowl dung I didn't know was there. It was all in my hair and up the barrel of my gun, and my lever had this unmentionable stalagmite of green hanging on it. I looked around and saw there wouldn't be any decent playing in here until maybe I was twenty.

I wasn't thinking about the birds or the cane this other day, walking out for the papers at the end of the drive, when the peacock all of a sudden beats out of the deeps and starts hammering at my thigh. I ran and finally shook him off. Now I was afraid of him, but I wasn't about to detour around the cane walking back on account of any bird. I picked up a piece of stick I'd thrown at the mailbox a week ago, pretending the stick was a grenade and the mailbox was a German's mouth; it was a healthy length of hickory, and wasn't ever a very feasible grenade. I walked back on the cane edge of the drive, and got to where the cock ambushed me coming out. The old boy was roosting about four feet off the ground this time, and jumped on me at head level, making a loud racket in the cane as he launched himself. This terrified me, but I stood still and swung on the peacock with both arms. I caught him on the head, and his beak swerved like plastic. He dropped on the bricks like a club, his fantail all folded in. I toed him. He was dead, with an eye wiped away.

The old man sails into the drive in his Buick. He's overdue home from the factory, and thinks everybody is thrilled by his making the turn so perfectly into the narrow brick drive. He rams to a halt, seeing me and the dead peacock. Up beside me faster than the shadow of a passing airplane.

"It's not dead, is it, son?" He leans over and peers at the cock's head. "Pray to God. He *is* dead. Why would you kill a lovely bird like. . . . You know who he belongs to, don't you?"

"He came at me. Twice."

"This small, beautiful bird came at you. You better tell the truth, buddy. What do you think we're going to do about this?"

"Put some lime on that sucker, he'll melt into the ground without a stink in three-four days." The old man's jaw dropped.

"Who taught you about *lime?*"

"Aw. The Nazis used it on bodies in concentration camps."

"Oh yeah? You're really getting an education, aren't you?"

"Yessir. You want me to handle it?" The old man was looking away at some hopeless horizon.

"I want *what?*" he said.

"You want me to handle this peacock? I'll drag him up in that cane. You get me a little lime, and nobody'll know nothing." Now the old man's roasting me with a hard look.

"You get your little fanny up to the bathroom and get your pants down. I'm going to handle *you.*"

But he snuck and got the lime, and lied to Ollie Sink when he called a few days later wanting to know if we'd seen Bayard. By then Bayard—God help me, I did remember the sucker's name—was a crust back in the deeps.

No more than a week later the old man and I are standing at the bay window looking out at the leaves dropping from the trees and running north over the yard in an early cool autumn wind, while the old man is trying to explain the concept of a yard-chore and what it had to do with Duty. He wants me to *rake* the yard, he means, every Saturday for the next ten years. He says a man gets to know the earth like that, by such simple acts as touching a yard rake to a decomposing nut. Quite incidentally, too, I'd haul away uncountable yellow tons of leaves in a wheelbarrow before I even got my growth. I personally always was of the school of let them lay and rot, and just imagining all the moldering beauty underneath they must be causing; I couldn't bear to think of moving a rake against them. Meanwhile, I could learn about all this unspoiled earth grit by watching our female terrier, Maggie, go wild up against our screen door when she was in heat; and her suitors—bird dogs, a spaniel, a Doberman, and two beagles looking so gruesomely depressed by their own desire—standing politely on the porch for two days and then, fed up, mauling each other with high croaks. Finally, only the Doberman was left, and he and Maggie would stare balefully through the screen at one another. He was a grand black thing, with somebody's chain around his throat. Nobody went out the front door while he was still there. He saved me immediate Duty on the leaves; no child could've been expected to go out in the front yard with him there. The old man took it hard that the Dobe was doing a mountain range of turds round the front step. What if one of the Sink boys accidentally dropped by to see how our household was progressing? Even though neither one of them ever even sent a Christmas card?

But the old man couldn't do anything about the

Doberman, either. It was that gentleness of his that my mother always bragged on him about. I didn't see this side of him, or wasn't ready to see it, until a couple of days later, when it was too sad to miss.

Toward the last pales of Maggie's heat spell, there was a day when the Doberman was gone from the porch, and we thought it was all over. But the morning after, there was a new suitor-dog outside. He wasn't on the porch. He was out in the edge of the cane. He was a sick, scabby, and practically hairless combination of Spitz and setter. From way over in the cane, he watched Maggie at the screen with wheat-colored rheumy eyes. You could see he was trying to respond more than he was; he just lay there nodding and raising his ears, then falling asleep unwillingly, it seemed. There was a mule with him. The mule was emaciated and showed burnt, hairless marks where an old harness had been. His nosey face looked older than stone, and he crumbled around the knee knobs with tremens. This mule stood in the shadowed bend of the cane behind the dog. Apparently the mule and dog were friends, joined up to see the last of it together. They were both clearly terminal. A big mule like he was, by the way, is a sensational sight to behold when you get up early and just look for the usual cane and St. Augustine grass. He seemed to be looming back and sponsoring some last romantic wish of the Spitz-setter in front. I think the dog had brought them as far as they could go.

The old man and I saw them together at the bay window. Both of us were looking for the leaves, and then, surprise!

"All right, Daddy, I'll go be getting the lime in the garage while you get the shotgun. Better put in some double-aught shells."

"Just hold it. . . ."

". . . Put both those scarecrows out of their misery in a minute, you get a good shot to the brain on 'em. I can tell they ain't gonna run." I was thinking, "Big game. See something *big* collapse at last."

"You better quit running your mouth that direction, Harry. I don't want to hear that kind of. . . . We're just going to leave those poor fellas alone. They look like they're on the move." My mother had come up, in her robe.

"That's the strangest thing I ever saw in my life. Did you ever see a mule and a dog go along together?"

"I believe they may have hydrophobia, Donna. Now what we're going to do is just ease out to the car, me and Harry, and see if we can't just not disturb them driving out. And they'll go on away. But honey, you don't go outside till they do."

"You want me to call the sheriff?"

The old man faked three paragraphs of thought.

"I don't think so. We don't know anything for sure yet. They look like they're on the move. Don't they? You ever seen a mule and a dog hang around together more than . . ." he chuckled, and kissed her. He took me to school in the car.

The animals didn't leave. They were still out there four days later. The old man's sense of beauty was hurt. The mule looked like an upright hewed-out cow-chip, the dog just a mangy rubble. We had a lovely yard, ordinarily. He sent me out to scare them off, but there was a massive odor coming off them when I got near; I quit waving; they'd ignored me anyway. Another day he sent me back in my room for my air rifle. He wanted me to pop them. I was groping away at the lever in an unworldly bliss and breaking out the screen door, when he called—

"Wait!" he said. "Don't do that. No use to hurt them if they just *can't* move." The old man's as gentle as a nerve, I find out. It got him into wells of trouble later. When he gave me money, and other prizes; when he raised up Harley Butte, a mulatto, to foreman over white workers at the mattress factory. There were certain bawling natural demands he couldn't deny. He thought Harley wanted the foreman position to a suicidal degree; he thought the mule and the dog had seen enough trouble.

"There's an organization I've heard of that handles these type of animals," he said. The dog and mule outside were getting sicker. The mule lay down. The dog attempted something drastic toward Maggie. It brought him out to the middle of the yard, and the mule wallowed loyally out in the grass too, ten feet behind him.

There was no SPCA around, burrow the phone book as the old man did. He would not call the sheriff, or any kind of exterminating veterinarian. Everybody knew that the Dream of Pines vet was an incompetent softy who always advised death for the least bruise on dog or cat, such a hater of animal pain he was.

I was spying in the cane one afternoon and caught him, the old man, out in the yard right by the dog; he was whispering something to the creature, and smiled. The dog lifted up, grunted pitifully, and moved a couple of feet over, then collapsed. I moved in to the old man's thigh, not caring about any secrecy then. Where the dog had lain in the grass, hair remained, and hundreds of maggots. The old man winced, and groaned.

"Harry. This is the first time in my life I ever knew God let things like this happen." The old man was born on a farm, but he was the spoiled child, with his mother taking her hands off his eyes only at the daylight of a '30's village called Town, Louisiana, twenty miles east of Dream of Pines. "Don't let's tell Mother about this now."

He looked over at the mule.

"I guess you're getting worked on too. Old fella."

He scanned his yard beyond the mule, with his eyes full of tears.

"I've read books about it," he said flatly. "But somebody has been keeping the real information from me. When things die, they get eaten by worms. They really do." He milked the cleft of his chin with a hand.

He hadn't wanted the sheriff to come over and finish the animals with a quick .32 slug. He didn't want the sheriff's checkerboard demarcated car in his driveway. The old man, as a snob, thought he was better reputed than that. He knew that a number of people in Dream of Pines worshipped him as the boss of the only clean and decent factory in town, and stood in line to apply for work under him, quitting the paper mills because of toxic dirt in their skin, and the old man gave a ten cent better wage per hour. Because of gentleness, a modicum of gentleness on his part: He thought no one should work for eighty-five cents an hour, be he a wino goof-off, even. He was not a hero of humane feeling; this gentle portion of himself mixed up his mind quite a bit, and landed him in protracted confusion, when some simple act was called for. In his study, thinking about a case like the dog and the mule in the yard, he'd get a box of matches and strike them one after another just to see them burn. Like me, he'd have to *dream* an answer before he knew it was right. He'd wake up and know what he ought to do, having just seen some righteous movie version of himself in his dream. Either that, or my mother told him in a simple sentence what she thought he ought to do, and he'd do it immediately, the old man thinking, like me, that the voice of a female was God's direct edict. The old man and I always tended to trust every girl we ever knew, and little else but our own dreams in sleep.

Mother didn't say a word this time. The animals stayed two weeks in the yard. The old man came into breakfast beat-out and his mouth curled around a Camel. His eyes were dull and bloody. He drank coffee like there was bourbon whiskey in it. Who knows what he thought on in the office, a little acoustically insulated glass cell on the mezzanine of the factory.

Then on a Saturday night he woke me up sometime way into the sleeping hours. He wore these dull flannel pajamas with duplicated scenes of the Hawaiian Islands on them. My mother was up; I heard her rustling around the old man's study, and calling out softly to him asking where the cigarettes were. A cigarette was a rare experience with Mother, like fireworks once a year every July Fourth at the country club. I knew something extraordinary had happened. He'd dreamed something, or the old lady had risen up in the night and commanded something in short, simple English. She was a fading brunette babe like Elizabeth Taylor in the shadows, and had to be listened to.

He said he wanted me to be up at six to go out in the yard with him. There was a fellow he'd phoned a while ago who owned a tractor and would be waiting to drag the animals off with a special sort of chain harness. He left me feeling drab and alarmed in the borders of sleep. I wanted to personally shoot the big mule sucker and see him cave in; and wanted to go to sleep at the same time. Mother came in and sat on the end of my bed.

"You do know why Daddy's waited so long to kill them, don't you, Harry?"

"No, Ma'am."

"He thinks he can shoot them in a kinder way than what the sheriff would." She caressed my foot under the covers.

"A bullet to the brain is just a bullet to the brain, though, isn't it Momma? You can't die quick in different ways."

"I don't like to hear you talk like that, Harry. Little boys aren't supposed to be thinking about bullets to the brain."

"But Daddy's waited wrong this time. They ought

88

to've been put out of their misery a couple weeks ago."

"Oh Harry. Daddy has to think it out. You don't have to do that." She'd smoked her annual cigarette and was looking around my room for somewhere to put the butt. I was the last child, and had a married brother and sister living out in far parts of the South. Mother always looked at me like I was not quite real, having come as late to her as I did—when she was thirty-eight—and I was an experiment, bizarre in the natural order of things. We'd also had an informally adopted foster boy who was making it big out West. Her children, the children of the thirties, must have been appearing to her mind when she looked at me. I was born in 1942, and was as strange as World War II. She always treated me as if I were an interesting waif. I was at the house as an only child from the time my brother married, when I was seven.

"You know you were a happy surprise to us. Daddy and I want you to turn out especially good," she said. I slept on that.

The animals weren't on the lawn as the old man and I came out at six. They'd gotten in the cane and smashed it up, wallowing. The mule was lying dead among some broken stalks. The dog lifted up his head in the foot-high pinplants on the edge of the cane. He smiled when the old man shot him with the twelve-gauge.

The man with the tractor was late. We just hung out between the cane and the porch and had ample time to study the corpses. A dead mule was such a big thing my mind couldn't really scope it. I had to think about him in pieces, like the dead feet, the dead eyes, the dead backbone. The wet pink scab of the dog, with the red shotgun dots on his skull.

The sun came up and we heard noises from the Sink mansions. At last the man with the tractor came up the drive. His name was Swell Melton; he regularly was

89

manager of the Self-Wash laundromat in Dream of Pines, but that didn't take all his time. All he did, as a matter of fact, was keep replacing the adhesive tape on the sign over the washers saying "Please Do Not Die In The Machines As It Colors Your Next Man's Wash." He was a lean, jaded fellow who got along with everybody, even the old man when he called him about the tractor at midnight. He wore the gray cotton pants and shirt which made you get the idea he was hovering about in a semi-official position.

He didn't hesitate a second about the dead animals. He backed up in the cane shallows, jumped off, and tied a chain around the mule's rear feet, then strapped the dog's corpse to the chain with a rope. Then he cranked up and towed them off. The dog hung off the load in a grotesque way as the tractor dragged him and the mule, scraping, out the drive and to the Pierre Hills road.

The old man and I were hypnotized by the sight. He held on to his shotgun by the barrel, and we both wandered out behind the tractor to the road. Ode, the old man, looked like a moronic recruit in the marines.

We were standing out in the road beholding the tractor disappear at five miles an hour as Ollie Sink crept up to our backs in his black Chrysler. He wanted by, and we were blocking his way. The old man turned around and did an inane thing: he tried to hide the gun against his side. Ollie, a big red face above white shirt collars and a black coat, glowered at the old man like, yes, he now knew how his peacock Bayard had disappeared, with this early morning gunner Monroe running around the hills. Ollie's eyes were fixed, burning through his windshield, at the corpse-heap dragging behind the tractor ahead; then he observed the old man's shotgun and the old man's guilty face, and ripped off in his car. The old man was trying to get up a neighborly sentence to shout to Ollie. But a dead mule *and* dog, seeming to be secretly spirited away in the early hours like this—he couldn't say anything about the scene that Ollie was seeing.

I think he gave up trying to be a perfect neighbor to the Sink boys that morning. I don't know what the deal was when the old man got us into Pierre Hills, what clause in the deed said if he was to buy from those land-scathing barons, he had to like them reverently too. But he quit it that morning, and all I heard the rest of my years in the house was how depraved and ugly and destructive of the woodland the Sink brothers were. My mother flew into them, after the old man let out the plug, beginning with how tacky their big houses were and how stupid their wives were, at the bridge dinner and other social events at the country club.

"That peacock Bayard needed killing," said the old man, taking another cup of coffee with his Camel. "Don't tell anybody else, Harry, but I was proud of you when you bashed him. I'm not for causing hurt to animals—you know that." He let out a stream of smoke and closed his eyes so it made him look confident and handsome as Bogart. I imagine he was getting much petting from Donna in those days. After all, he was Ode Elann Monroe, slayer of the Spitz-setter. Puller of the trigger when the chips were down.

JOANNE GREENBERG

Joanne Greenberg was born in Brooklyn, New York
in 1932 and educated at American University, and
presently lives in Colorado. She is the author of a
collection of short stories and three novels, including
the pseudonymous *I Never Promised You a Rose
Garden*. Ms. Greenberg says of "Upon the Waters":
"The story . . . is a warning to the unwary."

UPON THE WATERS

*To Messrs. Stan Laurel and Oliver Hardy
with affectionate respect.*

It was a bright green day. The big trees on the side
streets were raining seeds and the wind stirred in its
second sleep. A long flatbed truck came rattling down
Grant Street and stopped by the new steel, chrome,
and glass building. The building's lines were so austere
it made Cephas wonder if anyone really worked in it.
Then he saw some women going in. Good. He checked
his appearance by hitching up to the rearview mirror.
He was wearing a clean white shirt and a bow tie, and
his thin grey hair had been slicked down with water.
When he was sure he was presentable, he got down
out of the cab of the truck, dusted himself off and began to walk slowly toward the building. It had been
many years—perhaps they had moved. No, there was
the sign: BOONE COUNTY DEPARTMENT OF
WELFARE. The last time he had been here the building was a temporary shed and the people were lined

up outside waiting for the relief trucks to come. That was in 1934, in the winter. His father had been proud of holding out till '34. He stopped and looked at the building again. Some secretaries came out, laughing and talking. They didn't look at him, being used to seeing people who came hesitantly to their offices to acknowledge failure in life. Cephas checked himself again in the big glass door and then went in. There was a large booth with a woman behind it and eight or nine rows of benches facing it. People were sitting quietly, staring at nothing, waiting. To the right there were a series of chutes with numbers over them. Cephas went up to the booth.

"Take a number," the woman said, without looking at him.

"Ma'am?"

"You take a number and wait your turn. We'll call you."

He took one of the plastic number cards. It said 15. He went back, sat down and waited. "Five," the woman called. A heavy woman got up slowly and went to the booth and then to one of the chutes. Cephas waited. Minutes were born, ripened, aged, and died without issue. "Number six." Around him the spring-time asthmatics whistled and gasped. He looked at the cracks in his fingers. "Number seven." An hour went by, another. A number, another. He was afraid to go out and check his truck lest the line speed up and he lose his place. "Number thirteen," the woman called.

So they came to his number at last and he went up to the desk, gave back the plastic card and was directed to his chute. Another woman was there at another desk. She took his name, Cephas Ribble, and his age, sixty-eight. Had he been given aid before? Yes. Had he been on General Assistance, Aid to the Needy Disabled? Tuberculosis?

"It was what they called Relief."

"Yes, but under what category was it?"

"It was for the people that was off their farms or else didn't have nothin' to eat. They called it Goin' On The County. It was back in 19 and 34. We held out till '34."

"I see. Now you are applying for the old age pension?" He said he wasn't.

"Are you married, Mr. Ribble?" She sighed. "Never had the pleasure," he said.

"Are you in emergency status?" He said he wasn't.

"All right, then, take this card and go to room 11, on your left." She pressed a little light or something and he felt the people shifting their weight on the benches behind him. Number sixteen, he expected. He made his way to room 11.

The lady there was nice; he could see it right off. She told him about the different kinds of what they called Aid, and then she had him sign some forms: permission to inquire into his bank account, acceptance of surplus or donated food, release of medical information, and several others. Then she said sympathetically, "In what way are you disabled?"

He thought about all the ways a man might be disabled and checked each one off. It was a proud moment, a man sixty-eight without one thing in the world to complain of in his health.

"I ain't disabled no way, but I'm pleased you asked me, though. A man don't take time to be grateful for things like his health. If the shoe don't pinch, you don't take notice, do you." He sat back, contented. Then he realized that the sun was getting hotter and what with everything in the truck, he'd better get on. The woman had put down her ball point pen. "Mr. Ribble, if you aren't disabled or without funds, what kind of aid do you want?" A shadow of irritation crossed her face.

"No aid at all," he said. "This is about somethin' different." He tried to hold down his excitement. It was his special day, a day for which he had waited for over a decade, but it was no use bragging and playing the boy, so he said no more. The woman was very annoyed. "Then why didn't you tell the worker at the desk?"

"She didn't give me no chance, ma'am, an' neither did that other lady. I bet you don't have many repair men comin' in here to fix things—not above once, anyway."

"Well, Mr. Ribble, what is it you want?" She heard the noise of co-workers leaving and returning from their coffee breaks. She sighed and began to drum her fingers, but he wasn't aware of her impatience. He was beginning back in 1934. Good God, she would have to listen to all of it!

"'34 cleaned us out—cleaned us to bone. You wonder how *farmers* could go hungry. I don't know, but we did. After the drought hit there was nothin' to do but come in town an' sign up on the County. Twice a month my pa would come in an' bring back food. Sometimes I came with him. I seen them lines of hungry men just standin' out there like they was poleaxed an' hadn't fallen yet. I tell you, them days was pitiful, *pitiful*." He glanced up at her and then smiled. "I'm glad to see *you* done good since—got a new buildin' an' all. Yes, you come right up." He looked around with approval at the progress they had made.

"Mr. Ribble . . . ?" He returned. "See, we taken the Relief, but we never got to tell nobody the good it done for us. After that year, things got a little better, and soon we was on toward bein' a payin' farm again. In '46 we built us a new house—every convenience, an' in '56 we got some of them automated units for cattle care. Two years ago we was doin' good, an' last year, I knew it was time to think about My Plan for real. It was time to Thank The Welfare."

"Mr. Ribble, thanks are not necessary. . . ."

"Don't you mind, ma'am, you just get your men an' come with me."

"I beg your pardon. . . ."

"I do more than talk, ma'am. You come on out an' bring your men."

Mr. Morrissey had come back from his coffee break and was standing in the hall. She signaled him with her eyes as she followed Cephas Ribble, now walking proud and sure out to his truck. He sighed and followed, wondering why he was always around when somebody needed to make a madness plain. Why did it never happen to McFarland?

Cephas was reaching into his pocket and they thought: *gun.* He took out a piece of paper and turned to them as they stood transfixed and pale and thinking of violence. "I got it all here, all of what's in the truck. Get your men, ma'am; no use wastin' time. It's all in the truck and if it don't get unloaded soon, it's gonna spoil."

"What is this about, Mr. Ribble?"

"My donation, ma'am, I told you. I'm givin' the Relief six hundred chickens, thirty bushels of tomatoes, thirty bushels of apricots—I figured for variety, an' don't you think the apricots was a good idea, though?—ten bushels Eyetalian beans, six firkins of butter—ma'am, you better get them chickens out, it don't do to keep 'em in this sun. I thought about milk, so I give two cans—that's one hundred gallons of milk, you know, for the babies."

They were dumbfounded. Cephas could see that. He wanted to tell them that he wasn't trying to be big. Everybody gives what he can. He'd even signed a form right there in the office about promising to accept donated food and clothing. Their amazement at his gift embarrassed him. Then he realized that it was probably the only way they could thank him—by making a fuss. People on the state payroll must have to walk a

pretty narrow line. They'd have to be on the lookout
for people taking advantage. That was it. It was deep
work, that welfare, mighty deep work.

"What are we supposed to do with all that food?"
Mr. Morrissey said. Cephas saw that the man was
making sure it wasn't a bribe. "Why, give it to the poor.
Call 'em in an' let 'em get it. You can have your men
unload it right now, an' I'd do it quick if I was you—like
I said, it won't be long till it starts to turn in all this
heat."

Mr. Morrissey tried to explain that modern welfare
methods were different from those of 1934. Even then,
the food had been U.S. surplus and not privately donated. It had come from government warehouses.
Cephas spoke of the stupidity and waste of Government
and rained invective on the Soil Bank and the Department of Agriculture. Mr. Morrissey tried again. "We
don't give out any *food*. There hasn't been any *donated*
since 1916!"

No doubt of it, these welfare people had to be awful
careful. Cephas nodded. "The others do what they can
—don't blame 'em if it don't seem like much," he said
sympathetically. "I signed that slip in there about the
donated food, so there must *be* some donated."

"It's done because of an obsolete law," Mrs. Traphagen argued, "one of the old Poor Laws that never got
taken off the books."

"—an' here you folks are followin' it, right today,"
Cephas mused, "it must make you mighty proud."

"Mr. Ribble, *we have no place to store all this!*"

Cephas found his throat tightening with happiness.
He had come in humility, waited all the morning just
so he could show his small gratitude and be gone, and
here were these people thunderstruck at the plenty.
"Mister," he said, "I pay my taxes without complainin',
but I never knowed how hard you people was workin'
for your money. You got to guard against every kind of

bribes and invitations to break the law; you got to find ways to get this food to the poor people so fast, you can't even store it! By God, mister, you make me proud to be an American!"

A policeman had stopped by the truck and was tranquilly writing a ticket. Cephas excused himself modestly and strode off to defend his situation. The two workers stood staring after him as he engaged the officer. It was, after all, state law that food could be donated. Had the department no parking place for donors? The policeman looked over at the stunned bearers of the state's trust. He had stopped writing.

"Could that truck fit in the workers' parking lot?" Morrissey murmured.

"What are we going to *do* with it all?" whimpered Mrs. Traphagen.

"All those chickens—six hundred chickens!"

"The poor will never stand for it," Mrs. Traphagen sighed.

"First things first," Mr. Morrissey decided, and went to confront the policeman.

Cephas's truck in the workers' parking lot blocked all their cars. As a consequence, the aid applications of eight families were held pending investigation. Six discharged inmates of the state hospital remained incarcerated for a week longer pending home checkups. Thirty-seven women washed floors and children's faces in the expectation of home visits which were not made. A meeting on venereal disease at the Midtown Hotel was one speaker short, and high school students scheduled to hear Social Work, Career of Tomorrow, remained unedified. Applicants who came to apply for aid that afternoon were turned away. There was no trade in little plastic cards and the hive of offices was empty. But the people of the Boone County Department of Public Welfare were not idle. It was only that the action had moved from the desks and files and chutes to the workers' parking lot and into the hands of its glad tyrant, Cephas Ribble.

All afternoon Cephas lifted huge baskets of apricots and tomatoes into the arms of the welfare workers. All afternoon they went from his truck to their cars carrying the baskets, chickens festooned limply over their arms. When they complained to Mr. Morrissey, he waved them off. Were they to go to every home and deliver the food, they asked? Were big families to get the same amount as small families?

Cephas was a titan. He lifted smiling, and loaded with a strong arm. He never stopped for rest or to take a drink. The truck steamed in the hot spring light, but he was living at height, unbothered by the heat or the closeness or the increasing rankness of his chickens. Of course he saw that the welfare people weren't dressed for unloading food. They were dressed for church, looked like. It was deep work, very deep, working for the state. You had to set a good example. You had to dress up and talk very educated so as to give the poor a moral uplift.

You had to be honest. A poor man could lie—he'd been poor himself so he knew, but it must be a torment to deal with people free to lie and not be able to do it yourself.

By 3:30 the truck had been unloaded into the cars and Cephas was free to go home and take up his daily life again. He shook hands with the director and the casework supervisor, the head bookkeeper and the statistician. To them he presented his itemized list, carefully weighed and given the market value as of yesterday, in case they needed it for their records. Then he carefully turned the truck out of the parking lot, waved goodbye to the sweating group, nosed into the sluggish mass of afternoon traffic and began to head home. The lot burst into a cacophony of high-pitched voices:

"I've got three mothers of dropouts to visit!"

"What am I going to *do* with all this stuff?"

"Who do we give this to? My people won't take the Lady Bountiful bit!"

"Does it count on their food allowance? Do we go down Vandalia and hand out apricots to every kid we see?"

"I don't have the time!"

"Which families get it?"

"Do we take the value off next month's check?"

"It's hopeless to try to distribute this fairly," the supervisor said.

"It will cost us close to a thousand dollars to distribute it at all," the statistician said.

"It would cost us close to two thousand to alter next month's checks," the bookkeeper said, "and the law specifies that we have to take extra income-in-kind off the monthly allowance."

"If I were you," Morrissey said, "I would take all this home and eat it and not let anyone know about it."

"Mr. Morrissey!" Mrs. Traphagen's face paled away the red of her exertion. "That is fraud! You know as well as I do what would happen if it got out that we had diverted welfare commodities to our own use! Can you imagine what the mayor would say, what the governor would say, the state legislature, the Department of Health, Education, and Welfare, the National Association of Social Workers!" She had begun to tremble and the two chickens that were hanging over her arm nodded to one another, with a kind of slow decorum, their eyes closed righteously against the thought. Motors started, horns sounded and cars began to clot the exit of the parking lot. The air was redolent.

As the afternoon wore on, apricots began to appear in the hands of children from Sixteenth and Vandalia Street all the way to the Boulevard. Tomatoes flamed briefly on the windowsills of the Negro ghetto between

Fourteenth and Kirk, and on one block, there was a chicken in every pot.

The complaints began early the next day. Sixteen Negroes called the Mayor's Committee on Discrimination claiming that chickens, fruit, and vegetables had been given to all the white disadvantaged, while they had received tomatoes, half of them rotten. A rumor began that the food had been impregnated with contraceptive medicine to test on the poor and that three people had died from it. The Health Department finally issued a denial, which brought a score of reporters to its door. During the questioning by reporters, a chemist at the department called the whole affair "the blatherings of a bunch of pinheads on the lunatic fringe." On the following day, the department received complaints from the ACLU, the Black Muslims and the Diocesan Council, all of whom demanded apologies. There were eighteen calls at the Department of Welfare protesting a tomato "bombing" which had taken place on Fourteenth and Vandalia, in which passersby had been hit with tomatoes dropped from the roofs of slum houses. The callers demanded that the families of those involved be stricken from the welfare rolls as relief cheaters, encouraging waste and damaging the moral fiber of the young. Twenty-two mothers on the Aid to Dependent Children program picketed the governor's mansion carrying placards saying *Hope, Not Handouts* and *Jobs, Not Charity*. Sixty-eight welfare clients called to say that they had received no food at all and demanded equal service. When they heard that the Vandalia Street mothers were picketing, a group of them went down to protest. Words were exchanged between the two groups and a riot ensued in which sixteen people were hospitalized for injuries, including six members of the city's riot squad. Seven of the leaders and four Black Power advocates who were bystanders were jailed pending investigation. The FBI was called into

the case in the evening to ascertain if the riot was
Communist-inspired. At ten o'clock, the mayor went on
TV with a plea for reason and patience. He stated that
the riot was a reflection of the general decline in American morals and a lack of respect for the law. He ordered a six-man commission to be set up to hear
testimony and make recommendations. A political op-
ponent demanded a thorough investigation of the
county welfare system, the War on Poverty and the
local university's hippies. On the following day, Mrs.
Traphagen was unable to go to work at the welfare
office, having been badly scalded on the hand while
canning a bushel of apricots.

Cephas Ribble remembered everyone at the Welfare
Office in his prayers. After work he would think about
the day he had spent in the city and of his various
triumphs. The surprise and wonder on the faces of the
workers, and the modest awe of the woman who had
said, "Mr. Ribble, you don't need to thank us," humbled
and moved him. It had been a wonderful day. He had
given his plenty unto the poor, plenty that was the doing of his own hands. He rose refreshed into his work,
marveling at the meaning and grandeur in which his
simplest chores were suddenly invested. "By God," he
said, as he checked his chickens, "a man has his good
to do. I'm gonna do it every year. I'm gonna have a
day for the poor. Yessir, every year!" And he smiled
genially on the chickens, the outbuildings, and the
ripening fields of a generous land.

PAUL SMITH

Paul Smith, now in his middle forties, is a product of the Dublin slums. All but one of his five novels have been banned in Ireland. Mr. Smith is now living in London and working on an autobiographical novel entitled *The Man. Annie,* a novel about a young girl's fight for integrity, will be published by The Dial Press in 1972.

ANNIE

It was a night in fall, smoky and spiked with the year's first frost, getting in quick, short stabs at my face. A night when hunger cramps, filling us with a fuel of their own on which we could operate, took us from our lane and Rock Street to the heightened silence and sad Protestant remoteness of the tree-lined roads edging the city. A night for hunting and robbing and boxing-the-fox. And at that hour when trees, ragged in a drunken display of the season's fading, purpled, and men and the shadows of men, in frayed peaked caps and upturned-collared overcoats, prowled the emptiness on foot and on bikes and muttered dark obscenities as we passed or tried with feverish eyes to lure us into lanes with offers of rides on crossbars and promised pennies.

On Northbrook Road, leaves falling from trees lay idle and curled, desolate on shorn lawns. And in big houses big fires roared in big fireplaces fenced in by big brass fenders, and in polished silences in big rooms

frilled-capped servants lit lamps—drew curtains of plush
and locked tight brass-armored doors. Behind the
houses on one side of the road, the lane into which we
had drifted stretched from Ranalagh at one end to
Leeson Park and the church the Protestants had lifted
at the other. In the lane, girls in caches of clothes gone
gray from too much washing stood tethered to fellas
who smothered with their mouths the girls' whimpers
of ruin. And within bottle-throwing distance of two-
penny uprights, loud-voiced in lusty loneliness, tramps
like Johnny Forty Coats and Gentle Josie took out years
like things from trunks and picked them over for
memories as they dragged on butts and counted
pennies before settling down for the night.

From the high, barbed-wired walls of the gardens
backing on to the lane, color fled the way it did from
the faces that were here and there raised to us as we
passed, but in the flowing red scarf on the woman who
had come into the lane before us, color smoldered like
blood, or fire.

"And *that's* not just anyone," Annie said as we
watched the woman stalking off into the distance.
"*That* wan's a lady. Outa one of these houses. And like
us, pushing herself forward on the scent of something."

"But what? And at this hour?"

"Right now, we don't care," Annie said. "Thing is to
get rid of her, because them wans are great at picking
up them telephones and ringing the police. We'll wait,"
Annie said. And, slowing down to a rambling caution,
we did wait, until the woman disappeared. Then, going
in the same direction, we headed for the wall and the
dense leafage of the Hogans' garden.

As always, Annie, with her superior agility, was over
the wall before I was, and by the time I touched
ground and was running through shrubs cold with dew
toward a maze of saplings, she had already reached the

orchard and the trees ripe with the fruit we were after. Laughing back at me, just as I reached her she told me to look, and beyond her, through trees linked with ribbons of silver made by slugs, I saw a lawn smothered under the weight of leaves and above them more leaves fluttering down to half-remembered things of earth. I saw a path unworn and cutting at crazy angles up to a terrace of gray stone, and then a house of long, narrow windows, over which the curtains had not been drawn and through which no light showed. Nevertheless, there would be people somewhere, I thought, looking into the shadows that lay with a greater hush across the house; and because silence had been intensified, thoughts fell loud and came out into the open.

"Maybe," Annie said, but it was the garden, with its aching wilderness of tangled leaf and fruit that was claiming and holding her attention—and mine, but for different reasons.

Looking for what I couldn't see, I thought it was gloomy and, in spite of Annie's shining excitement, full of sighs and uneasy rustlings, as if men or ghosts watched us from its outer darkness. And I wanted to go from it and the sudden sense of unease and the hush that was like the one that comes before an unknown trouble. But most of all I wanted to run from the silence caused not by a lack of sounds but by a waiting. And I said so. But Annie, now that her eyes were no longer shaded by hunger or anxieties, only laughed, the way I knew she would, and, pointing to the house, told me to feast my lovely wans on that.

But even the house, for all its upright elegance, seemed to me to have something wrong with it, and my frown of uneasiness said so plain. "So it's harboring a ghost in every room," Annie said, and the smile she flung was tinged with green and meant to draw. But into her mood I wouldn't be drawn. All I could do was stand there, stiffened and waiting, scanning the garden as if seeking something invisible and dangerous; not speaking, not even answering when what she said demanded an answer; and not moving, either, even when, with a wild, rising lightness, she began to spread the sacks at our feet.

Watching her go from tree to tree on footsteps that after a time slowed to a wander, I began to think it strange that, whereas even when there was nothing to fear, I was always an alien in the gardens we invaded, and walked soft and unsure on the ground under me, something new and entirely different happened to her. A change came in her I could never explain. It was as if, during the jump from the wall to the ground, something happened that took her from me, and not only from me but from troubles for which she had no remedy, to where nothing and nobody could follow. It was as if a garden was the goal of some journey, and when in one her face lost its set-for-strife look and laughter instead of rebellion bubbled up inside her. Also, something new came into her eyes, and from her voice all protest went. Anger also went: angers large and small, old and recent, left her.

Even the one against her mother, whose spoiling bitterness, dislike, and cold indifference she didn't understand any more than she knew what that dislike was based on. All she knew was there was something in and about her that her mother didn't want to have anything to do with. This awareness of what her mother felt was always just below the surface and was one of the things she had never known how to consider in her mind, any more than she knew how to deal with the threat of the factory or the feeling her family gave her of being a person with no real place in the world or why she felt like a stray, even in the crowded bed she shared with her sisters under the roof her efforts kept over their heads.

Looking at her now, and catching the apple she

threw me after first wiping it on her chest, some of the
things Annie felt swirled in my mind and crossed each
other the way her angers did, and listing those, they
included persons and groups she held a burning anger
against: some servants and almost every single policeman she came across. Sometimes the list flourished, till
it included telephones, which she said were a sleeveen
invention; rent collectors, and Jewmen who pushed
blankets, sheets, and holy pictures onto people who
couldn't afford them; landlords, and people who
were neither rich nor poor—shopkeepers who acted as
if she had come to rob them even when she hadn't;
all buildings, like chapels and churches, banks and hos-
pitals, whose workings she didn't understand and whose
usefulness she doubted; and at the end of the list, the
youngfellas she fought off who would never forgive
her for the difficulties she put in their way of loving
her. But then, Annie didn't believe in love, never
played at it the way Carmel Mac and youngwans like
Maggie Hyland did. She wouldn't've written notes to
youngfellas even if she could write, and once, when
Jim Mac sent her one, she put the tin hat on him.

Following the turn my thoughts had taken, I didn't
hear at first the question she flung, and when she repeated it I asked, "Enough what?"

"Why, fruit, of course," she said and dropped on the
ground beside me the load of apples she had gathered
in her pinny.

"What about it?" I asked.

"I was saying," she replied, "there must be enough
in this garden to keep us fed and in business for a
month. I also asked, how many fruit trees in this whole
orchard?"

"Twenty applers at least," I said. "And pears," I
added.

"But pears bruise easy," she said.

"And some were cherries," I told her. "Only the cherries are over."

"Even so," she said, "there must be thousands of apples and them alone should take us through the winter, and what's left of the flowers see us through Christmas. But c'mon," she said, "we've wasted enough time." And as she readied me and herself for a fuller future, I saw her face in its new way, topping her pinny, glowing like a plum in the long grass that had not been cut. And, caught suddenly on her mood, I heard her laugh. Then, all at once, her laugh froze, and in me there was a shock as if a knife thrown had struck and shivered in my chest. At the same time—and together—we stopped dead in our tracks, unable to take in what happened. There was somebody in the garden. A shape, a movement, over by a trellis of crimson-elbowed thorns fronting a clump of trees hiding a path that led to where we had not looked.

Strength rolled back, the way water does from a swimmer, and only Annie's hand, like a green nerve on my wrist, kept me upright.

It's the light. A trick of light, or a leaf falling, I thought. Or the wind, maybe, disturbing the sinister quiet. But the garden and everything in it was completely static, rigid, the equation of a garden.

"It's a copper," Annie hissed.

But the shape had been a double one. A dark, double shape. And the picture denting my mind was of two people coming together, and the image so strong I had to remind myself where we were: in a garden, big and unexplored, surrounded by a high wall spiked with broken bottle stumps and rigged with four lines of barbed wire to keep people like us out. A gate was let into the base of the wall. A gate that opened into the lane. A small wicker gate, locked. Gates always were. To get into the garden, you'd have to come through that gate, from the house, or over the wall. And nobody but us had come over that wall.

Annie let go my wrist and together we bent down and gently picked up our sacks. And then we turned. And saw. With the eyes of the vicious searching a face for wounds, we probed, and stared stunned. Annie's breath against the side of my face brushed cold. For there in the garden, not twenty feet away from us, stood two men, like abstracted forms to which shadows had been attached. Two men. One taller than the other. One older than the other. And the taller of the two, with his arm round the other man's shoulders, said:

"I'm tired of all this. I shall tell her. I shall tell her she must go away now."

The dry thread of the voice was one I'd heard before.

"Two men," Annie whispered, "loving."

And they were. You could see when they stopped moving and stood together, swaying a little until they found their foothold, the balance of one so dependent on the other that there was no way of telling where one man ended and the other began. Two men. And in that garden, on leaves that a sudden, sharp, erratic wind was stirring, the taller of the two, thinking himself unseen, went down on his knees in front of the other and an urgent, hungry labor took place. Two men. And the less tidy, younger, and rowdier stood and waited, his hands cradling the head of the kneeling man and the mouth into which he was thrusting himself. Two men. And the younger stepped back after a time, out of the other's reach, and, making a loose, shallow cup of his hand, let it fall on his prick. In the light that endured, he stood and watched steady the older man. Then, arching back, he brought his head forward to see his own body's richness, with its bluish undertones of snow and marble, burst upward on release before it poured sulkily down onto the indifferent earth. Two men. And the one on his knees cried out and up at the propitiating smile of the man on his feet, or his soul did, and another in distress echoed it somewhere in the great house or in the garden in the dark.

I heard Annie's breath begin, and in the seconds that began to flow again something or someone moved in the shrubs screening the gate. A cat, maybe, or in the lane a kid like us was pitching stones. I looked at Annie, but she remained motionless, suspended, unable to move back or forth. And then she did move, silent except for the friction of cotton on brown skin. From me and them she went, as if from some unspeakable mystery.

"Only two men," I said, following her. "That's all," I added, wanting to repair possible damage, while across my mind slanted remembrances of things heard and the scrawl of chalked things seen.

"One of *them* smells of cigars, hair oil, and leather," I whispered and waited to be asked, "Which one?" and when I wasn't I said, "Mr. Hogan does," for that's who the man on his knees was.

Annie's face, though serious, reflected nothing, but her shoulders under her pinny were high and set tense. "I'm off," she said.

"But the apples—" I began.

"We'll do without them," she said, and although sweat showed on her face, she somehow looked cold.

"We'll come back tomorrow night, then," I said.

And we did. But that first night all we did was go from that garden empty-handed, Annie in silence and me burdened with nothing more substantial than thoughts broken and scattered, thoughts about Mr. Hogan and the rough he had finally selected from the hordes roaming the roads. And going over the wall and dropping down into the lane, we came face to face with Mrs. Hogan.

Not hiding, the way Mrs. Kirwan and the rest of the gentry did when they tried to trap us as we left a garden. And not pouncing with a moistened hiss, the way Miss Lemon did and as we expected Mrs. Hogan would. But just standing untouchable in a shroud of silence, and looking not at us but at some other situation altogether, and, from the cut of her, one in which there wasn't much hope.

Eyeing her, we backed from her, straightening ourselves as we did so and *waiting*—to be noticed, to shout down the crimes she was bound to allege against us. And at the same time, thanking Christ we carried nothing and that our sacks were empty.

But she didn't accuse. All she did was stand in a tweed-warmed stupor, her arms tight against her sides, her spine backed hard against her own stone wall.

"Sick," Annie ventured, but only after the shock of the meeting had eased up some.

But the devil a sick, I thought into the fear that with Mrs. Hogan's silence was beginning to take possession. Women like Mrs. Hogan don't get sick in lanes. There was no need. Besides, I could see, in spite of my fear, that the disturbance Mrs. Hogan's dark eyes were sucking us into wasn't sickness.

"What, then?" Annie asked, and pity, I knew, was stirring and would any minute now be making her stubborn.

I didn't know, and I said so. Shriveled, even shrunken, in her tweeds and the crimson silk scarf at her throat, Mrs. Hogan was. But not sick: at least, not stomach sick.

"She must be." Annie bent on denying me my senses, and only because Mrs. Hogan was acting as if we weren't within miles of her. So maybe we weren't, but Mrs. Hogan wasn't standing in that lane, either, for even as Annie spoke I remembered the red scarf we had seen on the woman in the lane, and I knew instantly

where it was Mrs. Hogan had put herself. Mrs. Hogan
was on the garden side of her own stone wall, that's
where Mrs. Hogan was: hearing what we had heard
and seeing what we had seen, except that, from the
look of her, *her* eyes would never be used for ordinary
sights again. And it wasn't sickness crippling Mrs.
Hogan. It was disgust. Disgust, plain and simple. A
deadly disgust, disfiguring Mrs. Hogan's face, until it
changed, and her expression then seemed to contract
till it reached some point that went way beyond disgust and rage, and even pain. And a loud cry, strong
and clear, tore from Mrs. Hogan—and, turning her face
to the wall, she let the bricks take it.

We could hear, then, her teeth begin to grate. Like
teeth on teeth, the sound was, till Annie moved. Half
a step she took in front of me, and in quick anxiety she
went toward Mrs. Hogan. I could almost feel her heart
against my own, and I shivered, the way I did when
Miz Robey let me hold the ashes of Mr. Robey in my
arms. And then my hands begged and my voice swam
up as my hair bristled, and in the lane the encroaching
dark was flung back and the light, like teeth, bared
itself to consume. I spoke again, but Annie went on as
if I hadn't. I could hear her feet, narrow and bony,
splaying on gravel, and the snarl of twigs under them
snapped. I heard her say, "Mrs.—" and add, "Ma'am,"
and I wanted to shout, "Look out!" and I did, but late,
for the sound Annie was making was already off-guard
and as soft as the smile on a sleeper's mouth.

I saw her touch the tweed elbow. And then I saw
the tweed elbow shoot out and strike, like a streel, like
an upright belting a man begging love. Mrs. Hogan
struck Annie's hand from her. I saw the clean creases
in the clean tweed sleeve, and Annie's unbelieving stare
and, in the depths of her eyes, the shocked and stricken
look was plain, and awful. Backing from my sudden
venom, Mrs. Hogan's mouth twisted open, but to the

side, as if it were going to or had already displaced itself permanently. And words only half understood came through what was only a gap—words I couldn't make out but, mulling over after, I thought she must've been saying a long time, for they were all heavy and coarse and swollen. I saw her stop and rub hard the arm Annie had touched. And then she turned, Mrs. Hogan did, as if nothing had happened. And walked away. Through our stares she went, stretched thin, like the last of bread. And straight. Like a dead saint.

THOMAS SANCHEZ

Mr. Sanchez began *Rabbit Boss* when he was twenty-two, working on a cattle ranch in the High Sierra. He got his master's degree at San Francisco State College where he taught until the student-teacher strike in 1968. *Rabbit Boss* begins with the cannibalism of the Donner Party in 1846 and follows four generations of Washo Indians through 110 years. Alfred A. Knopf, Inc. will publish the novel.

RABBIT BOSS

"It's five gold dollars to drink at this here stablishmint for Injuns."

"We got five times ten a that and then some." Squirrel leaned over the polished oak counter and stared into the face that had half an unlit cigar clamped between its teeth.

"Put it up then." The bartender's words came around the cigar in a blurred lump.

The two Indians laid their money down, got their drinks and made their way through the crowded room, straining their eyes in the smoke-blue air searching for some spare space. The tables jammed with men, elbows cocking and uncocking as they drained the glasses clutched tight in blistered fists. Not all were blistered, one pair was gloved, raising the glass daintily to pursed lips. Taking the liquid in, meditatively, the man pushed back in the chair, eyes drifting in and out through the thick redwood-raftered ceiling, wandering over the elk head that grew from the main wall, monstrous, glaring down through lucid amber glass eyes. The man fastened on the eyes, raised a finger to his thin nose and stroked it, let the finger run off the smooth bridge, touch the moustache, lips, caress the trim lines of the beard. He turned, looked straight at the two Indians, the one light on his feet, cased in stained leather shirt and pants, beaded sash around the waist, tight mean eyes. The other dressed heavier, large body, not quite fat, but you can't tell with an Indian, scar on the left cheek, eyes shot full of red. "You boys," the man raised a gloved finger in the air. "You boys!" He shouted into the thick roar over the piano that pounded out songs by itself.

Captain Rex saw the gloved hand, the white broadcloth coat just slightly frayed at the cuff. It was a Bummer. He nudged Squirrel, they shouldered their way through the pack of men separating them from the table.

"Ahhh," the Bummer stood, his back straight as a board, his checkered pants showing over the tabletop, tipping his high shiny black hat a fraction above the hairline. "Glad you boys could make it through that gang. Truckee is no place for a soul to be by himself to enjoy the quiet of his own good company with a decanter of excellent Cuban rum. Cuban, that reminds me," his hand slipped inside the coat and came out with three thin cigars. "Sit down boys, have a Cuban smoke." He handed them cigars as they sat, sliced off the tip of his own with a slender silver pocket knife, placed it between his lips, struck a match, held it a half-inch in front of the tip and sucked the flame into the tobacco. "Hard to come by a good roll like this," the words glided from his mouth on slivers of smoke. "Light up boys, don't be bashful. That's right, smoke them right up, get some of that tropical jungle air in your lungs. What tribe you boys from?" He turned the cigar in his teeth, pointing it towards Captain Rex.

"Paiute," Squirrel answered. "I'm a redblooded Paiute."

"Is that so," the Bummer's eyes opened wide, the thick lashes beating into one another. "I didn't know there were any left. I thought we nabbed every little squaw between here and Santa Fe."

"I was born before you came." Squirrel lowered his eyes to the liquid in his glass.

"And you, Injun, what tribe you from?"

"I ain't."

"You ain't, ho, you're the funniest-looking Swede I ever laid my eyes on. You got to hail from some tribe, boy, all you Injuns do, that's your way."

"Washo. I'm Washo. We have no tribe."

"No tribe hell, that's the damndest thing I ever heard, no tribe, all you Injuns got tribes, that's the way you live. You must take me for green boy. Why an Injun without a tribe is like a bull with brass nipples."

"We go now, mister." Captain Rex pushed his chair out and stood.

"Hold on one minute, boy." The Bummer reached down beside him, brought up a gold-handled cane and stretched it across the table, pushing the tip lightly against the Indian's neck. "Just hold all your ponies down," he smiled, the lips pulled back exposing the two front teeth capped with the same metal as the cane handle. "Sit yourself down, Injun boy, and behave like a whiteman. You Injuns get more uppity everyday. Think you can come and go as you please. Don't have a stone's idea of how much you owe us. Sit down I said," he poked the cane harder.

Captain Rex looked at the man with the gold metal shining in his gaping mouth and sat.

"That's right, now there's a good fellow. I see your drink's up. Tender!" He shouted without taking his eyes off the Indian. "You boys prospectors?"

"No we ain't, we just—"

"Shut up, boy. I was talking to this Injun here. You just keep your trap shut and finish on up your drink. Here comes the tender now." He settled back as the glasses were refilled, picked up his, holding it in front of Captain Rex. "Here's to a pleasant friendship, Injun." He drank, watching over the rim of the glass to make certain the Indians followed his example. "Now then, what was it we was discussing? Yes, you was going to tell me if you was a prospector or not."

"I ain't."

"You mean you ain't now. All you Injuns are, you just ain't saying, just waiting while we white gents run around for years making a fool out of ourselves then you're going to walk on over and pick it all up, now that we give you something to buy with it and it's worth it to bend your back just once or twice stooping over to get it."

"I ain't."

The Bummer put the cigar to his mouth again and drew deep, blowing a pile of smoke out. "That's a pity, you could make a fortune. I bet you know where that gold lake is up Downieville way."

"Never heard of it."

"I didn't ask you if you heard of it, I said I bet you know where it is."

"I never been there."

"Sure you have, all you Injuns have, you been all over this country. You know that lake's up there someplace by the Yuba River, you know men been digging around that country for a long time now, trying to find that lake with gold glowing up from its bottom."

"I never been there."

"That's too bad for you, Injun," the Bummer ground his cigar in the can in front of him. "You know, Injun, I seen sights like that in my day. I was down in Trinidad country in '52 when old Mama Ocean herself was tossing up cartloads of golden nuggets on the sand. I seen it once and I aim to see it again. Everyone is shouting silver now, but that gold had just barely begun to be touched. It's still there where it always was and I'm cashing in. What do you think, Injun? You think I'm going to cash in?"

"Don't know."

"No," the Bummer looked at Captain Rex, his eyes riveted on the scar that slashed the cheek. "I guess you wouldn't. Then again," he winked, "maybe you would. What was it you said you did?"

"Nothin," Squirrel answered, setting his glass down. "We don't do nothin but lie round in the sun all day."

"I told you to shut up," the Bummer smiled his lips in a tight curve. "So shut up! You going to answer my question or not, Injun?" He turned back to Captain Rex.

"Odd jobs."

"Is that a natural fact, odd jobs. Most Injuns can't even speak, let alone learn how to do an odd job."

"We learned."

"I bet you did. What kind of odd jobs is it you do?"

"The odder the better," Squirrel laughed.

"I told you to shut up!" The Bummer jerked around. "If you make one more sound," he placed his hand lightly on the glistening handle of the cane, "I'm going to ram this right through one of your beady eyes, then you can have a glass one put in like that elk hanging up there on the wall; you'll see real good then."

Squirrel gulped the rest of his drink, his eyes rising to the elk.

"What kind of job is it you do, Injun? You trying to play funny games with me? Make me repeat everything twice?"

"For the Iron Road I work," Captain Rex looked straight at the Bummer.

"What could you ever do for the railroad?"

"Odd jobs."

"Don't get smart with me, Injun boy, this little stick here can go through your eye just as quick as it can through your sidekick's, it's not too choosy."

"I take the people on the Iron Road so that they can pick pigweed along the iron tracks."

"Pick pigweed, what the hell would someone want with a weed that only grows out from rocks and railroad tracks. What the hell could somebody do with it, let alone an Injun?"

"Eat it."

"You sure you're not playing games with me, Injun boy?" The Bummer laid his gloved hand on the cane.

"You asked. I told."

"Now I'm going to ask again. What is it you do?"

"Odd jobs."

"Lookit, you lying Injun," the Bummer leaned across the table. "You don't come in this barroom where they don't give a redman a drink for less than three gold dollars American. You don't come in this bar with gold jingling in your pockets an' expect me to believe you just saved it up doing odd jobs. I ain't green, Injun, so just you suppose you tell me where you and your sidekick come running into all those coins? If what you say the first time out don't set right with me I'm going to put this stick right through your head, sabe?"

"John Chinaman."

"Where?"

"Back in behind the place called Emigrant Gap."

"That's true," the Bummer nodded. "John has been up in that part of the country. I done a little tax collecting myself, but you don't have the right to tax John Chinaman, Injun boy. What you did was an illegal act. John has a claim on that land and he doesn't have to pay out one cent to you. You and your partner here could be hung up by your necks right outside in just a matter of minutes if I was to announce to these honest gents in this room that you tax-collected off a legally deeded mine. You're in a pack of trouble, redman. You're in more trouble than you ever thought you could get in outside of your tepee. Let's just examine your case. One, I could declare right now what a lawbreaker you are and you would be put to quick justice in short time, and the fairest I might add. Two, I could go for the district marshall who just happens to be in these parts right this moment over at Donner Lake and turn you over to him to atone for your sins against our mountain society. Three, you could ease your conscience and relieve yourselves of that burden of packing all that money about and simply transfer it to me to make certain it is transported back to the lawfully wronged owners. And last, number four, being a sportive man, I could invite you two boys outside and down the street for a little gambling. What do you say, Injun boy, pick a number, anyone a winner."

"What kind of gamblin is your number four?"

"Ah, my good fellow," his trim eyebrows raised high up into his forehead. "I should have known you were after my own heart itself, fair as I tried to lay it out, a true sport you are. Badger." His eyebrows came down, the smirk on his face melted by a scowl. "Badger baiting."

"In a box or barrel?"

"Barrel."

"What's the stakes?"

"Ten to one, on the dogs of course, dear boy."

"Do we get to throw our own bet?"

"Now don't be silly, Injun boy, sport is sport, and you, good fellow, have the badger. If you don't think it's right choose number one, two, or three. Hang or get yourself a chance at earning five hundred dollars American."

Captain Rex took a drink of whiskey, swishing the liquid around in his mouth with his tongue, the taste of alcohol rising in his nose.

"Make up your mind quick, Injun boy."

Captain Rex swallowed, looked between the Bummer's eyes at the delicate bridge of the nose. "Mister," he spoke slowly without moving his eyes, "your bet is on."

They made their way from the bar into the dust of the street, the man with the gold-handled cane walking jauntily in front, his stovepipe black hat tilted atop his head at a truculent angle, the two Indians trotting behind. The man strode regally through the mob of noisy men flowing in hard dirty currents along the high boardwalk, streaming into others, human islands back to back with faces in newspapers, noses almost touching the printed words. He picked his way nimbly through the forces, adroitly darting in and out at a moment's opening, riding with this wave and that; a sleek racing boat, the two Indians in tow. He steamed down an alley, simply navigated through a squall of galloping horsedrawn wagons, drifted onto another boardwalk, a calm one, and proceeded down to the end where the town ceased, suddenly broke off, the mountains towering up in all directions. The gambling party made its way up a short rise to a small box of a corral with men sitting around on the rotting planks like bears on a branch, dogs leashed beneath them, tugging at the sagging boards.

"John C. Luther!" One of the men dropped from his perch with a thump, the club of a hand held out in greeting. "Where you been? We been sittin round here since before noon seein who could collect the most slivers in his behind."

"Very good, very good," the Bummer shook the offered club warmly. "I was fortunately detained up at the Silver Elk, couple of boys begged me to be let in on the proceedings. You know me, Elliot, what a puddle of pudding I am beneath it all, never one to refuse a couple of boys some fun."

Elliot looked at the two Indians, his gaze going right between them. "One body is good as nother I s'pose, makes for higher stakes." He turned back to the Bummer. "Why don't you come over with the boys and have a snort. The badger ain't here yet."

"It's not!" The Bummer slammed the butt of his cane against the ground. "What's holdin up Ike!"

"Cain't find a barrel big enough to get the badger in," Elliot grinned. "He's a big un."

"Well then," the Bummer took the neatly folded silk handkerchief from his vest pocket, swirled it over the metal cane handle and replaced it. "We do have time for a bit of refreshment before the festivities. Boys," he nodded to the Indians. "Would you care to join us gents?"

"It would honor us," Squirrel nodded his head gravely.

"He has a voice." The Bummer looked at Elliot in surprise. "He's been silent so long I was beginning to wonder if some one had slit his vocal cords, poor boy."

"I'm surprised he speaks English at all." Elliot's face grew into a sour mask.

"Now you shouldn't go judging every creature by the color of its skin and the way it smells, Elliot." The Bummer touched the end of his cane to the man's chin. "Don't be too hard on our boys here. They're educated, no longer simple heathens, coming up in the world."

"How bout that drink, John C.," Elliot shifted impatiently.

"That we must, Elliot. First, why don't you collect ten dollars apiece from these two boys for the privilege of refreshing themselves with us and for the advancement of their education."

Captain Rex reached in his pocket, put his hand around some coins and closed his fist; they felt hot, heavy like stones, he could feel the sweat on his face, beneath his arms, trickling cool down his sides, the sun burning through the trees on the back of his neck.

"Are you or are you not going to pay this gent for a privilege, Injun boy," the Bummer asked loudly, looking down as he swirled the handkerchief on the metal again.

Captain Rex kept one of the coins in his palm and held it out. The man took it.

"I said ten dollars apiece," the Bummer glared at Squirrel. "You pay too. I thought you boys were smart, now it turns out you're proving me wrong, that's something I don't like."

Squirrel handed over his money.

The Indians walked up to the corral, the barking dogs tugging at their ropes, yanking their necks as they lunged at the intruders.

"Curious," the Bummer smiled. "Canines are not partial to Injun scents." He mounted the corral and sat rigidly, the two Indians getting up at his side. "Nice little gathering of spectators," he beamed, scanning the men sitting on every available space around the wooden box, their mouths opening only to jam in another bottle neck. Elliot handed him a filled brown bottle. "Pardon me," he held the bottle in front of the Indian next to him. "Would you be so kind as to free the opening of this decanter?" Captain Rex yanked the cork with his teeth and spit it out. "Thanks very much," he took the bottle back, wiping the opening with his handkerchief then taking two swift gulps, he emptied half the contents. "Your turn I believe," he offered the whiskey to the Indian who tipped it and drained it, tossing the empty glass to the dirt.

"What bout mine," Squirrel jabbed Captain Rex in the arm. "That was for the two of us."

"Nobody said nothin bout two. I just drank my share."

"Who do you think you are? Just what do you think

you are!" Squirrel's tight eyes faded in his face, he grabbed the front of Captain Rex's jacket and tumbled him from the fence.

The laughter around the corral whirred through Captain Rex's head, pressuring, closing like a vise as he stood up. He could feel the sun, could feel it burn as his fist shot out, knocking Squirrel in the chest, toppling him over backwards. He watched Squirrel fall, it was as if he himself were falling, spinning, smashing into the dirt, the blood pounding in his head, the birds singing their songs, primitive, antique sounds smoldering in his chest, welling up through his throat, tearing from his mouth in ancestral fury, the air of the corral conquered in the winging beat of feathered relics, his head swung back and he sang in the sun.

"It's the badger!" The words split the sound in the corral, piercing the man who sang from dreams, submerging the echo of time, the sound of birds escaping into trees.

The buckboard slammed in by the man, the horses' hooves throwing up dirt digging into the ground, and stopped. Two men struggled the large barrel off the back of the wagon, working it to the ground, then turning the team of horses around and riding out of the corral. The men cheered, waving their hats in the air. The Bummer strode to the middle of the clearing, put one gloved hand on the barrel lid and held up the other for silence.

"Gents! If you please," he coughed into his gloved hand and continued. "The game will now begin." The men fell silent. "The rules are, as you know, that the game is divided evenly into three sections. You may bet on all sections, or just the one of your personal choice. The first section is that of drawing the beast out of the barrel, you bet on whether the hounds will or won't. The second section begins when the beast is out, if the dogs can't bring him out we'll kick the barrel over; this section will be individual fights only, if you think you have the dog to beat him then go it with him. The last section, if the beast survives, will be against all dogs left. The odds in all sections are three to one on the dogs. Mr. Franks is going around presently to collect and record all wagers before the match; no verbal bets will be taken while the game is progressing. Remember you are at your honor in all occurring debts."

"What's your bet, Injun?" the little man demanded, his swollen eyes staring at Captain Rex behind thick glasses.

"I'm going with the dogs."

"House odds?"

"House odds."

"What's the name?"

"Rex, Cappin Rex."

"Last name?"

"Don't have none."

"What do you mean, don't have none." The little man's eyes jerked from his scribbling, his pencil poised over the black book. "You got to have one, ain't legal if you don't."

"Mr. Franks," the Bummer appeared behind the little man. "I think I can speak for our friend here, he is with my party."

"Oh Mr. John C., I didn't know," the little man apologized, his gaze dropping from the Indian. "I wouldn't have bothered him if I had known he was with you."

"You did right Mr. Franks, all men here bet, now what's the problem with the Injun boy?"

"I was just recording his bet but he don't have a last name to go by, you told me to put down first and last names, no exceptions."

"That's right, I most assuredly did, a man must have two names, first and last, it's only Christian."

"Yes sir, it's certainly natural, even for an Injun."

"Most certainly so Mr. Franks," the Bummer patted him on the shoulder. "Now then, Injun boy, tell the man your name so he can put it down."

"Cappin Rex."

"Rex what?" The Bummer leaned against his cane.

"Rex nothin, that's all of it, that's all *they* gave me, that's all *they've* ever called me."

"They must of given you a full Christian name."

"I'm not Christian."

"We're all Christians here, bud," the little man poked a finger in the Indian's face. "Injuns or not."

"Just put it down as it is, Mr. Franks, the men are anxious for the game, we'll attend to it later."

"But Mr. John C., I think we should get his full name," the little man licked the lead of his pencil nervously.

"I don't give a damn what you—"

"Birdsong. Call him Birdsong," Squirrel leaned over the corral fence, pointing his finger at Captain Rex. "Birdsong his name should be. Hah. He's always singing like some wild bird beast, like some crazy loco Injun!"

"Like some drunk Injun you mean," the Bummer smiled. "Put it down that way Mr. Franks, Rex Birdsong. What's his bet?"

"House odds on the dogs."

"You lying cheating Injun," the Bummer's face filled with red, as he aimed his cane at the Indian's throat. "Ten to one, Mr. Franks, that's what this filthy Injun's bet is! Ten to one on the badger! Mark that down, and this one too," he poked the cane at Squirrel. "The same odds. Get their money." He swung the cane again at Captain Rex, "And I'll settle with you later." He turned his back and moved to the barrel, holding his hand up, "Gents, all opening bets have been covered! Mr. Elliot, would you please commence!"

Elliot came to the center, "Get all those dogs in here pronto!" He shouted at the men standing by the tied dogs straining at their ropes. "They smell that cute lil badger," he laughed.

The men brought the dogs in, unleashed them and stepped back. Elliot flipped the lid off the barrel and leaped away as the dogs lunged at the large wood tub, surrounded it, pressing their noses against the wood and barking, their tails slicing through the air behind them like flags. A long red dog leaned up on his hind legs against the barrel and stuck his head over the opening. A claw swished up, slashing for an instant, ripping the dog's nose, sending it flying back and yelping off. The other dogs circled faster, their barks blurring into one fierce threat, building to a point. They charged, hurling their bodies against the barrel, trying to break through the barrier, knocking it over, rolling it to its side and scrambling for a position at the opening. "Go em dogs," one of the men on the fence yelled. "Go em all the way!"

"Get them damn dogs out of here!" Elliot jumped off the fence, waving the men to hurry up as they ran to their dogs, grabbing them behind the neck, dropping nooses over the heads and pulling them away.

"Who wants to go first!" Elliot shouted.

"My dog'll take it on," a man in a red flannel shirt rolled to the elbows stepped forward, his dog tugging at the leash in front of him.

"He's all yours," Elliot jumped on the fence.

The man slipped the noose from the dog's neck; it sprung across the ground, disappearing into the barrel. The only sound the men heard was the gnashing of teeth and a long hiss, then a howl blasted the dog from the mouth of the barrel, the badger's teeth clamped on a front leg. The dog ran, spinning his body, but the badger held onto the dog twice its size. The man in the red shirt rushed forward and kicked the badger in the head, knocking him from the dog. He picked up his losing entry and hurried out of the corral.

"Who's next, you men?" Elliot hopped down again.

"I got a dog's half-wolf," a man walked out to the center. "Timber wolf is what he is," the man grinned and pushed the sweat-stained hat further back on his head.

Elliot looked at the dog standing calmly at its master's side, the razor slice of nose, the powerful legs pushing up from the ground. "No," he shook his head. "That dog'll kill em off too fast. This here badger's got some more fight left in him fore we cut em off so quick."

"That's right," a man shouted from the fence. "Let some other hounds have a go first."

"Yah," cried another. "Hold your wolf on back. We got lots o time. Don't want to settle that beast's hash too easy."

"We'll go er," a fat man fingering a moustache lumbered out next to the man with the wolf dog, a yellow mongrel with half a tail trotting behind.

"Your show, pardner," Elliot waved him on.

The men spoke low making individual bets as the yellow dog cautiously approached the badger who was plopped down in the thick dust, coiled in a steel gray ball. The yellow dog stopped, sniffed at the air and scratched the dry earth. The fat man waddled up, kicking his boot into the dog's rear. "Get on up there, you lazy coyote." The dog jumped to one side of the badger, then hopped to the other side. The badger did not move, its belly flat to the ground like a snake, its wary eye fixed on the dog's every action. The dog growled with his nose pointed at the badger and circled, poking tentatively at the coiled body. "Come on, you lousy cur!" A shout came from the square of spectators, "Fight em! Fight em you yellow dog coward!" The dog moved to the badger's front, sniffing closer, almost touching the furry head with the slash of white down the center of the face, the badge. He stamped his paw in front of the animal; the badger's head darted up, the flash of teeth exposed for a moment in the sun. The mouth clamped beneath the chin, sinking into the throat with one hard twist. The yellow dog gave a short whine, staggered to its knees and fell on its side, his throat gashed open.

"That's it! That's it!" A man screamed. "Bring on out that there gent with the wild wolf dog! Give us a show for the money!"

The man with the wolf dog released it. Straight across the clearing it advanced to the badger. The prey sprang up, its back hunched high, lips snarled over the gums, two rows of needle teeth ready. The dog came on fast, the massive jaws wide, saliva dripping from the corners of the mouth, the tail up rigid, a sharp spoke of rudder; smooth white scars from previous battles crossed the ribstretched hide. He headed into the badger, feinted with his head as if to strike, then moving quickly, seeking the opening where the needle teeth would not be. One paw whipped, catching the badger on the side of the head, flipping him. The attacker dashed in for the kill, but the badger was ready, waiting for the strike, and hit with his own paw, a quick fierce bite sinking into one side of the dog's mouth, ripping into the lip. Both animals locked together. The battlers rolled over, thrashing in the dust. The men jumped from the fence, closing together on the fight, eyes burning as they stared into the dirty pulsating cloud and heard the gnash of teeth against bone, the tear of flesh.

"Waahoo! There he goes!"

A form leaped from the dust.

"It ain't the badger. It's the wolf dog!"

The dust thinned. The men huddled silent, hoping, until the dust cleared. The badger was reared back, swiping the air around him at the men, his panting mouth full of hair, tongue bleeding, his small face caked with dust and blood, a gash down his side.

"That damn beast ain't never goin to die!"

"Bring in all them dogs! Let em go it agin all of em!"

"No! Make it fair! Stand back and give him breathing space first!"

"I'm for bashin his brains out with a club!"

"Give it a drink! It's thirsty!"

"Kill him is what I say. Kill him now!"

"Gents!" the Bummer held up his gloved hand as he poked his cane playfully at the badger, the animal slashing futilely at the gold tip. "Rules is rules. We abide by the law. Let all the dogs have at him at once in even match. Then, if they don't whip him," he raised his gloved hand in front of thin lips, "then, gents, then you can kill him."

The men backed up, spreading out their arena, those with dogs ran and got them, holding them tight on their leashes in a circle about the badger.

"Release them!" the Bummer called out.

The dogs broke from their ropes as they smashed in against the animal, the men laughing, shouting into the rising dust, clapping their hands together until the last dog trotted off from the humped rag of body.

BARBARA KEVLES

Barbara Kevles is a young New York writer whose
profiles and interviews have appeared in *Atlantic
Monthly, Paris Review, New York Magazine* and
elsewhere. Of this excerpt from her book which
Doubleday & Company, Inc., will publish, Ms. Kevles
says: "It was radical feminist Ti-Grace Atkinson who
suggested I write about the Grove Press action from
my own viewpoint. At first, I was reluctant to. I intended to use the action as part of a profile on Ti-
Grace. Then I decided to try it though I had never
been successful with a first-person piece before. I had
to; I didn't understand why I had gone to jail nor
what had happened there."

RAISING MY FIST FOR
FEMINISM:
I DISCOVERED THE
MOVEMENT IN JAIL

I must get home for a call, though I long to continue
conversing with this engaging, well-recommended historian, to linger in the safety of this New York bar
amidst Tiffany light and twenties decor. In half an hour
I expect a prominent radical feminist to phone with
either an invitation or a refusal of permission to accompany her tomorrow on a secret action which, I was
told, is guaranteed to produce arrests. I want to cover
the action for an exclusive profile I am writing on this
radical. The waiter. My companion scratches a check

in the air as I nervously smooth a leather miniskirt before lifting myself out of the low booth.

Outside the April temperature bristles though Puerto Ricans cluster on orange crates beside the corner grocery. The men don't hiss because I am with someone. We walk and I relish the sensuality of his tight funky clothes and shoulder-length curls nearly hiding his eyes, mirrors of deep sadness and need. He slides an arm over my shoulders and referring to a second divorce in progress confesses, "They always leave me." I would not, for his honesty suggests a malleable openness, a man who could live with a writer. He wouldn't mold me into the kitchen-oriented *frau*, the *balabatash* women prized in my father's family of poor Russian immigrants, my first models of a female who were valued for cleaning so well you could eat from their floors. But candid as we are I have wound a clamp around my emotions the entire evening. He is tenured at a university in California, and I am too practical or too scarred to risk a nubile liaison to the distance of three thousand miles. So clasped in step and touching as we pass by the brownstones long ago quartered into apartments, I savor the moments of respite against the promise of another lonely night.

Finally, the phone. Ti-Grace Atkinson. An apology for lateness, ". . . a few of us stayed to work out the issues." I appreciate the thought, knowing she owes a reporter no explanation. Then with a voice shimmering with firm tensile strength and contagious excitement, she invites me to come. I am elated by her trust. I don't know how I'll hold up or react to the action. Seven years in New York and I've never marched, never demonstrated. "No press will be coming and people will attack me if they know you're a reporter." I swear I'll write up my notes in visits to the john. She laughs and, more seriously, asks, "Are you going to be arrested?" Her tone is not demanding, not proselytizing, rather measured, as if at her Columbia doctoral seminar. With sheer bravado of inexperience and dreams of a reportorial coup, I reply, "Of course, I'll be arrested." No knowledge of bust procedures or the rights of a prisoner, "Of course." On my couch, the historian who has written about revolutionaries breaks into a smile of approval as he listens to me pledge to be one, the geisha girl, instinctively ready to please, if only for the sake of a romantic fantasy.

New York Times lying on the doormat to Ti-Grace's East Side garden apartment. It's too early to bend over, even for a good friend. It is only a little past 7:30. Door opening, Ti-Grace. I wave feebly and she retrieves her own paper. A navy sweater and slacks shroud her statuesque, Maillol figure. I am aware her outfit is deliberate, a political statement debunking women as sexual objects, a self-imposed price for her beliefs. We whisper "hi" and smile. I am glad to see her. I always am. I tiptoe into the darkened foyer, relaxing some, as if crossing her welcome mat means I have reached a temporary safety zone. Following the tall form of Ti-Grace past her elegant family heirlooms, the heavy furniture which needs anything but the backdrop of pink stucco walls. Neither Ti-Grace nor I have chosen occupations which guarantee much money, certainly not for survival *and* lavishing on our apartments, too. Down the long hall. Ti-Grace closes her bedroom door, almost dancing on her toes and clapping her hands gleefully announces, "We're taking over Grove Press."

Giggling at the news, not knowing why, not even sure I like it, I sink into a flowery armchair, pulling out my 5"x8" cards from a green book bag. "Why Grove Press, Ti-Grace?" the question my attempt to turn researcher-writer, to place aesthetic distance between my fright and the militants' action. Accustomed to me as an alternative shadow and sleuth for some months now,

Ti-Grace settles on her unmade bed to brief me. Robin Morgan, radical feminist, fired a week ago along with two men and five women after working at Grove Press for two years. Grove claims reorganization, but most fired were union organizers. "When anyone in the movement gets hit," she says, "you make the company pay, and we've been after porno for a long time. With Robin we get two at once. . . . Profits from Grove pornography will be used to finance. . . ." and she lists the militants' nonnegotiable demands, the bases for a veritable feminist socialistic republic. I suspect Ti-Grace had more than a little to do with their formulation. She concludes, "This is a legal act, after all. To allow Grove to print sado-pornographic literature, why this is as illegal as the abortion laws." In the past, I've always had the option, as reporter, of believing "They're her ideas." Today, I no longer have that choice, as co-conspirator. It's very different, very. "Did you ask anyone else to come?" Putting on her coat. I do, too. "They gave excuses like 'This is an ego trip for Robin.' I tell you, it's about time someone got on one. More ego trips and tomorrow women'll have some self-respect."

Riding downtown, I have difficulty breathing. Ti-Grace, relaxed, reclining back as if she were heading for full treatment at Charles of the Ritz. "I'm going to Grove: I'm not backing down," I say as if trying to convince myself, revive my seeping courage, "but I do want to know," prefacing as I do questions which might offend, "what legal right do we have for taking over Grove Press? What gives us the right to criminal trespass?" Promptly, Ti-Grace answers, "I'm holding this property in trust," and launches into a highly complex political theory of private property framed in obtuse language and sentences of Jamesian length, and I encourage and prolong the intellectual gymnastics, perhaps as a distraction.

As a child I lived so much in a world of pain. Simple

criticism would prick my confidence and drain away an afternoon. For instance, when I came home, wind-swept and quite disheveled from the rain, my mother might say, "I don't see how you live with yourself; you're no child of mine." I could rarely satisfy my mother's standards for appearances, in any category. I rarely saw my father. The ninth child of a poor Russian grocer, he, like many Philadelphia schoolteachers, held two jobs. And when we did meet at the dinner table, my father often would quiz my older brother and me on math problems, displaying the male wit at the expense of mine. My admission to Bryn Mawr surprised everyone, most of all me. I had no sense of self-worth. So when Ti-Grace springs seminal-level political philosophy on me, I never stop her because she is giving the schoolteacher's daughter the highest praise possible, assuring the smarting child within I have something worthwhile, something of value—a mind.

Traffic tieup, taxi stopped. Listening half groggily to Ti-Grace complain about the New Left women who won't be arrested for feminism, the sloppy planning for the action, the lack of style and the irresponsibility in the women's movement, and then, "The agent didn't contribute anything." I nearly fall off the seat as the taxi lurches forward. Government agent? I didn't think this action was important enough for the government. Oh, Jesus! My notes will be subpoenaed. No one, Ti-Grace admits, confronted the girl suspected with the charge, but she proceeds, nonetheless, with a nerve-tingling account of the "agent provocateur," ending with "But the real danger, once up there, will be getting people to act, and not to explode." She sighs, "We'll be better off with agents; they're more together." I feel as if I'm watching some grade-B imitation James Bond film and want to laugh, but I can't because I'm in it. Into the Park Avenue underpass, the driver gives the only words of normality yet. "Time? 8:15." A political inductee heading for the front lines too soon, I blurt out, "The pact, Ti-Grace, I forgot to write it out." "Don't worry, I trust you."

Ti-Grace and I met in the summer of 1969. Betty Prashker, a Doubleday book editor, had privately suggested to me that Ti-Grace Atkinson would make a fascinating profile. So I phoned. Then one evening, Ti-Grace, by chance nearby, stopped by my West Side apartment to deliver a thick envelope of speeches. The speeches, I realized, were rather a transparent excuse for an inspection on a night I was bogged down in a disastrous first draft of another article. However, I couldn't refuse. Never having encountered a feminist, I expected the author of *Vaginal Orgasm as a Mass Hysterical Response* and other papers to be a harsh, arrogant woman. On the contrary. Except for a militant tiger-print sheath, Ti-Grace appeared quite vulnerable, an impression accentuated by cropped blond hair that ringed the nape of her neck like an infant's, and long, slender hands with exquisitely tapered fingers, like those I always imagined for heroines of nineteenth-century novels. In six months' time, having survived a series of near-fatal political crises by herself, with calls from the press on her service each day, Ti-Grace would have the confidence to take a direct tack with anyone. That evening, still wearing proper heels and stockings and very new to the radical feminist underground, Ti-Grace delayed, detoured, backtracked into her past while I duly jotted down notes for a proposal which, I hoped, would inspire a magazine commission and, more important, an advance. With prompting, she described her present life with a staccato, "FEMINISM, FEMINISM, FEMINISM . . . I have just about no personal life left. For a woman to demand humanity for herself is to cut herself off from men . . . it is a very painful and gradual thing." Although unalterably opposed to marriage, she admitted nonetheless to liking my recent cover story on Joan Kennedy (wife and mother of three). She argued, though, she was perhaps reacting to a portrait written through the filter of my sensitivity, sensitivity not possessed by Mrs. Kennedy. Ti-Grace seemed unconvinced by my arguments and circled the subject until finally she revealed the real purpose of why she'd come. She said, "I tell you, if you write about me, you must be brutally honest and raw, even if you have to be cruel. Otherwise, I won't be real to other women. . . . People are afraid of feminism because they are terrified of what it will do to their lives and my life is my best political statement." Her hands fluttered all the while off and on her lap, seemingly as removed from her words as she from her conventional marriage and sheltered Louisiana girlhood. Trying to be as candid, I confessed I couldn't promise because from article to article my greatest difficulty is . . . that I continually must force myself to see people as they really are, without myths. "Naive and nearly thirty," I said, "I write with discomfort about what some consider faults or weaknesses, and others, just human." And I complained bitterly of an impossible second draft for a profile on a New York single girl. Ti-Grace just listened, hands stilled, and when I finished, said, "You must put in the fantasies about men and her despair because it is so much a part of every single woman's life." I remember Ti-Grace and I talked till very late that evening, beyond the time I'd allotted in my writing schedule. After that, the range of our conversation expanded, as do talks between any new friends.

Gradually, Ti-Grace confided in me. I was the first to know she was considering leaving The Feminists though she had founded the radical group. She debated whether she would protest the cell's views of the equality issue, the issue she had pioneered in the women's movement as president of the New York chapter of

NOW. At a recent meeting, certain Feminists had proposed the resolution, No contact with the media for any member except with group approval, believing that "Everyone deserved equal treatment," meant "Everyone possessed equal talents." All should receive the media exposure enjoyed by Ti-Grace, equally. I advised, "Do what is in your self-interest," wanting her to make an objective decision without pressure from me. I knew that continued membership in The Feminists meant the end of my writing the profile on Ti-Grace, and if she severed these ties of a year and a half for principle, Ti-Grace would be very much alone because her friendships spark primarily from political alliances. Without The Feminists, I would receive too many long phone calls I couldn't easily disconnect, which proved to be true.

After the ninth magazine rejected the proposed profile, Ti-Grace and I vied masochistically for the blame with the same excuse, "I'm not well known enough." I began to feel my five months of research disguised either voyeurism or an elaborate subconscious plot to escape confronting my typewriter and current assignments. Most general news magazines were publishing movement surveys. When at last *Life Magazine* requested her story, Ti-Grace wrote the editors, demanding no picture of her be used without my text:

> I am on very shaky ground to think that there's any chance for having a 'fair' trade between instruments of the oppressor and the oppressed. But this is worth a try. If *Life* tries to fuck any of us over, they get nothing.

Life preferred a staff writer and Ti-Grace told me, "Not until yours is sold. Your style is the closest to autobiography I know and what your article will say is what no one else can after the standard six weeks of research." Such is the nature of our friendship—on the plus side, mutual encouragement, criticism, exchange of confidences, and loyalty; on the debits, a surfeit of mutual psychotherapy and voyeurism. I know Ti-Grace would not bring just any reporter on a secret maneuver and I probably would not chance the trauma of a first political act without support implicit not as a profile subject, but from a friend whom I would prevent, if I could, from rashness or blunder that will incarcerate her and stymie her political effectiveness in repressive times.

Greenwich Village. 8:35. Ti-Grace snaps her change purse shut and I slam the taxi door. We are five minutes late. I am surprised. Only a few women waiting by the wide pillars of the Bleecker St. Cinema. Relief. Some of them wear eyeshadow and mascara, too. I nod "hello" and turn to watch Ti-Grace, for cues. We remain apart from the rest. No one offers her name, nor do I, afraid someone will remember it in testimony later. The green tote bag, heavy. I drop it on the pavement and stare toward Circle in the Square's marquee and Sixth Avenue. I try to pick out the militants as they approach. I can't. Every female a possible demonstrator, till she passes. Crowd now, East Village types, Afros, well-dressed working girls. Majority, I estimate, mid-twenties. I am roasting under layers of winter lining. I unbutton my coat. I can actually hear my heart, thumping. I'm so scared. Ti-Grace is pacing, angry at the delay and the latecomers. No other Feminists yet. A Volkswagen pulls up. Male driver with a small girl, long hair held back with a barrette, neatly, waves from the front seat, rather pretty. Robin Morgan, I presume, publicly announced practicer of the bisexual marriage, hugs and kisses fellow members of the Gay Liberation Front, WITCH, RAT, and all, nearly. Fired Friday and returning Monday, not with a plea for recommendations, but a protest action. Former child actress, her face is composed sweetness, as if she could do evil with a

fixed expression of innocence. Someone gives me a leaflet with demands for feminist profit-sharing with Grove
Press, *Evergreen Review*, and other corporate enterprises. I skim it, uneasy without a pen for notes. Ti-
Grace, nearby, busy greeting her admirers, perhaps
scouting for new friends to fill the vacuum left by quitting The Feminists. Perhaps even testing me, for in all
our months of traveling, I have preferred to listen and
question, nurture a trust for the unguarded outbursts
of private confession, as always, gathering all the facts,
the schoolteacher's daughter, wanting to be right, implying with silence support for her extremism though only
flirting with radical feminism in my head. My desire
to cover Ti-Grace today through the action, to judge
her in relation to other members of the movement, I feel,
is somehow secondary for Ti-Grace and perhaps for me
as well. A whisper, move out in twos and threes. I pick
up my tote bag from the pavement and pass the order
on.

We trail the rest. Ti-Grace's shopping bag handles
hitting her chin. She repeats her strategy, perhaps for
courage, "I'll fight the hardest if the police make an
assault, I'll take plenty with me because I'm going to
stay till I get justice!" No remnant visible of the woman
I first encountered, the ex-editor of *Art News* who after
a divorce tried painting in a Greenwich Village loft
till she enrolled for a Ph.D. at Columbia because she
couldn't take loft life. I miss the complex intellectual
with a grounding in art now camouflaged by simplified
radical rhetoric. I don't know how to answer her. My
radical mask doesn't fit well, it's a masquerade, I feel
it. Skirting construction machinery and python hoses in
our path. Crossing to the wide pavement funneling
around the Washington Square apartment complex
lawn. Odd . . . me . . . with so many militants. I feel
out of place because I assume they, like Ti-Grace, give
men all the credit for women's niggerization. I do not,

believing my failed relationships a private dilemma. In reach of a man's caprice, my sense of self erodes without scheduled writing, and when I write, conserving my stamina through isolation from men as well as all distractions, I inevitably injure myself, perhaps as punishment, with burns, cuts, and this past winter, while working beside a small home heater, I burned the moisture from my skin. Only recently have I realized that my mother's choice to live through a man does not have to be the only choice except loneliness. Heading for the action, I view the marchers ahead, one by one, through orange-tinted lenses: uncommitted to turning private matters into radical politics, while Ti-Grace in her blue glasses multiplies each militant's maced loves, careers stunted by marital cul-de-sacs or childbirths, every maladjustment to conventional biological female roles, into a political movement for women's rights.

We stall outside Grove's new headquarters till, at last, a signal from Robin, "The Little General." All clear. Inside Grove's lobby, no security, just workmen. We cross toward the elevator. A man in baggy grey shirt comments, "I wonder if it's safe to be in office buildings nowadays." Ti-Grace counting, watching the rise of the forward guard to the executive floor on the elevator dials. "Four, five, six," and we cry, "They did it, they liberated Grove Press. They did it." The elevator doors open and it is our turn. Sixth floor. A corridor of desks and, at its end, a huddle of women forming where one, facing the rest, her back to the door, with a sideward glance slams a tiny hammer through an opaque wall panel and turns. Glass shatters and I am chilled as from a breeze after a warm bath. Mind, paralyzed. My eyes are like cameras on the moon, recording, sending images of invading revolutionaries to Houston. Everyone into the office of president Barney Rosset and I follow. I'm afraid, but someone assures me Grove will not tarnish its liberal image with arrests of demonstrators, at least not for several days. Rosset is in Denmark today, buying porno films, he won't know for hours. Everywhere opulence, cushy leather chairs, aluminum lamps and plants ceiling-high, but Rosset's bookshelves are almost empty. His world-famous collection of pornographic books, probably still unpacked. Even I'm disappointed. Coats off, Ti-Grace draws a hammer from her shopping bag.

More glass splintering in the corridor. Women carrying not groceries, not twenty-five-pound toddlers, but couches, chairs, cartons to build barricades. Rope. Who has it? Ti-Grace forgot hers. I stand aside, wanting to say later "I didn't do anything." All secretaries' chairs have disappeared. Beyond the desks, an avalanche of furniture hides the fire escape door. This is better organized than I imagined. A trio hobbling along with a wide chrome table. I help, grab hold. A few steps. The glass top falls and cracks on the floor. In Rosset's office behind the couch, my coat and in the tote, tissues. Someone passes, but I keep wiping the fingerprints from the chrome. A girl arrives with broom and dustpan for the glass. We smile knowingly. Even behind feminist barricades, we are unable to divorce our cultural roles. Shouts. They are hanging a women's liberation banner outside Rosset's windows, and humming a jubilant "Marseillaise."

Slouched against a wall on executive row. I glance at the phone on the secretary's desk opposite. Every button lit, every outside line in use. Relaxed, I'm in no hurry. I look down at the yellow pad of paper under my arm containing scribbled information from our organizational meeting, plus some undetected research notes. I check a second time to see I have it, as if the pad of notes were an identity card. Ti-Grace emerges from an executive's office, "I keep calling some Feminists, but they keep going back to sleep," and she leaves.

Before anyone else, I spring to the phone she's vacated and dial out. I ask for Channel Thirteen's news desk, hoping no one there knows me from my four years of free-lancing in television production. A woman answers for the local ETV news unit, and raising my pad, I boast, "I'm calling from a zone liberated by women. Women have seized Grove Press because corporate enterprises have earned millions off . . . humiliating, degrading, and dehumanizing women through distributing sado-masochistic literature and pornographic films like *I Am Curious: Yellow* and . . ." I take a breath. The woman interrupts, the newsmen won't be in till eleven. I hang up. I have nothing to do, and I'm suddenly bored. I wander outside. Women are doctoring framed Grove film advertisements with signs lettered THIS EXPLOITS WOMEN. One sign, like a first-prize blue ribbon, hangs across the corner of a poster which . . . I stare for a moment, to let the image have full impact . . . a woman on all fours, like a mongrel, grovels at the heels of an ignoring man. To the sign's right, the film title, *The Joke*. I'm amazed. It's so savagely hostile to the woman. I am really incensed. I can vividly see the Puerto Ricans gathered on orange crates on my corner, making their lewd gestures as I walk by and hiss hints of split-second conquest which I ignore and detest. . . . Maybe I am getting back at them by being here. . . . The militants waive my offer to help. Alone again, I pause and then drift toward the back. Earlier, women deserted through the rear barricades and I'm worried about our security. The sentinel, commenting on a heavy black box atop the barricade, tells me, "It will knock the head off of whoever comes through that door." The box is precipitantly tipped against the door. It's frightening. I try to move the box. It is too heavy. I can't even lift it. I don't doubt it will kill. The sentinel agrees to help me reshuffle the furniture for a "more stable construction." Leaving . . . did I save us from a murder charge? Jesus! That woman really hates men. The phones on secretarial row, too public. Privacy of an office. Outside line free to contact my lawyer, Gerald Dickler, someone in whom I confide, who encourages me like a surrogate father. I tell him where I am and my reasons for the research. His counsel, "When the police come, get the hell out of there."

We converge for a meeting in the middle of the corridor, even sentries must attend. The Little General has heard from our spies with management on the lower floors. The circle, much smaller than this morning's, wedges between two desks. The Little General announces Rosset's called from Denmark, the cops are downstairs, "Who are the dead bodies?" her question and tone flickering with condescension for any identified. Immediately, one girl says, "I can't, not with a 1:30 rehearsal," and no one contradicts her excuse. Then the roll call for "Who doesn't want to be arrested?" begins as I jot down one-word mnemonics though inwardly dreading the new requirements for the part as actress in my own autobiographical film. One after another, the first three women choose jail, with no hesitation, as I gape, wide-eyed, with astonished admiration. The next, "I've got a drug bust." Accepted, an honorable out. Can I desert? Is it enough to say I'm a reporter, I'm not a member of any movement because professional objectivity is prerequisite to what I do? I'm in agony. No press were to come. I can't tell who I am. Only a few more till me. Too fast, too soon. Now, Ti-Grace's turn. Seven women have agreed to be busted. Ti-Grace repeats, "I'm holding these premises in trust," and suggests bringing more women on the floor because "we legally believe we can be here." But she doesn't expose why I'm here, or our pact, allowing me no reconsideration, demanding that commitment to the woman's movement at my typewriter, but now, I am last. I give the only "Undecided," barely audible, an answer as schizophrenic as I feel. The meeting is almost over. Ti-Grace, with concern, reminds the group of the one "undecided," neither with contempt nor approval, rather as obligation. In the distance, I hear the sound of the front elevator door slamming against the chair which obstructs its closing. The door hits the chair and flaps back, slams and rolls back.

The guards leave for their posts. Everyone is dispersing. I just sit on the rug a moment longer, back against a desk, trying to decide. I can't. I get up. By the front fire exit, a small hall leads to a window and there, Ti-Grace beside the rolled blinds, very preoccupied in thought. I join her. A good-sized crowd has gathered for the union rally being held for Grove employees on the sunny lawn across the street. The union is protesting with their rally the same firings we are protesting behind feminist barricades. The speaker points toward the feminist flag outside Rosset's window, red clenched fist encircled, sex sign for women, now for militancy. The newsreel cameras follow his gesture, but I don't understand the connection. All but one of the demands on our leaflet is non-union. I'm really confused. What am I doing here . . . are we being arrested on union grounds . . . that's not what I. . . . Two more police cars are parking and Ti-Grace is talking about the raids on Columbia. She recalls, ". . . they came like ants, in droves . . . I always said I wanted my first arrest on a feminist issue." Directly below us sit two gigantic police vans. A bullhorn. Its garbled message resonates off the walls. "Come on down. This means everybody." An off-duty sentinel warns us back from the window and exposure to the cameras. She mentions the "dead bodies" have made their escape. They have taken the back elevator to the safety of our spies on the fifth floor. Another messenger. The police will break down the back door, which siphons off almost everyone. I can't think.

149

My pulse is pounding. I hear it and that's all I'm aware of.

"Hey," and we turn from the window toward the guard. Her hand waves us to come fast to the fire escape door, almost hidden by a skid of book cartons, and we hear the sound of keys being tried in the lock. Men's voices, probably cops. "The glue is holding," Ti-Grace whispers. I don't know what to do. The guard, in stocking feet, climbs onto a chair and angles her thin arm through the packed cartons till, at last, when her body is almost a taut chain, we know she's got hold of the door handle. Ti-Grace brackets her arms around the guard's waist and digs her feet into the rug for a foothold, cornered, but pugnacious still. Without words, I lock my arms around Ti-Grace. The three of us, a human bolt to support the door from opening out, as it is designed to, toward the police. Metal scratching on metal, a crowbar picking at the door hinges. My cheek pressed against the bristly wool of Ti-Grace's shoulder, I'm following her lead, holding on, when suddenly, up, out of my guts . . . I want out. Instinctively, I let go, separate myself from Ti-Grace and I say it out loud, as if Ti-Grace has the omnipotent power to save me from arrest when I've loitered till the last minute to make up my mind. She whirls around for a scorching, "You'll disgrace me in the movement!" I reel under the impact of I'm signing for you as a friend, no press were to come, don't expose me; you exploit a woman's action as a reporter and at the arrest claim press, deny you are a woman, we can't be friends, *you* will be a disgrace to me! Her eyes throb with that maternal look I have fought since childhood, that look of "I-know-better-than-you-what's-good-for-you." She means if I leave, I will embarrass myself in the movement, giving me an ultimatum, as if I, like her, were a radical feminist.

I stumble away, round the receptionist's desk, and pause at the beginning of executive row. A moment to catch my breath and I stumble on, very shaken, clutching still the illusion of press card immunity. Midway down the corridor, the Little General materializes. Again, I submit, "I want out." She responds, "You're released on your own recognizance." Women passing say the cops are removing the door from its hinges. Jesus! Radicals on one side and in a few minutes the pigs on the other. I'm faced with the symbolic confrontation. Radicals claim, "Either you're with me or against me." To admit I'm press, I choose the side of the enemy. The Little General stands beside me, waiting for my decision, with placid control. "Oh, well," I say, and shrug my shoulders, "I'm here," and with that heroic line proceed after the others into Rosset's office to join the feminist movement. Mind a montage—red fist on white flag, standing up for women's rights behind the barricades, Grove's exploitative policies, being a romantic guerrilla, profile, friendship, loyalty to Ti-Grace, trust in her political judgment. My motives impure as anyone else's.

6TH PRECINCT: There is one chair in the room; the police take turns using it. I have improvised a seat atop a supply cabinet. Some of the radicals are leaning against the wall or just milling about as they have for over an hour. Ti-Grace, across the room, is flipping through the announcements of the FBI Wanted. So stuffy and warm. Stiflingly so. My heavy leotards are chafing my legs, irritating the skin condition I treat daily. Almost unbearable, as if my legs are being jabbed by electric cattle prods. I try to concentrate on the continual comings and goings through the nearly room-size doorway. I know where this precinct is located. A couple of blocks and the Eighth Avenue subway. In forty minutes, I could be home. I could be in an air-conditioned room. Home . . . what am I doing here . . . in jail . . . what the hell am I . . . I scan the other women from the action, trying to remember their names. I can't. We said them once, when we assembled in this room after the van ride. The first time we could see who had crossed beyond the rhetoric and the glamor of "I was there, I was at the demonstration," to be arrested. Nine of us. One by one, each woman filled in the "I am . . ." for the rest, confiding the identity she'd held back for the last five hours. In those moments, I felt an extraordinary closeness, almost a kinship with every stranger, as if each with her name pledged, "I trust you . . . we'll get through this together." Thinking of that now, my pulse slows, a little. Trying to bear up, to get through this. My legs . . . Ah, that policewoman, through the doorway, her breasts bobbing like baby seals under her blouse. Before she can choose her next frisk, I've hopped down and am complaining again, the heat, my skin, and in best Bryn Mawr charm, "Could I possibly. . . ." My civilized approach works. She leads me to the front of the station house as I inwardly preen at the special attention I always, even if subconsciously, assume I deserve. The office where she searched me. Again, I remove my boots and leotards, hoping as I stand in the rear recess that I can't be observed through the tall windows facing the street. And there I start swabbing with lotion from my tote, blithely, as if I were applying *Bain de Soleil* to a bad sunburn on the beach. Some of the viscous lotion falls, eddying into a smear. The frightened guard, protected from assault by the desk between us, pretends not to notice. I hurry, but spill more. "I can't let you do this," the guard says, panicking, "this is a *captain's* office." "I'll clean it up," I offer, and genuflect respectfully to blot away what I can. I smile politely, aware this policewoman has the right to stop this and cause me to spend the rest of my incarceration with one-third of my body in pain. I am almost finished, when she confiscates the medicine. She places it in a brown envelope for safekeeping; prisoners shouldn't have glass bottles in their possession.

A crowd now packs the reception room, and only that one chair. My arresting officer, Stephen Driscoll, as before, leans on a filthy window sill filling out his report cards in triplicate, one by one, without carbon paper. Driscoll, with the blond altarboy profile, claimed in the van a wife in NOW and, as he booked me, confided, "Morally, you're right to close Grove; legally, your tactics are wrong." The liberal wearing the badge of the establishment, the two of us like sly chameleons who have tried to slide through the system without taking sides and, as yet, are undetected.

The last duplicate done, New York City's daytime commandos, the Special Events Squad, renamed by us the Sexual Exploitation Squad, promises us better accommodations upstairs. The detectives' office. At the end of the office, a narrow cell. We sit down, cramped butt to butt in this five-foot square. "They've got the fucking fantasy they've always wanted," says blondie with care, "they've got nine women in a cage." I pull out Cokes and raisins and pass them. Ti-Grace jokes; for a first arrest, I'm well prepared. I call to Driscoll, what about my phoning the Deputy Commissioner for Press Relations, needling him with the hint of a connection higher up. The cage door swings open. "Don't get too chummy with the pigs," from one of the radicals, suspecting me, I suppose, of turning informer before their very eyes. I practically skip to the desk where Driscoll is dialing, frisky as an animal let out of confinement. His voice changes into a very respectful tone, then to me, "He isn't in." Not in? No friend to verify my reporter's credentials? I don't believe Driscoll and ask to talk to the officer who's answered. I'm allowed to, with no better results. Dejected, I return to the cage. Ti-Grace, talking with the blond, misses my glance. During the arrest, Ti-Grace scuffled with the police. I remained in another part of Rosset's office, smarting from my forced baptism to the movement, till Ti-Grace screamed as two cops bent her wrists and her back arched, quivering in pain, and I moved, unavoidably, toward her. I arrived powerless to do anything but protect her shopping bag till access to the elevator was cleared. In the police wagon, we sat side by side, skating surfaces, taking cues from our roles, the radical and the establishment reporter. Our personal rapport at its most strained since the start of our friendship. Wool coat prickly on my lap and overbearingly warm. A leg, I feel it, pressing against mine. Shifting and still that leg. I stand up, the air above the other eight an unexpected privacy from the cramped suffocation. I hold onto the bars as I saw another prisoner do last summer. This man with holes in his tee-shirt and pock-marked cheeks was brought in, the detective said, for stealing a car. Now that pimply car thief and I, to all the cops outside the cage, look the same. Both criminals. Spurts of tears fill my eyes and I force them back. Swallowing not to throw up. Too many head changes too fast. Am I a woman-writer or a writer who happens to be a woman? What's the priority? If I'm a writer, then what am I doing in jail? What the fuck am I doing in jail? I went to the action as a reporter, I wanted out, but then I got busted, as a radical. How in the world? Why did I . . . Ti-Grace and I first through Grove's back doors into daylight. Behind the rim of policemen, the union representatives and Grove employees, cheering us, facing us with a bristle of raised fists. Newsreel cameras rolling, my arm shoots out, hand curling awkwardly. I've learned the sign, but no idea what I'm saying with my raised fist . . . or my body in jail. . . . I give Driscoll my lawyer's number. Paint on the ceiling above, flaking. The sickening green walls are curling like carrot peels. I picture my lawyer's penthouse Park Avenue office with its opulent view of Central Park.

Suddenly, I flush, ashamed to be in this grisly station house. I don't know what I'm saying. I reach for the receiver, but Driscoll's superior says "no," buttressed by something about the "literal interpretation of the law for demonstrators." Driscoll will talk for me. I am deprived of that comfort I need from someone who knows me, who can reassure me I am respectable. Driscoll questions, do I want my lawyer to come to the precinct? He's offered to. I'm glad, I'm nearly joyful. But . . . I stand there, nibbling my nails. How can I have a male counsel extract me from a radical feminist action? How can I? I return an "I don't know," like a schizophrenic shuttling between two identities. Driscoll relays my indecision while on some unconscious level I'm aware my lawyer's my last contact with the outside till my release, and I've just broken that connection through a second party . . . I'm holding up, at least I'm not crying. At least, here I can think by myself, above the rest . . . in this aerial privacy. I look through the bars at the detectives. Nothing interesting happening. And turn. Robin, hunched against the opposite wall, is saying the press won't be allowed to come up to the cage. "Why not?" I boom out, and instantly know why. A picture of us in this cage would make page one of *Pravda*. Robin studies me curiously; "That's a pretty naive question." I want to defend myself; I want to add, but I'm a member of the press and I'm here. Instead, I keep quiet and in a couple of moments face the bars again. I can't tell anyone who I am. No press. The pact. No one can give me a reflection of who I am. Nobody can know. This is horrible. I got busted as a radical. . . . What the fuck . . . I'm dissolving. I'm freaking out. . . . The policewoman, belt cinching a line for her waist, guides me to the door and I step down inside a closet-size, soot-coated bathroom. I hear the cops on the desk two feet from the door, but before I can close it, that policewoman walks in and entrenches herself

like a miniature tank in front of the window. When I
bend over the toilet, she is so close I see the veins in
her legs. The cold water spigot works. . . . I grasp the
bars tightly and tilt my head down, so the blackness
will pass. I wait. I don't faint. Is this how they get their
jollies? The blackness again. I slide my arms through
the bars and just hold on. When I open my eyes, I
pretend it's a mirage. It has to be a mirage. No, it is
Flo Kennedy, chic cowboy hat, ties dangling under her
chin, expensive leather vest over her blouse and slacks,
with her lawyer's attaché and a big lucite ring, coming
through the doorway. Someone cares. Someone cares.
It is Flo, speaking in her impressive, inimitable patois.
Flo, with her indomitable authority, gets the door open.
Someone cares. The whole cage seems to float into the
air. Everyone up, giving Flo numbers to call. Everyone
enthusiastic. She explains Ti-Grace left a message on
her service. . . . She's checked . . . as first arrests, we
should be allowed out on *vera* summons before arraign-
ment, but for some obscure reason, we can't be released.
We can't be released. I sift down to the floor and cover
my head with my hands, unable to imagine the remaining hours in jail, not wanting to. To anyone else, I look
as if I'm trying to sleep. In truth, I'm trying not to
scream.

CRIMINAL COURT DETENTION PEN: "I ain't
no freak," spits out the leather-suit prostitute, jumping
up at the matron's order to move from the long bench
opposite the open toilet. I don't know how she had the
strength to stand that odor and not faint. The smell of
urine foul as rotting garbage reaches as far as my bench
corner. She bypasses the vacant spaces farther down by
the Grove people and joins the other whores lined up
like a jail cell tribunal of street fighters on the short
bench. Wedged in the center, Ti-Grace hasn't stopped
exploring with Sugar the new issue for the movement,
prostitution. Sugar wears a black matronly card-party

sheath and her eyes are like the tiny slits on an infant's face, only hers are encrusted and lined, as if she had weathered much more than the twenty-five years she claims. We have passed hours together. We are all waiting to be fed to night court and released, we hope without bail. I focus on the girl outfitted in the pretty patchwork leather. She wears her eyes Twiggy style, with precise stick strokes and more makeup than I've ever seen, which rather awes me, because I don't have the time, the inclination or, admittedly, the skill to achieve such a sophisticated image every day. I study it with minute interest, as a distraction from my fractured identity and dislocation. To get out of myself, I ask a few interview questions, but the girl doesn't mind and garrulously sketches a Midwestern childhood and coming to New York to model and turning to this. "It's more money." "Why, Jackie Kennedy has the richest trick of them all," this from Petunia at the bench's farthest end, by the cell bars. The whores agree wholeheartedly, while some of the radicals laugh at the comparison of prostitution and marriage. Undaunted, Petunia, in kelly green vinyl, luminescent to taunt the cops and tease the customer, Petunia, with more bluster and more stories about her clients than anyone, who has transformed her end position to stage center, launches into the topic of police harassment, "The pigs jump off buses, hide behind trucks, and one motherfucker tackles you, so I just stand still when I see him and I plead for him not to jump me." Sugar raises her head, "I know the one you mean with the flying tackles, he broke my leg in three places," flexing the right one, "I feel it when it rains." She bends her head again toward Ti-Grace. "They're so intent on quotas," Honey adds, from beside Ti-Grace. "They picked me up today in Woolworth's! That's right, in front of my two kids." She muses a moment nervously smoothing the coat in her lap. "Lucky my mother was with me." Petunia, as if never interrupted, bitches, "I've been in jail every day this month, and last one, too," thoughtfully, "must be my skirt." In sympathy, I point out that my skirt is short, too, and stand up. She gets up, too, about my size, only scrawnier, and we compare. My hemline rises about six inches above my kneecaps, but her skirt ends just under her crotch. I lose and sit down, but we smile, warmly, the gesture of camaraderie crosses whatever divides us.

Ti-Grace, I notice, draws out a white paper from a pocket and hands it to Sugar who waves the Grove leaflet in every direction. She shouts, "I want to read these demands," and calls out "WOMEN HAVE SEIZED THE EXECUTIVE OFFICE OF GROVE PRESS BECAUSE:" as the cell quiets down, "Grove Press and its sub . . ." Ti-Grace helps her, "subsidiaries," Sugar goes on, sounding out the multisyllable words she doesn't know, when necessary, *"Evergreen Review,* Grove films, and other corporate enterrr-prises have earned millions off the basic theme of humiliating, degrading and dehumanizing women through sadomasochistic literature, pornographic films and. . . ." Weighted with fatigue, I try to concentrate, too pressed out to fathom whether I've supported an action which, it occurs to me now, favors censorship of some kind. Meanwhile, Petunia resists the desire to upstage Sugar and is listening attentively. Along the benches, initial interests wander with the mention of demands farfetched from their tenement lives, like retraining programs for Grove's divorcees. Sugar, again, waving the leaflet, yelling down the growing din with, "Now listen, this is really somethin'!" and her commanding manner rivets attention again, the excited enthusiasm in her eyes, on her face, mesmerizes two benchloads of prisoners as she hammers out, "The profits from Venus Books, Zebra Books, and Black Cat Books, the hard core of Grove's pornographic subsidiaries, must *all* go to those women," she pauses for emphasis, "who are the *special* victims of this propaganda, by . . . a bail fund, to free each month a minimum of one hundred political prisoners," another pause, "most of whom are prostitutes, from the Women's House of Detention." Clapping, shouting, even feet stamping, a communal spirit permeates the cell, as I felt this morning when on Grove's sixth floor in a whirlpool of action, women not knowing each other's first names built barricades together. At this instant, I feel an intense bond with the whores, radicals, addicts, thieves, with everyone in the cell, identifying as never before on the basis of being a woman with other women. Above us, on the ceiling, reached only on another's shoulders, scrawled with burnt matches by previous prisoners, their "Joe," "Ritchie," "Phil," "George," . . . tielines with roles of lover, wife, mother that supposedly mean a female is "more a woman" in American society, which, though absent, at this moment, do not chip away the knowledge we were born women, we are women still though inside a prison cage that symbolizes the cages outside of myths, conventions and law. Despite color lines, class lines, we are all sisters, reinforcing.

Jolting sounds. Gurgle of a toilet being pumped. A girl rises from the long bench, jaws swelled as if stuffed with sourballs, and she makes it to the toilet, before splattering up her guts. I cower in the corner, head in hand, always terrified by vomiting and lack of control. "Someone help her," Ti-Grace cries, and the blond and another go behind the not-so-high wall, and Ti-Grace approaches and hovers outside, hands on her chest crossed resolutely, ready to hold the girl's head if necessary. Honey tells me she could be put away for years on Rockefeller's "rehabilitation plan," if the matron found out, just as the eight o'clock sandwich wagon, unwanted now, rolls to a stop in front. Honey winks at me, motherly, "The tea is always good." I glance about to see how the others are reacting. Nearby, Robin is talking to another radical. I am amazed. After all these hours in jail, her voice possesses the same martinet sureness with which she countered the police trying to arrest us in Rosset's office. "We don't recognize male authority," she told them, "we want to be arrested by policewomen." And for a few moments, Robin subdued an entire squadron into silence. The offensive attitude she took then, as now, seems to insulate her from the fears of the victim flushed into her oppressor's power. I see the blond and another girl have the addict lying down now. The two take turns clamping down her mouth when she, yawning, veers toward a fracture of the jaw.

In response to urging from Sugar, Petunia begins to tell a hilarious story about her first LSD trip. "I was ironing like this," she says, gesturing as if she were sanding a ten-foot piece of plywood, "and I was burning more brown spots on my blouses, so I stopped and sat down. My boyfriend was laughing . . . he knew . . . well . . . that chair . . . I was slipping backward to eternity and I jumped up so fast. I got out of that chair so quickly. . . ." She stops. The matron is at the door. She motions for the prostitutes, calling names we never heard, to file out, the spirited street fighters who never bother as I do about whether chivalrous cigarette-lighting or door-holding compromises them as women, and the whores leave, taking with them the affection I reserve for Shakespeare's walkons who soften audiences with laughter, suspend the motions of destruction, encourage hope against hope before the arrival of the unwished-for news.

Robin sits down beside me, giving me her Cheshire smile. She has been collecting details of the happenings in night court. She tells me the judge faces a packed house, that press have come, and everybody is waiting for our appearance. I brighten at the idea of a courtroom filled with supporters hollering and waving feminist banners. Then Robin begins to list the bails the judge has doled out—$1,500 for the girl with wrinkled stockings who sits on the bench snapping and unsnapping her dimestore pearls. Fifteen hundred dollars bail for stealing food for her kids from a hotel kitchen. My eyes widen; I'm shocked. I have less than $100 in my own checkbook. She's just surfacing from her abortion, he's out of work, film business slow; she's added a new wing to the house; she's not getting alimony. Robin finishes, citing the outrageous figures set for the junkies. Looking at me she says, "I won't leave till all my sisters are out on bail," and trembling with indignation, "even if I have to stay here several nights." Her bravado is backed by $1,000 ready bail and more funds available from the underground haphazardly interconnected by telephones, mimeographed papers, meetings and years of demonstrations, all sharing the radicals' "With me or against me paranoia" which multiplies the voltage of a jar from "the system" into a major assault, while I take put-downs as isolated acts, to gloss over, shelve, forgetting past examples. They interpret against their class-women, and to their own receipts of discrimination, doubling each other's, escalating irritation into heightened fury, but I'm not there yet, and I resent the pressure to put more on the line than eight hours in the movement justify. "I don't know what I'll do," I reply, and she moves on to recruit for Robin Morgan's new action, while I seriously juggle the worth of my writing about women versus the worth of my body in jail for strangers, on behalf of the nebulous "Movement."

10:30 P.M. Male voices in the corridor. The Sexual Exploitation Squad. I start removing bobby pins. My hair cascades onto my shoulders for the courtroom cameras. Outside the cell, I joyfully retrieve my green tote. Who's come, I wonder, will the TV lights blind us?

Halls, impersonal yellow blocks. We are pinned in by cops guiding up ahead and trailing behind. Up a stairs, a door, and suddenly we emerge into the night in a courtyard. We are being herded toward a parked police wagon. Absolutely bewildered, I drop back to find Driscoll who informs me our charges have been raised to a felony because Grove lawyers insisted. "I spent the last hour arguing with the DA," his words flail only air. The damage to Grove's property, he explains, exceeds $250. I imagine it to be more, far more. The damage gives the DA the right to push the charges up. He inhales the night air slowly; a felony conviction means a year in jail, or more. Police van, a butcher's Frigidaire, to take us to yet another precinct to be fingerprinted. Square mesh grating on the door reminds me of the design of a sewer cover. "We Shall Overcome" sings itself out after a few bars, all of us salvaging what strength remains in silence. When I asked Driscoll if the lawyers who had visited us at the sixth precinct knew or would find out our whereabouts, no comment. Anticipating a night in jail as a political prisoner, incommunicado, I am numb.

5TH PRECINCT: "Barbara Kevles?" A man in street clothes and catfish jowls beckons to me. I am to be first. The radicals and I hunched on desk tops across from the pigs. I tentatively step away and cross to the standup desk. Robin said, "Try it." As the cop rolls my thumb in the ink pad, I do, I announce, "I'm press," goodnaturedly, willing to be released because of the special classification, with no hard feelings, to forget the nearly twelve hours in jail. "Oh, that's nice," he says, blandly, and proceeds to fasten the thumb to the top block of a card. No reprieve, none at all. Not knowing what else to do, I hold out my fingers obediently, trained to middle-class reverence of the law. The jowly man presses the fingers of my left hand, one at a time, in the middle row, clearly for a future FBI researcher.

Forehead hot, I keep shutting and opening my eyes on my record. He stops to scan his work. "Sorry," and he smiles so his jowly chin dips into his shirt collar, "I used a card for a male, I'll have to start all over again." I understand. According to the system, I am classified breasts with skirt over my sex. No dividing prisoners by profession, just biologically, second-class white nigger, a woman. "Jesus! JeeZUS!" My fingers are dipped in the ink again and suddenly, Ti-Grace behind me, "I know, I know," laying her hands on my shoulder for support. "I know," with that encouragement I have come to rely on when I call, and Ti-Grace consoles me that I am not the only one paying a high price to do what I want to do. Now, as with those talks, her gesture revives me, turning down the power of the electric shock machine. Her fit of fanaticism has passed and, I realize, my furious anger at her, as well. We are friends still. She sympathizes. I don't have to be afraid alone. I take several deep breaths as the ink on one set of prints dries and we start another card. An arch, another loop. Was I breathing? I must have. I take several long breaths to be sure, momentarily, relieved.

Three sets of prints completed. Someone from Grove points out I have ink on my forehead, a sign on my head. Sink stained with dirt and soot in an adjoining room. Cops sprawled about, but I wash anyway, long hair tucked in my sweater, rubbing grime from the morning action, the afternoon and evening in three jails, setting my soap back on the rim for the next. Driscoll at another school lectern with more queries for the files. My pedigree report. It is nearly midnight as I must stand and listen to "Are your eyes large, small, deep-set, bulging or hooded lids?" "Are your eyes artificial, contact lens, bloodshot, squints with blinks, different colored?" I raise my hand to stop, a breather. "What will happen to me?" the geisha girl imploring help, the

163

exchange, I assume, for male authority over me, because it is my nature in time of stress to look to a man to protect me, and despite failures of this philosophy, despite the fact that men exploit their authority and often use you, I still haven't shaken my upbringing entirely. "If convicted, you can't get a civil service job or work on a newspaper." Limply, I deny that I even want to, but I shiver at his threat, as if it were the "last word," that once the charge is proven, free-lance work will shrivel away. Leaning toward me, Driscoll says in a choirboy tenor, sotto voce, "My brother was arrested, and I couldn't get in the FBI," with a stern nod to insinuate the untold damage to *my* family. He raises the sheet again to the light for another question, "Are your ears cauliflowered, scarred, discolored, amputated, deaf?" I ponder all the slots of deformity, convinced I must have one. Another cop, "You don't have to use that," in surprise. A whispered conference. Driscoll tears up the sheet and glaring at me blurts out, "I don't trust you." Moored to the other side of the issue, I turn away from the ex-liberal to find a typewriter and write, a refuge I can control, reliable, that will not fail me or hurt back, to wait out the delay because they've run out of cards "female."

Around 2 A.M., the Sexual Exploitation Squad calls for "the girls." A few sturdy ones shout, "Call us women!" On the wagon ride, the cops prove they can do with us what they want. The driver chooses every cobblestone street he can find, as we sit in the dark, hands clutching the next woman, bouncing and slamming down on the hard bench, bobbing uncontrollably, every two seconds, with no real food in our stomachs for thirteen hours.

14TH PRECINCT—PIG PALACE! Driscoll heads into the matron's office. After several minutes, he returns alone and disappears up the stairs to the cellblock. I suspect the matron is always on a 2:30 A.M. coffee break.

One chair in this drafty foyer, everyone gracious, so all nine of us stand. Suddenly one of us, a stress diabetic, pitches forward, laughing, wildly, hysterically. Someone grabs her. The strange party-joke laughter grows shriller and two more get a hold as the girl collapses like burning paper. She was lucid just an hour ago. The girls are edging her toward the single chair. She cries for "Ti-Grace," and "I just need food, that's all, just food." The on-duty sergeant arrives, stomach an enlarged eggplant dangling from his belt, face of an A&P Food Store clerk. Ti-Grace relays the request which the sergeant refuses with "We can't get food at this hour," bureaucraticness. And I holler, "What do you mean? This is New York! You can eat somewhere in New York City twenty-four hours a day!" The sergeant caucuses with a huddle of S.E.S., loudly, to be heard, "If she's sick, let's send her to a hospital." From the chair, the diabetic screams, "I'M NOT SICK, I JUST NEED FOOD, do you understand me, I haven't eaten since breakfast yesterday morning." The rest of us bunch around her, protectively, menacing as a militia. The sergeant adopts conciliation, some of the S.E.S. will take the excruciatingly long trip to the corner, to the all-night grease-joint, for sandwiches.

Lo and behold, the matron. Repressively baggy skirt, that suggests she might have been laid last in the early forties. The first chosen to sample her privileged hospitality, Ti-Grace and I trail our hostess up the stairwell. The walls glisten, cavernous limestone. Beside the doorway, a wooden chair with armrest and another lectern whose shelves hold rolls of toilet paper carefully stacked as in a museum display. The matron opens her record book, "What do you want for breakfast?" trading the promise of food in the morning for our co-operation now. The catch, we have to pay. The corner restaurant fills the orders. Ti-Grace asks, "What about prisoners with no money, do they eat?" The matron, nodding, assures us, they are fed, too, unlikely as it sounds. Her pencil poised, I quickly order bacon and eggs, "scrambled in butter, please," toast and tea. Ti-Grace follows with nearly the same. I forage for a five-dollar bill at the bottom of my tote, while looking quizzically at the matron for the price of the meal. "What's it worth to you?" she asks and adds, "We only ask for a contribution." I hardly ever eat breakfast out. I silently decide on $1.25. "And don't forget the tip," the matron remarks, with a trace of condescension. "$1.50," I say, not wanting to appear cheap. Ti-Grace has a dollar, so I pay for both.

Ti-Grace in her fur vanishes around the corner of the cellblock with the matron. I am rocking on my feet, half-asleep. I've been awake since 6 A.M. yesterday, nearly twenty-one and a half hours. "Hey, Barbara, I have to strip," Ti-Grace calls, "tell the others." Down the limestone conveyor, I announce the news. Quiet below. From Ti-Grace, "Ask them if everybody is going to strip," in a measured tone, but the breaks, the tremolo alert me. Through some wireless intercom between us, I know Ti-Grace is remembering the shocked Columbia bust victims emerging from the police station with hideous tales of vaginal examinations, and the pained confidences of a black friend forced through a brutal physical, and remembering them, she is scared. I move to the doorway and repeat the question, "T.G. . . ." using the abbreviation for her name, the first time ever, my way to put distance between myself, and this jailhouse and what is happening here to a close friend. I suddenly comprehend the question. Ti-Grace is foxing out a test case of the strip and squat technique for federal courts. Anyone else who wants to fight this jailhouse normality can join her. I want to . . . I want to go with her. Because Ti-Grace hasn't insisted, because she isn't playing the role of leader in search of a disciple. I lean against the wall to keep standing, so tired. Out of my guts, out of my being rises mutely, I can't . . . I can't do it . . . not this time, I'm not there yet. . . . Murmurs below, dimming. Robin retorts, "We've decided it's up to the individual conscience, but most will strip. . . ." I face the cellblock and pass the message from the movement on. In moments, Ti-Grace rounds the corner, buttoning up the side of her slacks. I hear the matron order Driscoll up to watch the prisoner. She will be handled later. Ti-Grace sinks into the chair, shaking, ignoring the matron's threats, dragging her reluctant body after the integrity of her mind. And I stumble after the matron, to get on with it.

Cellblock corridor, aggressively lit. As we pass the first cell, an old gray-haired lady in shadows peers out, timidly. At the next one, the matron stops and my eyes burn with tears from the odor of disinfectant slamming out of the open cell. The matron barricades herself from me with a table, its top gashed by knives. I brace myself, "I have to . . . it's procedure," as for a physical with my family doctor. The tote empties onto the table. She flattens out every tissue, and there are many, and then piles one atop another, with a meticulousness I never hoped to encounter. We chat about her night shift and her studies. In answer to "Where?" she says, "The police academy," and I shiver, nervously, and stop talking. She unwinds the tie of the brown envelope with my medicine. I plead to have it to soothe the unbearable itching. She decides the lotion bottle will remain outside my cell.

"Remove your sweater," she orders. My long hair catches in the zipper. A moment longer, and I hand over my navy wool for inspection. I didn't know. I didn't know it would be like this. "The blouse, take it off." I do and expose my braless torso to the corridor spotlights and the matron's stare. Every curve, every crevice of my breasts, visible. "Hold up your arms," goose pimples spring to my skin. I ask for my blouse back. She gives it to me. "Hey, T.G.," I shout, buttoning the red buttons, slowly, trying to deflate what I really feel, "I've liberated my chest." My voice jocular, as if a facade of bravado can cauterize the pain of humiliation. I don't want to feel this experience. I just want to get through it. Sobs, hard sobs are coming from the corridor linking the cellblocks, where Ti-Grace sits. "The boots." She lifts one upside down and knocks her hands against its leather side. Then the second. She keeps them behind the table, to barter, for my continued cordiality. "Your leotards." The sobbing rises like the shriek of a siren. I call to the matron, "Wait!" holding up my hand and dash past her. I round the corner and halt in horror. Ti-Grace, at the end of the other cellblock, is clutching at the corner's spiked edge with one hand and with the other arm is hiding her eyes, embarrassed to be crying before a male pig. Driscoll, motionless, at the doorway. I am stupefied, because I've never seen Ti-Grace cry. I run to her and take an elbow to guide her back and help her into the chair. "She needs tissues," I tell the matron who unwraps a toilet roll and obliges with some scratchy sheets. Ti-Grace, sobbing and gasping between sobs for quick breaths, takes them. She blows her nose, but she won't look up. Her wet face hangs hidden in the military blue sweater, between her shoulders; only her blond hair protrudes. I clasp a shoulder and press her to me, and softly, "Ti-Grace, come on," at the same time massaging her bent neck. "Ti-Grace," chiding as I might a terrified child, attending to her because her pain is greater than mine. She is shaking, convulsively. "I know," I say, offering the words of encouragement she gave me earlier, gently, to tell her I'm OK, I'm holding up, to make her forget how her pact led me to this stripping and the moment of arrogance which foiled my confession and release, to bring her back past this tornado of guilt from the crazy. I'm too tired to be angry. I just want her back, to sanity, to control. "I know, Ti-Grace, I know." Her sobs lessen, gradually. In several minutes she straightens up, dabbing her eyes, revived enough so I can leave her.

Then back to complete my narcotics dossier. Brave, because I haven't heard Columbia bust stories. My naiveté, my shield. "Take off your underpants." I balk, can I keep my skirt on. The matron hangs on to her ritual, it's procedure. I beg, hard. "All right, keep your skirt on." I lower my pants modestly from underneath and put them on the table. "Hold your skirt up," she commands. No choice. I've agreed to be stripped. The sad reward of female meekness. I obey. I raise my skirt. "Higher." The hem of the flowered print blindfolds my eyes. I cannot see the matron. To her, I am a headless pair of legs and ringlets of black genital hair. Her stare, much too long. I swallow and swallow again, not to cry. "Turn, turn now and squat." My head twists for one last look of "please, not this." What have I done? I was so cordial, so nice, I cooperated . . . I don't deserve this. "Squat," she repeats, as I face the sterile, friendless cellblock in her power. My skirt tucked in my fingers, I plié, bare from the waist down, buttocks exposed like two tiny, smooth-skinned melons in the food market. Ti-Grace's wracking sobs suffocate the corridor. Ti-Grace, my Greek chorus, wailing loudly at the blank walls the pain I have sealed in with my pride. Driscoll's voice down the stairshaft, "Get some food, fast, I think she's cracking." As the air climbs my squatting cheeks, I feel . . . I feel the system has made me degrade myself. The ultimate humiliation.

The matron removes her key from the cell door lock. I grasp the front chain strapping my bed to the gray metal wall and lower myself until I am sitting on a hard, flat board. My forty-two-dollar, plastic glasses have been taken away. I fear the matron put them on the tepid radiator, but I am so nearsighted, I can't tell.

My fingers feel further down the board to the bundle of gray I know is my coat. The whiteness beside it, the pile of tissues. Searching, touching, zigzag, toward the back wall, I find nothing. No sheets, no rolled-up mattress, no pillow, no thin wool blanket for the wind-chilled night. All I have is this scrawny three-inch plank to sleep on. I adjust to the fact, any human comfort is denied in this cell. I put my coat on. Luckily, she didn't confiscate any of my clothes. I'm still cold. I slide back against the wall, glad for the space, to sprawl, to pull the heaviness of my feet up and rest. Looking around. Next to the edge of the plank, a blur of white against the back wall. I move closer to discover a bowl-shaped sink tinier than the cheapest motel basin. Below it, a murky hole circled by white. A latrine, I guess, gleaming ghostly in the slit of light from the corridor. I look out, another authorized striptease in progress one cell down. I'll wait . . . a little longer. Ah—my body stretches out. I lie down for the first time all day. Mind joggled by so many jail transfers. Do they know, I'll bet they still don't know where we are. Metal jangling against the table. Robin's voice. The matron with her litany. "Take off . . . now remove . . . yes, that, too . . ." forcing Robin to expose herself as I did, violate her own privacy, the punishment by the priestly pigs in the church of the establishment, the police station, psychological insult, the penance distributed in the name of "the law," the holy father, J. Edgar Hoover, and the son, John Mitchell. A couple of inches from my eyes, a dark brown spot in the light wood, and another brown knot inches from that one. I concentrate on the grain, to arrange my mind, think out my confusion . . . I'm a writer, not a career activist . . . does it matter . . . what I do . . . in prison . . . arrested for a felony . . . but I'm special, I have special status, I've created a life out of the merits of my talents . . . when special . . . with that treatment . . . did you

suffer differently from anyone else? . . . deprived of
food and hungry, detained in a cage, no place to sit
. . . on the floor, in view of any cop . . . examined
for dope, like every prisoner, naked . . . your special-
ness it blinds you . . . it's escapism, even outside . . .
I have professional status, I use my brains to make a
living . . . I'm no stereotyped dumb female . . . what
I think of myself doesn't matter . . . admit it . . . not
to the police . . . not in the eyes of the system . . . the
system classifies you "woman" . . . a loser mentality
. . . a woman, a body . . . another body. A lover? A
wife? A mother? no . . . a white nigger . . . or at best,
someone's special nigger . . . his baby bearer, his pleasure dome, a biological fact. I hear the orders of the
matron. I hear her give the command that welcomes
every female prisoner tonight to her cell, "Now turn,
that's right, turn and squat." In bitter anguish, I question, Is this all human nature can accomplish? Is this
system the best mankind can do? I don't accept it. I'm
worth more. Every woman is worth more than this.

I struggle to wake up, and I do. Stillness, as in a vacant hotel lobby approaching dawn. I open my eyes.
My neck is warm with sweat. I touch the nape and
feel the wetness of my hair, stringy at the damp roots.
I prop myself up on my elbows, tucking the coat under
my body to keep warm. I breathe, aware that I am
taking a breath. Then I turn my head to study the light
on the latrine, pure whiteness on white, losing myself
in its pristine sterility. Is anybody? I stare till my elbows
hurt. Sliding my legs to my chin, to keep warm, and
sleep.

"I'm lying here in a pool of blood." It's blondie. "They
even took my Tampax."

"That's because," responds Robin from next door,
"they thought you would hang yourself on a two-inch
string."

I turn over, adjusting the tissues between my head

171

and the plank. No lice, please. Please, no lice. Sun blurs on blue windows opposite my cell. Last night, I remember Ti-Grace, and I shout, "T.G., T.G." Blondie, Robin, the entire corridor is awash with "T.G., T.G., T.G." "Are you all right?" Tense silence. And the chant is repeated. From very far away, an answer. "Nearly." I close my eyes and open them slowly. Relief! I sit up keeping my coat close to my shoulders and exhale. No smoke. Should be. I scrunch my neck down and draw the coat closer. It is so cold! Sporadic spurts of water in toilet bowls. Oh, some of the others aren't waiting. Suddenly pounding, thumping on the bars, and in unison, "Breakkkkkfasssst," and everybody gets off the final "t" together. Again, "Breaaakkkkk," it is so loud, "ffffassssstttt." Why not? And I am up, beating my fists at the bars, bellowing like everyone else. They ignore us. More calls. And I'm tired. Someone booms out with the cheerfulness of a scoutmaster, "Let's have a flush festival." "One, two, threeee." The gushing water begins. I squint to find the chrome button and press. Niagara Falls churns through the cellblock. And I'm smiling, eagerly anticipating the next imaginative act, the next ingenious harassment of the authorities. Someone at my cell bars. Long skirt. Must be the matron who's squeezing something through the iron slats. I move my coat and myself along the bench. My order. Entombed in cardboard, my eggs. And I stuff my mouth quickly and swallow. Oh! They must've been scrambled in hamburger grease. Oh, well. I try the toast. Lukewarm wood pulp. Pressure in my pelvis and I squint at the white hole under the sink. Another sip of scalding tea. From my coat, I ferret out more tissues and mop the latrine seat. I get up, shed my coat onto the plank and roll down my tights. Then hanging on with one hand to the sink and with the other to the latrine, I direct myself in my nearsighted condition onto the circle of white tissues. A chill spreads up my back, momentarily, from the ice-cold seat. Nonetheless, I look out the bars at the blue blur of window, quite content. Except I can't lean backwards, but have to curve forward because the bottom of the sink juts out over the toilet cutting right into the small of my back. Whoever installed this plumbing must have been a sadist or a contractor who got a bargain on straight pipes. My flush solos through the cellblock. I don't care. I really don't give a damn who knows I'm on the john. It feels so good. And another flush. My knees are cold. I pull my coat over my lap. Someone at the cell bars. I don't move. I just remain where I am, very annoyed at the intrusion. The matron. She excuses herself, her voice mincing with embarrassment. My lap is covered, what's she ashamed about. She saw more last night. Oh, she wants the fork. I point to the cardboard, and she reaches through the bars for the highly dangerous weapon, a Goddamn plastic fork. As she retreats, I holler, "Fuck YOU! FUCK you! FUCK YOU!" Because of the interruption. She interrupted me on the john. But I'm not at all embarrassed. I passed her kind of middle-class mentality as of yesterday. Male voices. At the bottom stairs to the cellblock. Like most blind people, I have excellent hearing. I alert the others, "The S.E.S. are here." From Robin, "You take your identity, vertically, from men." I detect a sisterly attempt at consciousness-raising. "Not any more," I sing out through the wall. My leotards around my toes, my underpants at my ankles, marooned on the can in my jail cell, spilling out a stomach of prison food, my back forcibly contorted, imprisoned by male authority, freezing, exhausted, no bail money, victim of the strip and squat technique sanctified by male law, I say, "NOT ANY MORE." And I mean it.

The largest van yet. I'm so squeezed between Ti-Grace and someone else, I feel I'm going to pop into the air like a button. What are we waiting for? And more women are climbing in. More. The taller and more portly offer their laps. We know about these rides. No one chooses to sit on the floor. The van is so filthy the color of the floor is debatable. I look at Ti-Grace, expecting some comment, some witticism. One hand holds her fur jacket closed, the other . . . I fix on it. The fingers are moving. One by one, in sequence, forefinger, middle finger, they touch the thumb and spring back to place. I don't think she's aware of it. At all. Her blue glasses hide her eyes, but she faces ahead, as if in a trance or deep meditation. The motor starts, at last. Ti-Grace signals me and I bend my head closer as she begins speaking, very low, so her voice will not carry to the agent seated across from us. "Last night, last night . . . I don't know what time . . . after all of you were in cells. . . ." I forgot to ask, I suddenly realize, I forgot to ask what happened. I suppressed it. "They brought me to a room. I was crying . . . I was alone with a dozen pigs, maybe more, maybe fifteen. I couldn't stop . . . crying. Before, when the rest of you were being stripped . . . Driscoll said my tears made me human." She pauses. "That pig, the cop who said he hunted four months of the year," I nod knowingly, "he wanted to rough me up . . . he threatened to . . . Driscoll stopped him and held him back." She takes another breath. "Then instinct took over. You're dealing with power, you've got to get the power out. So I told them, '*Life* wanted to do a story on me, and now I'm going to do it . . . so I can make you all famous.' And the hunter, the one who wanted to beat me, I told him, 'You'd be a credit to Auschwitz.' Can you imagine . . . telling the S.S. I'm making this a test case for the Civil Liberties Union? I mean, I could have been killed."

"Ti-Grace, what happened? What did they do to you?"

"They were waiting for another matron to arrive. . . . More cops came in with their night arrests, their quotas, you know . . . then they took me to a cell. I don't know where. Maybe another cellblock. The other matron was there. The two matrons started to handcuff me to the bars, but I told them, 'You're half pig, but you're half women, too, and I'm here on behalf of women's rights.' So they got smart. They didn't want charges of assault. They called in Driscoll and let him shackle my hands to the bars. He . . . he stretched my arms as far as possible, spread-eagle, you know . . . and he kept saying, 'Does it hurt?' . . . while he was doing it, 'Does it hurt?' Then they stripped me. They took off all my clothes . . . my sweater nearly throttled my neck . . . my panties . . . even the Band-aid on my toe. They didn't miss anything." She's crying. I pull out a tissue. It's clean. She takes it and blows her nose. I turn away. The other women pretend not to notice or maybe they've seen so much it doesn't mean anything. Everyone's in her seat. The driver hasn't hit a cobblestone street yet. He must have a hangover, the smooth ride can't be for our benefit. "Listen," Ti-Grace says, and I lean toward her again. "The only way I survive this . . . is . . . is because this is my life . . . because I am somehow groping through to something I don't know whether it exists and there's no evidence of it . . . but it is humanity . . . otherwise . . . I'd commit suicide . . . but there's no point in your staying close to me after this . . . I don't think it is humanly possible . . . to go past this point . . . to live through something as a voyeur, perhaps as a man . . . but you've got to back off, I've gotten you into this, I didn't want you to embarrass yourself in the movement, but now you've got to step away. Otherwise, they'll break you, they'll break your back." Is the warning for me? is my first thought. Or, is she talking to herself? I can't be sure. Her fingers rhythmically are beating out the shock from her forced stripping.

The police lock slides back noisily. I am home. I feel a public mask falling away, and a weight. I am at ease for the first time all day. The lamp by the secretary is on as I left it. I glance everywhere without moving from the foyer. The apartment is intact. The red pillows are puffed on the couch, as if it were yesterday, no, the day before, when I had the choice to be arrested or not on my first action. By the straw trashbasket in the foyer, newspapers. Good. I open them up and stand on a double page. A whimper escapes, and another. What have I done? A felony? What will happen to me? Good lord! I take my boots off. My coat I hang on the front doorknob. I push the sweater over my head and lay it on the paper. Step away, as if the wool were infested with vermin. The blouse, too, with the sweater. Then the rest, inspecting each piece. No lice. I couldn't stand that. Not now. Not that, with all this. I empty the extra clothing from the green bag into the paper, and stand there. It's so warm. Radiator wheezing like an old granny. I'm shaking as I start the bath water. While the green tub fills, I return and roll up the papers, put them in a foyer corner to be delivered to the cleaners, later. What time is the press conference? 6:30. I'll contact the TV stations after my bath. Oh, it's so warm, so warm. Winding my hair up and sticking a pin through to hold it up. Into the bath. I am sobbing as I stare at my own wall, something familiar, the first time in two days. The sobs start somewhere around my waist, and widen at my shoulders before they channel their way out. I hear the sobs. I hear nothing else. What did that judge say? Oh, he told the Assistant DA, what was it? "Do you think they'll come back for $500 bail, they're all first arrests." Oh, this is incredible. That prosecutor looked like a fat butcher. He thought he had us. I have a felony on my head. I can't believe it. Trial in three weeks. Who will call? Who will be my friend now? Water getting cold.

I draw the washcloth down from the towel rack, sobbing, sobbing, sobbing. After the bath, I pull out an orange suede skirt from a closet, something bright, and a pumpkin sweater. Then I put on makeup and I begin to recognize myself. If we go to trial, those radicals will make the Chicago Seven look like a sewing circle. Am I going to be part of that? What to do? . . . To the secretary, to dial. ABC's local television news desk. As soon as I begin giving information, I calm down. My old professional distance returns. I'm holding together. "I'm one of the Grove Press nine. We were just released . . . yes . . . after 23½ hours in jail, I should say five jails. Half our incarceration, we were held incommunicado. During that time, the DA raised our charges from misdemeanor to a felony," and punching out the words, "without our lawyers knowing. Also, we were subjected to the strip and squat and when one of us refused, she was forced to . . . handcuffed to her cell, spread-eagle, stripped. We're holding a press conference to give the details. . . ." Then I phone the historian at his hotel to invite him to the briefing. I repeat what I've told the TV station, but between us, there is an undercurrent, an unspoken plea, that I'm scared, that I want him to stay in New York, for my sake, a couple of days, to see me through this, that I can't handle this alone, because I am terrified.

The Grove Press felony charges, miraculously, are dropped. Several weeks later, I am in the office of a friend, an editor of a traditionally literary male magazine sold nationwide. Our meeting is an excuse to see each other, but we have always manufactured literary pretexts to resume contact—a call from him for the names of Russian poets or from me, to title an article. We have patterned endings, too. One of us discovers something unacceptable about the other and we both flee from commitment with the cloying delusion we deserve someone more perfect than ourselves. Sometimes, in despair, I compare the relationship to a seed in an infected womb that cannot hold it, but today I have hope. I am wearing the same clothes I was arrested in, that I now wear to write in, because since the action, I don't dress up, put on a face, but bring what I am ordinarily, everywhere, even to the man I'd live with.

I am sitting in his desk chair while he moves about his office, austere without distracting decoration, to complete his day's agenda before we leave. I'm so delighted to be with him. Anyone else in my recent past seems vulgar or mediocre by comparison. As always, I stare, especially at him, his waist, the pivoting tip of a tall buoy, or his legs, outlined by tight bells, thin steely pins when I am pressed against them. I am excited to be with him because given his brutal unreliability countered by my retreat to work, we rarely are together. Our fights, more often than not, take place by telephone, our tenderest emotions, our promises of sterling fidelity have been expressed, in most cases, to a hard, cold telephone receiver.

Another editor, thin tie type and very married slouches through the door. Probably just back at four from some lunch where his note arrived at the wrong table of ladies and the infuriated recipients got him thrown out. A lunch like that. Edging in, careening, tipsy, he strikes out blindly, "What kind of eyeshadow are you wearing?" "Taupe," and so he'll stop squinting, I rise and come around the desk. In his state, he interprets my cordiality as an advance. Emboldened, he asks lewdly, "Why can't I screw you?"—not with the soft *machismo* of a corner whistler, but loudly, so I can't avoid the question. I'm astonished, bewildered, simultaneously. I look to my friend now seated across the desk, expecting him to tactfully deflect the remark. Rather than defend me, he watches, like a voyeur. So, in a low voice, I start to answer, "I've recently been arrested for protesting pornography at Grove Press, I want you to know," snipping my words. "Do I look like a bar-stool girl? Is this office a bar? I'm not a sexual object. I'm a human being. Either treat me like one or . . ." glaring I point toward the door. "This office is a *sanctus! Sanctorum! Sanctissimus! Sanctorum!*" Without a word, the editor staggers out. I'm stunned, stunned at the outpouring of my own rage. I'm no longer the geisha girl willing to laugh and giggle for male approval. The action has changed me. My friend doesn't oust me for the insult. Surprisingly. "He was complimenting you," he apologizes, "it was a compliment." I can't accept it. Nor can I deal with what he is saying. I don't have the words. I haven't sorted everything out, but I know I have discovered the movement in jail, that I will be an action of one each day and that I will protest with other women for our rights as a political class. And I'm afraid. Then I remember, once when Norman Mailer, arch male chauvinist, was photographed leaning back in his swivel chair, he asked the photographer not to publish the low angle shots, the ones through his crotch upward. Well, if Norman Mailer doesn't want to be identified or known by the angle of his crotch, why should I or any woman? Why should any woman let society degrade her, humiliate her, and limit the options to her life because of that perspective? Why?

OSCAR LEWIS

The late Oscar Lewis, renowned anthropologist and author of several books including *La Vida* and *The Children of Sanchez,* left, at the time of his death, a large manuscript tentatively entitled *Six Women.* Sofía, who figures in the following excerpt, is one of those women. The entire work will be published sometime in 1972 by Random House, Inc.

SOFÍA

The Trouble Begins

Whenever I'm nervous I stammer. I've done that ever since I was a child. So it's very hard for me to explain things properly, like when I'm in court or talking to a doctor. I can manage to say the first word, but then all the other words struggle to get out at the same time and I can't talk straight again for about five minutes. Sometimes I try so hard that the wrong words come out, words I never meant to say, and I'm terribly sad because I hurt people that way. It's especially bad when I argue with my husband Antonio. And we've been arguing a lot lately, ever since we moved back to La Esmeralda.

We came back just before my sister Dolores got sick. That was in 1966. For about six years before that we had lived at Stop 18 in El Fanguito, a stinking place. When the federal government decided to knock down all the houses in that area, including ours, it wasn't much of a loss. In fact, it was our gain because they gave a thousand *pesos* to everyone owning a house there. With some of the money, Antonio bought a house in La Esmeralda. The house he liked was by the sea, near Dolores's, and it cost 750 *pesos*. I tried to talk him out of buying it because Dolores had paid only a little over 300 *pesos* for hers, but buy it he did. That's the kind of man Antonio is. When he wants something, he goes after it and gets it. But I didn't complain. He was a very accommodating man in many other ways. If he had a dollar and saw somebody in a jam, he'd give it to him. Antonio had a good job, too. He was a long-shoreman and when the work was steady he earned about 7,000 *pesos* a year. It's true that he gambled a lot, but he never let us go hungry. His greatest virtue was that he was a good father. He adored our two boys, Antonio Luis and Orlando, and he was never un-kind to Ruben and Sofía Jovita, the children I had be-fore I met him.

Antonio and I had lived in La Esmeralda before we got married. At first I was happy to be back and close to my sisters and my *mamá* Carmen again. Antonio was happy too. He got along well with my family, and when *mamá* came to live with us he was very good to her. And if any of my sisters needed money, Antonio would always lend it to them. When Lola got sick and suffered her first hemorrhage, Antonio told her, "Either you come home with us or I'll call the police to drag you to a hospital." No one wanted to stay with her at her own house, so Antonio picked her up and carried her to ours. She stayed with us about a week, but finally got so sick that Antonio took her to the hospital. While she was there Antonio and I used to visit her two times a week.

Lola was always my most troublesome sister, but I never paid her back with anything but good. Her son Millo stayed with us while she was in the hospital, and between *mami* and me we scrounged up fifty dollars to buy his food. We bought a few little things like smocks and slippers for Lola, too. And when Lola got out, do you know what she had the nerve to say? She claimed that Millo had been left to go hungry because Antonio drank up the fifty dollars. Well, that was a lie, and it was Millo who told it to her! Each time he visited his mother, he'd tell her we spanked him and didn't feed him. That's why Lola left the hospital before she was well enough to come home. She said she was dismissed, but I found out later that she simply went out on a three-day pass and didn't go back. If it hadn't been for Millo's lies, Lola would be alive today.

When Lola did come to get him, Millo didn't want to go with her. I myself had to put his suitcase in his hands and tell him to go. He knew well enough the kind of life he'd have at his *mai*'s house. She put him to work earning money as a shoeshine boy, washing the dishes, cleaning the house, buying the food. In my house he never had to do a thing. And in return he stole a dollar from me one day and went out to play the daily double. But I never told Lola about that.

Lola looked healthy and plump when she came out of the hospital, but a month later she was very sick in bed. She was staying at my sister Alicia's house and, when she knew she was dying she called for the priest. He came right away and confessed her, but couldn't give her the Host because she kept throwing up. He said we would have to wait for a day when she wasn't vomiting. As things turned out, her throwing up got worse every day—she was never able to have the Host. I've heard a lot about purgatory and heaven, but the only way I can picture them is according to something Lola said the day we took her to Alicia's house. She was almost on the way out, and all of a sudden she cried, "Ay, mi madre! I dreamed I climbed a very tall staircase and I saw lots and lots of flowers, but to get to them, I had to climb a ladder and cross a great big garden."

"Is that all you saw?" I asked her, and she said, "Yes, that's all. I saw lots of beautiful things. But why didn't they let me stay there?"

Finally she got so sick that Antonio had to take her to the hospital. They admitted her around midnight and by two o'clock the next morning she was dead. Before we buried her we brought her into San Sebastian Church where the priest blessed her. He said, "God forgives the good and the wicked." You see, he knew all about her.

Ay, I'm so grateful for what Antonio did at the time of Lola's death. He took the rest of the thousand *pesos* out of the bank and paid for all the funeral expenses—the coffin, the crown, the glasses for the wake, everything. Then he rented out Lola's house and put *mami* in charge of collecting the monthly rent, which she put into the bank for Millo so he can start a business when he is older. Later *mami* sold the house for 300 *pesos* to a spiritualist named Tomasa. Tomasa gave her 200 *pesos* down and promised to pay the rest in monthly installments.

A few months after Lola died I became pregnant again. I've never gone more than three months between pregnancies. Sometimes I've had miscarriages, sometimes I've aborted, but I've never taken pills to keep from having babies. I hear they make you feel sick, and besides, if you take them for a while and then stop and get pregnant, you're liable to have twins. That happened to a girl in La Esmeralda who was on pills. She forgot to take them once and lay with her husband. She got pregnant right away and had twins, so she was worse off than she was without pills.

There are many other ways to keep from getting pregnant, but I've never used them. I'd rather bear twenty children than use a liquid or any of those devices a woman puts inside herself. Once before, when we lived in El Fanguito and I got pregnant right after Antonio Luis was born, I said to Antonio, "No, *mijo,* this is too much! If I don't find a way to remedy this, we'll wind up with twenty children!" That time Antonio agreed to let me be sterilized at the clinic, but when he found out it would cost him $150 his answer was, "Well, doctor, she'll simply have to do without the operation."

When one is poor one shouldn't have more than three children. After all, what you may be able to buy for three, you sure can't afford to buy for five or six. Still, I didn't mind being pregnant again. Children grow up so soon and I always like to have babies around the house. I'm not like my sisters when it comes to my children. I can't quite explain it, but my feeling for them is so strong that I can never get them out of my mind. If I go anywhere without them I feel uneasy. If I am given food and my children aren't there to share it with me, I start to cry. Sometimes, though, I wish I could be like my sister Eva. She loves her children, too, but she can forget about them for a while. She goes to parties and eats and drinks and dances. Not me! Oh, I could never do that! All of my children I have loved from the very first moment. The day I miss my period, that's the day I start loving the child in my womb.

I've heard it said that my sister Magda has been a good mother to her children, at least in the sense that she puts them in school and sends them off clean. But I also heard, and straight from *mamá*'s lips, that Magda gave away her first child, a girl named Gloriá, so she could run off with another man. If that's true—and it's only when *mai* is angry with Magda that she says such things—then I have a very bad opinion of Magda as a mother. Surely a woman who loves her child would never do a thing like that. And to do it for the sake of some guy makes it that much worse! When a woman leaves her children to take off with a man, it means she prefers the man to her own children. She's a bad wife and a bad mother. My sister Alicia is no better. She gave Delfin the two boys and two girls she had by him. Later she gave away the little girl she had by Pablo, too. She seems to have no interest in that child, either. She doesn't give her presents and never even goes to see her. That isn't my idea of acting like a mother. As long as I had my health I wouldn't think of turning my children over to someone else, no matter how bad things were. My God, no!

I used to think my marriage was different from my sisters' marriages. They and their husbands were always fighting and picking on each other. When they weren't separated, they were in court. But I really and truly respected my husband. Before I knew Antonio, all men added up to nothing as far as I was concerned. If a man told me not to do something, then that's exactly what I'd do. But if Antonio so much as looked at me severely, I'd get the shakes. Honestly, I don't know what that man did to me! It wasn't that I was afraid of him, because he never used to hit me. I just loved him so much. It seemed to come from deep inside me, from my soul. I pinned all my hopes on him. From the day we were married by law, I thought we would live out our lives together, and even die together.

I guess that the farther away I am from my sisters, the better off I am, because with less visiting back and forth we have less trouble. As long as Antonio and I lived far away from them, we got along well. But a little while after we came back to La Esmeralda, Antonio began to change. He went bad on me. He had a friend named Arguio who ran a bar in La Esmeralda, and whenever Antonio wasn't working he would spend all his time there. Arguio had a wife named Pascuala, a much older woman, and I could tell Antonio had something going with her. He'd come home drunk as a dog. I've always known what he was thinking, and when I told him I didn't trust him, he said I shouldn't be jealous. He reminded me that Arguio was his friend. He said that if he had wanted to have an affair with Pascuala he would have done it long ago because he knew her before he met me. So I let things ride, but sometimes I'd look out my window and see the two of them whispering together and doing God only knows what other damn things! You can imagine how I felt. I was Antonio's legal wife, and when a man and woman get married by the law it's a far more serious thing than simply living together. That's why I expected Antonio to treat me with some respect and not like some *corteja* who had no rights.

Until that time Antonio and I never quarreled. If I had some objection to make, I always used to call him aside into the bedroom where we could talk privately. But after Antonio began seeing another woman we lost our respect for each other. We'd insult each other at the top of our voices for everyone to hear. He'd yell at me and I'd yell right back, but then I'd begin to stammer. That would make me madder and I'd hurt Antonio without even realizing it because the bad words simply slipped out. It was my nerves' fault and I explained that to Antonio, so sometimes he'd keep quiet after we started to argue. But once I got so mad I thoughtlessly called him *cabrón* and he told me, "Next time you call me a cuckold, I'll cut you up." Before the day was over we had made up. Antonio begged me not to call him names and I never did again. Somehow I managed to control myself and that's something I've done for no other man!

As long as Antonio isn't drinking, he's a good man, but when he drinks he's like his father. The moment Antonio puts a beer in his stomach the blood rises to his head. It causes him to *see* blood. His eyes begin to look very red, just like a dope fiend's, and he acts as though he were in a daze. According to his *mai*, he was even worse when he lived with his family in the country; they once had to tie him down there. Why, his *mai* claims that one day he got drunk and punched a woman. He didn't remember it, and the next day when the woman came around, Antonio said to her, "My God, what happened to you?" She turned on him in a fury and said, "Listen here, you big piece of filth, you're the one who punched me!"

Antonio always drank too much at Arguio's, and one night he came home looking as if he saw blood. Never had he so much as laid one finger on me unkindly or even scratched me with a metal instrument, but that night he came after me with his knife. He was trying to slash my face, but he missed and cut my arm instead. He didn't even know he was doing it, but I have a terrible scar there now.

Even though I said nasty things when I got mad, Antonio should never have cut me. And with me five months pregnant! When his sister heard what he had done she really gave him a bawling out. And his sister's husband is a good guy, too. He told Antonio he should never do that to a woman, and that if he felt in a cutting mood he should cut himself. We were in one royal mess by that time. It was drinking and fighting all the time. Antonio even went after *mamá* once with his knife, but she got out of his way in time. I blamed Pascuala for it all. She was driving Antonio crazy.

For a while I had an urge to kill myself. I'd say to myself, "You've got medicines there in the cabinet. Why don't you swallow them?" And when I looked at a piece of rope we had in the house I'd say, "Why don't you string that around your neck?" But then I'd say, "And what would become of your children? Antonio Luis and Orlando have their father to look after them, but what about Ruben and Sofía Jovita? I am

mother *and* father to them. What if they were left
with Antonio, or with my own family, and were mis-
treated? An orphan suffers, no matter whom he is
with." So when those ideas came into my head, and
they did plenty of times, I'd ask my dead *pai* to make
them go away.

Now and then I thought of leaving Antonio. I could
have gone to live with my sister Eva in New York.
She and I were always very close and it seemed I was
destined to follow whatever path she took. She left her
husband, too, and was living in New York at that time.
When she came back just before Dolores died she told
me people treated you better in the States. She said
one could easily get a good-paying job and live a hap-
pier, more peaceful life than in Puerto Rico. As for her,
el Relief supported her and gave her money and food
for her children. In Puerto Rico the government gave
a measly seven dollars a month for old people and only
the simplest kind of food. You had to earn the money
for clothes with the sweat of your brow; if you didn't
you went bare.

Eva wanted me to come and stay with her, but I
didn't go because I was pregnant. My nerves were in
a terrible state, though, and I didn't like the way I was
making the children suffer on Antonio's account. I
hoped that God would make Antonio pay for all the
things I did to my children because it really wasn't my
fault.

Our little girl Teresa was born in July 1967. My labor
pains started on June 29 and lasted until July 4. Six
days, imagine! When they started, I didn't tell Antonio
because he's the kind who says right away, "Something
hurts? All right, let's go to the clinic." But on the Fourth
of July I got terribly sick; not only did I have the pains,
I was also choking with *fatiga* because the baby was
pushing up instead of down. Antonio took me to the

hospital then—just the two of us because *mami* stayed
with the kids. Antonio was plenty scared! While I was
in labor, the nurse told me the doctor said I would need
an operation after the baby was born or else I would die
in labor if I bore another child. So Antonio didn't have
to pay the hundred and fifty dollars for me to be sterilized. God was with me; I was so sick that they had
to operate gratis.

I had planned to call the baby Carmen Sofía after
my daughter who had died, but Antonio objected to
the name because some people say one should never
call a baby after a dead relative. *Mamí* objected for
the same reason and because she felt I would always
be remembering the child who died. Antonio's *mai*
wanted the child named Josefina Sofía after *her*
daughter who had died, but Antonio would have none
of that. Why, when I was pregnant, his *mai* made a
little shirt and pillowcase for the child, but after the
baby was born she asked me not to use the pillowcase
because she had embroidered the name Josefina Sofía
on it. Antonio insisted on naming the baby Teresa, and
Teresa she remained.

I didn't feel any changes in my body after the operation. The only way it affected me is that now and then
I get such pains that I writhe on the floor. But the
pains don't come too often, and as long as I'm not having them, I feel fine. I have heard people say that some
women feel free to have intercourse any time they like
after an operation like mine; Antonio himself told me
that. Not long ago he said that the operation had
changed me, that *every* woman who got sterilized became a showoff. But I have *not* changed. It was Arguio
who put that notion in Antonio's head; those were the
very words he said to *his* wife right after she had the
operation. Antonio was simply repeating Arguio's words.
It is true that *some* women, when they don't have to

be afraid of getting pregnant, start going out with other men and doing anything they like. I can say truthfully, for instance, that *comai* Eva was very different before her operation, while she was living with *compai* Arturo. But no sooner did she get the operation than problems started. Finally she put the horns on Arturo and they broke up. I suppose that is why men are afraid to have their women sterilized. Antonio showed he really trusted me when he let me have the operation.

In certain ways I am glad they sterilized me; in other ways I'm not. I don't think it affected the way Antonio felt about me. Actually, it was *before* the operation that he changed towards me, and that's the real reason I am so glad I was sterilized. If it's God's will for Antonio and me to break up sometime, at least I won't have any more children. But I'm sorry too, because if I did want more, I would not be able to have them.

As far as sex is concerned, well, I'm not the kind of woman to start pestering her husband the minute she crawls into bed. I just don't care one way or the other. But I believe I used to satisfy Antonio in bed. Yes, I really think I did; that is, as far as I could tell, I did. And of all the men I've had, Antonio was the best lover. He's a very hot man and in the beginning he'd get into me and come quickly, never caring whether or not I was satisfied. He'd want me as soon as he got in bed at night and then again in the morning, every single day. But after we were married awhile he really began to make an effort to have me come, too. He'd start kissing me and playing with me before he went in and I enjoyed it. Sometimes I'd even take the initiative in bed. I didn't let myself come when he did, though. I used to hold back, afraid I'd get pregnant, because that's what happens when the man and woman come at the same time. If one comes first and the other later, the woman doesn't get pregnant. After my operation I didn't have to worry about that any more and

I'd let myself come at the same time Antonio did. We were very compatible then and Antonio began to change for the better. He even stayed away from Pascuala, but only for a little while. Pretty soon he went back to drinking and staying out late.

There were some things I always refused to do in bed with Antonio because they weren't right and normal. For instance, before my operation I wouldn't let him lay me during my period. I respected those days because doctors say that a man who has sexual contact with a menstruating woman can get sick. It was partly for fear of making Antonio sick that I refused him at those times. But it humiliated me to have him ask certain other things of me in bed. It was against my conscience because they were dirty things, against the natural order. Ay, what Antonio wanted was a tart who'd stop at nothing! Why, he came right out and told me one day, "I'm going to get myself a real hot mamma and live with her. What do you say to that?" My only answer was, "Do as you please. Get the kind of woman who'll suck your cigar, if that's what you want! If that's what you expect of me, you're in for a big disappointment. There are some things I will *never* do! I'll serve you in bed as a wife is bound to serve her husband, but as a slave, never!"

After we moved back to La Esmeralda Antonio began to complain that I was not what I used to be in bed. "Well, what do you expect?" I asked him. "When we moved here, there was a big change in *you*. I warned you that if the situation kept up I'd change, too." And I *had* changed. I was never the one to start making love any more. I'd have relations when he wanted them and let him go as soon as it was over. I stopped letting him lay me in the morning. I'd only let him do it in the nighttime and even then, not always. And when I said no, I meant no! Sometimes he'd try to kiss me and pester like before, but he didn't seem to have the same passion for me, and if I wasn't in the mood for it, I'd lose my temper the minute he touched me. In a way it was better when he went right in as though he couldn't wait because then the sex act was over quickly. Antonio said I was cold, but I wasn't. It's just that a woman needs some sexual satisfaction, but not as much as a man. Many's the time Antonio said to me, "If I should let two or three days go by without using you, you'd begin to miss it." Well, he couldn't have been more mistaken! Antonio was the one who was screwed up without sex. He really needed it. Once, when he went away for a few days I realized I didn't need him in that way at all. I needed him in only one way—for the children's sake. And if he had left me then, I wouldn't have taken on any new men.

It got so I wouldn't let him sleep with me when I suspected he'd been out laying another woman. God knows what he might have caught, out one night until twelve-thirty, another until one! On those nights I'd say to him, "You're not going to eat a single grain of my corn!" I'm not one to rush to suck the dog's nipple and risk getting all balled up myself. My sisters, who are experts in those things, said that if you were going to have relations with a man and wanted to find out whether he had the clap, you should pour some drops of lemon right on his prick. If he screams in pain, then he's sick. The same thing is true of a woman. If after having relations with a man she presses her stomach and it hurts, then she knows she's sick. Doctors say those illnesses may heal up on the outside only to be driven into your lungs or some other part of the body. That's why so many people die of tuberculosis, why so many women have to have their wombs cut out. Holy Mother! I didn't want to find myself in that fix! Not me! I love my body too much. If it was God's will that some of my guts had to be taken out, let it be because of a tumor, something that couldn't be helped, and not because Antonio got a case of hot pants and I was fool enough to accept him after he laid another woman. The doctor told me it takes nine days for the clap or those other illnesses to show up on the outside, so that's how long I'd make Antonio wait. Then I'd ask him to swear by his mother and by his virgin daughter that he hadn't been having any affairs during those nine days. If he wouldn't swear to that, I wouldn't get close to him in bed, no matter what. I'd tell him, "You sleep that way and I'll sleep this way, back to back." But one does miss a man! When a woman is used to sleeping beside a man, the two of you putting your arms around each other, and then you quarrel, you suffer terribly. Believe me, I *know*.

Antonio didn't seem as unhappy about the situation as I did. Sometimes he'd come to bed, turn his back to me, and sleep until morning. What hurt me most was his saying I was frigid. I didn't even know what he meant by that, but it cut me to the heart. I asked myself, "What the heck did I do to him that bothered him so?" But I hadn't done anything. He even ordered me to take the baby's crib out of the room, which amounted to telling me to get out, too, because if the baby woke up in the night I had to be next to her where I could hear her. At first I didn't take the crib out. I thought, "If Antonio doesn't want to sleep with me, let him move!" But a few weeks later, after a bad argument, I moved the crib and our spare bed into the other room and slept there.

In a way I blamed myself for what happened. I *deserved* a husband who'd stick it into every hole in my body for being such a dope—I didn't even go as far as the corner without his permission. I spent the whole day behind locked doors, and if I did open them it was only a crack. Why I did it, I don't know. If you get a man in the habit of keeping you locked in, you're ruined. I tried to be a virtuous wife to Antonio, but he didn't give a damn about that. What he wanted was a whore, not a wife. He was even hanging around Miriam, my sister Alicia's daughter. I told him that girl would let anybody do it to her.

"As long as she's hot and willing, what do I care?" That's the answer I got!

Oh, I had my ways of getting back at him—like fixing myself up real fancy every night to make him jealous. I'd use lots of green eye shadow and eyeliner. Antonio would get furious, but I wouldn't pay any attention to him. One Saturday morning he came in, sat down on the edge of the bed, and said to me, "You know something? Yesterday one of those street women came down alongside the boat and invited me to go home with her."

"Well, my boy," I told him, "you should have gone with her."

"You think I fall on my face for every broad that goes by, don't you? Well, I know exactly what I'm doing."

Ay, Antonio wanted to give me the business, so I let him have it, too! If he got an invitation like that, the least he could do was not tell me about it! I told him, "Remember the other day when we had that fight? Well, after that I was standing on the porch when a boy passed by, and do you know what he said to me?"

Antonio got a very serious look on his face and said, "Who was he?"

"Just a fellow. You don't know him. It was the first time I ever saw him."

"What did he say to you?"

"That I have beautiful eyes."

For a while after that he hardly ever went to Pascuala's. In fact sometimes he'd go out and hide and then all of a sudden he'd appear from nowhere. Like one day he said to me, "I'm going to San Juan." But within half an hour he was back. I said to *mamá*, "This guy thinks I'm a jerk. If he has an idea he's going to catch me off base, he's nuts." He was still my husband and I respected him too much to put the horns on him. I just wanted him to respect me, too. But he didn't. He went back to hanging around Pascuala again.

About a year and a half after we moved to La Esmeralda the big waves came and carried our house away. That was in December, 1967, when Teresa was almost six months old. *Ay*, I remember the time well! It was about three in the morning when the first waves hit, and I realized from the beginning that we were in for trouble. The first big blow of waves poured right in between the wall slats of the house, and I screamed for *mamá* and Antonio to wake up. All I could think of was getting the children out; I grabbed them up and took them to Alicia's house, leaving Antonio to get our belongings out. He took the clothes but balked about moving anything else, thinking, I suppose, that nothing really bad would happen. But when the neighbors assured him the worst was going to happen, he went to work and got everything out. *Ay*, it was horrible—people crying, screaming! Magda's house was carried away and so was Dolores's. The woman who bought Dolores's house still owed *mamí* money for it, too. By ten-thirty in the morning our house was very shaky, and soon after, the sea swept it completely away. It was a tremendous blow to Antonio watching the sea waves carry away the house. He liked living there and felt he had made a lot of sacrifices to buy the house. I felt sad, too, thinking of my children without a home, but at the same time I was relieved, because I knew we would be better off somewhere else.

Antonio asked Arguio to store our furniture for us until we had another place to live. We were assigned an apartment in the Juana Matos public housing project in Cataño, which is pretty far from La Esmeralda. Antonio was very unhappy about that because all his friends were in La Esmeralda and he didn't know any people in Cataño. It took him longer to get to work in San Juan, and he complained about all the money we'd have to pay for rent. But I was glad to go there. Our apartment was in a new cement building where everything was modern and clean. The children would be better off there. And Antonio wouldn't be forever hanging out at Pascuala's. As long as we were in La Esmeralda, the two of them carried on right under my nose, and loving him as I did made it that much worse. If Antonio did go to La Esmeralda after we were living in Cataño, at least I wouldn't have to know about it. That way I might be able to keep our home together for the children. I didn't want them to know what a broken home was like, as I did when I was a child.

ALAN SCHOLEFIELD

Alan Scholefield was born in Cape Town, South
Africa, in 1931 and now lives in England. He is the
author of several novels, including *Great Elephant*,
many articles and short stories. The following excerpt
is taken from Scholefield's *The Young Masters*, a
novel set in South Africa. William Morrow and Co.,
Inc. will publish the book in 1972.

THE YOUNG MASTERS

Hugh Hutcheson Howe arrived at Meade House at the
beginning of 1944 and became fag to Posthumus. At
first everyone called him Hugh Hutcheson Howe out
of sheer enchantment but later he simply became
"Flash." There were several features about him, ex-
cluding his name, that singled him out from the other
new boys, indeed from everyone in the house. There
was his size: he was barely five feet tall and yet there
was nothing about him that suggested a stunting of
growth. Everything, hands, feet, face, shoulders, legs,
all were built to a precise scale so that each exactly
matched the others, giving him the most elegant pro-
portions. It was apparent that nearly all the growing
he had to do, unlike others who shot upwards and outwards with the unexpectedness of fast-growing vines,
was already done. Where Paul and Rhino grew at the
rate of a new blazer every year—for the latter part of
which more and more of their wrists slid into view—
Hugh Hutcheson Howe, if he grew at all, increased

gently by a uniform fraction of an inch. He was always neat and his limbs seemed under perfect control; he was also extremely beautiful with a pale face, high cheekbones and wavy golden hair. At first his expression had been described by Paul—then in the midst of *The Old Curiosity Shop*—as wistful, but it soon became clear that he was no more wistful than Ebenezer was white.

What Paul had mistaken for emotion was the purely physical expression of a face behind which things were running a little slower than normal. When Hugh Hutcheson Howe was a child he had been described as "dreamy"; now, in Horse's phrase, he was "grotesquely idle."

He was incapable of speed and abhorred hurry. When he had first arrived at King's, Drop du Plessie, the master in charge of rugby, had stated that Howe was the perfect build for a scrum-half. But after three or four practice games during which Howe ambled about the field as though the game was, in fact, cricket and he was fielding on the boundary, Drop relegated him to that particular hermaphroditic hell which existed for boys who had no interest in rugby.

Since it took Howe longer to get up in the morning than anyone else, longer to shower, dress, eat, move, he was always late and so he was called "Flash."

That same dreamy, wistful expression that was appealing to house-masters' wives, caused a different reaction in their husbands, especially in Horse. Latin was first period every morning and Howe was late three mornings a week. Had he arrived flushed, hair awry and penitent, Horse might have been more forgiving, but Howe did not live like that. When he presented himself anywhere he was always perfectly groomed, so each time he entered the classroom he did so with a calmness and control that infuriated Horse.

"Good afternoon, Howe," Horse would say. "It's good of you to come," or "I hope we're not putting you out,

Howe," or "We're obliged to you, Howe, for gracing us with your presence. Better late than never, eh?" And Howe would simply say, "Yes, sir, sorry, sir," and place himself neatly in his seat.

As punishment Horse gave him great slabs of unseen and you'd have thought Howe would have been the leading Latin scholar in the school with all that practice but he seemed to have little desire for knowledge. Invariably, he would have to have a question repeated; infrequently did he have an answer. His notes were the neatest in class but he seemed to gain little from them. This infuriated Horse even more.

"Resting, Howe?" he would say as he came up to his desk.

"No, sir."

"Doubtless it has escaped your attention, but the others are assaulting, if that is the word, Caesar's Army in Britain."

"Yes, sir."

"Yes, sir . . . ! No, sir . . . ! You really must try to extend your range of syllables, Howe."

But the more Howe suffered from masters and prefects the better he was liked by the rest of Meade House. Apart from the fact that he did not bear malice, that he intrigued against no one and that his ambitions, if he had any, conflicted with no one else's, Howe had one priceless gift: he could make music. He could make it on anything, piano, guitar, Jew's harp, paper and comb, mouth organ, ukelele, banjo, anything, and this, as Paul remarked to Rhino, was what he seemed to exist for. No matter what he was doing, if someone wanted him to play, Flash would play.

King's College was not noted for musical tradition. The school possessed two pianos. The first, a Blüthner baby grand, was known as the "school piano" and was, for most of the time, locked away with the carbines and the two obsolete German machine guns in the armory, to be brought out only on special occasions when the National Anthem or the school song was to be sung. The second was known as the "rugby piano" and lived in a small room off the Minor Hall. It was used during the rugby season for sing-song practices and was taken across to the Recreation Ground and hoisted up into the grandstand on winter Saturdays when King's played at home. For several years no one at King's, among either the boys or the staff, had been able to play the piano so the Blüthner had remained in the armory and the rugby piano, manufactured years before by Messrs. C. J. Quandt in Germany—the "Q" had been changed and the "a" and "d" deleted and the ivories pulled off the keys—stood unused. This changed when Hugh Hutcheson Howe came to King's.

Almost any afternoon, except when he went downtown for private lessons, he could be found surrounded by an audience of half-a-dozen or more while he played the rugby piano. The school favorites were "Stardust," "Jealousy," "In the Mood" and "Prisoner of Love," all of which—and a couple of score more—Howe was able to dash off. He could play them in any key and with at least two bass accompaniments, the standard jazz bass promoted by the teach-yourself schools, and what was called the "crawling" or "boogie" bass, which fitted tunes like "Alligator Crawl." It was his mastery of this bass that brought Howe his greatest acclaim.

He could also play sterner stuff, Beethoven bagatelles, Chopin nocturnes, Czerny studies and Bach preludes, and these were tolerated by some, abhorred by others, as the price they had to pay for hearing "Deep Purple" and "Paper Doll." Rhino made no bones about his inability to appreciate any music at all but Paul, drawn at first by the jazz tunes, began to stay for Howe's practice sessions and found appreciation growing. He also, to his surprise, found himself in the company of Posthumus.

Posthumus had, at least, reached his matriculation year, having achieved the distinction of failing the previous year twice. He was now twenty years old and remained doggedly at school because his father had promised him one of the family farms if he finally matriculated. Dold had left the previous year, joining the army to fight in Italy rather than face his father, and de Klerk had passed his finals and disappeared. The Room had also vanished; it had become a reading room, its halcyon days of brutality, farting competitions, and group masturbation gone forever. Posthumus now lived in solitary splendor in a small room that had once been a bathroom, as far removed from the rest of the House as Horse could manage and where Posthumus's influence could be controlled. Horse was fond of describing him as "that elderly gentleman." Posthumus did not seem to care. He was isolated by age, distance and inclination from fellow members of the House. He smoked when and where he liked, drank beer, and was known to have a girl in the town with whom he did not just hold hands.

Paul was unable to understand the attraction Howe seemed to have for Posthumus. At first, when Posthumus made him his fag, Paul assumed that Howe's freedom to go downtown to his music lessons meant that he could be used as a messenger boy, a carrier of sweetmeats and cigarettes; but since Posthumus came and went as he pleased there seemed no point to this. Then Paul discovered that what Posthumus craved was music.

Over the years he had put together an unrivalled collection of records; almost everything, it seemed, that Artie Shaw, Benny Goodman, Dinah Shore, Duke Ellington, Count Basie, the Quintet of the Hot Club of France, the Mills Brothers, the Andrews Sisters, the Ink Spots, Joe Daniels and his Hotshots in Drumnasticks, Harry James, Tommy and Jimmy Dorsey, Louis Arm-

strong and others had ever recorded. The records lay
and stood and leant in piles against the walls of his
room, under his bed, on his table, scratched, dusty and
some, in their Parlophone and HMV paper covers,
broken by the weight of others on top of them. For
Howe, Posthumus's room was like a treasure cave.
Much of his time was spent listening to the records,
which suited Posthumus very well. He would lie on his
bed playing with a chameleon called Zoomo, enjoying
whatever Howe chose to play. Occasionally Paul and
one or two others would crowd into the small space,
but for the most part Posthumus and Howe were alone.
This led to a strange development in their relationship.
What had started off as a typical senior-fag arrangement gave way to a situation much less brutal than
Posthumus was used to.

"He's bum-rushing Howe," Rhino said to Paul by way
of explanation.

"Don't be coarse, Leslie."

"What else, then? You want to see the two of
them. . . ."

"I do . . . more than you."

"Christ, Posthumus was never like that when we
fagged for the Room. You remember how he used to
stripe us? I'm bloody sure he never touches Howe. Not
like that, anyway."

"Maybe he doesn't need to. Maybe Howe's so bloody
good. . . ."

"Balls. Howe's too fucking fast asleep."

Even when it had become apparent to Paul that
music was the bond, Rhino remained unconvinced.
"Posthumus?"

"Come and see for yourself."

"Learning the piano!"

"He's even written off for a jazz course."

The spectacle of Posthumus learning the piano
proved too much for Rhino and others. For a week

or so the small room off the Minor Hall was filled to capacity as onlookers shoved and pushed for a place near the piano. The whole thing should have been good for a laugh—and at first there was the odd remark from the back of the crush. But Posthumus might have been deaf for all the notice he took. He seemed to exist in a private world and his aloofness was so genuine that fewer and fewer stayed to watch the lessons. Rhino remained for an hour and left, still doubtful. But Paul went down as often as he could, fascinated by the sight of someone he had once defined as a human gorilla learning a complex new medium. The astonishing thing was that while Posthumus might have looked anthropoidal as he crouched at the scarred keys, his fingers apparently too clumsy to strike and glide with precision, he was, as Paul later told Rhino, making progress.

"He's no bloody fool about music," Paul said. "Look at his records."

"That doesn't mean he can play."

They were smoking half a Springbok cigarette in the school lavatories, passing it draw by draw until the butt was a single glowing coal.

"He can play 'South of the Border.' . . ."

"Only with one hand. Anyone can do that."

"Ungulates can't."

"Piss off!"

Posthumus could, in fact, play the first verse of "South of the Border" with his right hand. He could also pick out "Blue Skies" and "Take the A Train," but he could not put his left hand to the tunes. As the weeks passed this inability to synchronize his hands loomed larger and larger both in Posthumus's life and Howe's.

"No," Howe would say gently, "you've got to start it on the beat. Look, I'll show you." And for the hundredth time he would move his chair closer and at arm's length play the standard bass.

"You play the treble now. One . . . two . . .

three . . ." and off they'd go, Posthumus playing the right hand and Howe putting in the bass. Sometimes he would play the crawling bass and then Posthumus would crouch lower and concentrate harder.

"Christ, Hughie, that's the one I want."

"You'll never play it if you can't put your hands together. Try again. One . . . two . . . three. . . . No, no. On the beat. Dum . . . di . . . dum, dum . . . di . . . dum. Then you put the treble to it. It's simple."

"Simple, *shit!*"

Posthumus's repertoire grew. He could play "On the Sunny Side of the Street," "Shoo Fly Pie" and "Tuxedo Junction." But only with his right hand. Paul began, in spite of himself, to feel sorry for Posthumus. As he watched the intense concentration, the sweat beading the simian brow, he began to will the left hand to come in at the right time and hold the rhythm, but the synchronization seldom lasted beyond a bar or two before breaking down.

The twenty-four-week course arrived from a correspondence school in Johannesburg and this brought Posthumus added worries. Was that a crotchet or a quaver? What did a double bar mean? Why couldn't everything be written in C major? What was a dominant seventh?

"What the hell do they do in there all the time if they're not pulling each other's wires?" Rhino said one day as they passed Posthumus's room.

"Race chameleons."

"Cock!"

"I'm telling you. Flash races them on Posthumus's back."

"Bullshit."

"You remember how we used to have to scratch his back when we were fags? Well, he's got two chameleons now. He makes Flash race them up and down his back. He says he likes the feeling."

"Jesus, if Horse finds out he'll go mad!"

It took nearly three months before Posthumus's left hand responded to the stimulation of rhythm. Paul was there when it happened. Posthumus had been trying, for the best part of half an hour, to marry the bass arpeggio to "Red Sails in the Sunset" and failing, when suddenly he let his shoulders relax and simply pretended to be playing the piano as one might pretend to strike the notes on a pianola. Only this time his fingers struck the correct notes in sequence and in time. He played "Red Sails in the Sunset" nineteen times before resting his hands on the keys and turning to Howe. "Jesus, Hughie," he said, awestruck, "it worked!"

Within a couple of weeks he was able to play his entire repertoire with two hands, provided he could work out the tune in C major and provided he did not have to play too quickly. Meade House was impressed. Even Horse heard about it, for as he passed Posthumus in Middle Dormitory one evening he said, "I understand you have grasped your Muse, Posthumus. I urge you to hold her fast lest senility loosen your grip."

But after the first raptures of "Red Sails in the Sunset" Posthumus became dissatisfied with the vamping style of the jazz bass. His own favourite pianists were Fats Waller and Art Tatum. "That's how I want to play, Hughie," he said. "The crawling bass."

"You're doing fine with the other. Why change now?"

"Because I want to."

"It isn't easy."

"You'll teach me."

"I've got my own practicing to do, you know," Howe said mildly.

"You'll bloody teach me or you'll get striped," Posthumus said, letting Zoomo wobble along his forearm. "Don't forget you're just a fag."

So the process began again. The first bass had been achieved by reflex action and did not help with the new one. Winter gave way to spring, spring to early summer, and still Posthumus had not mastered the crawling bass. During this period, Howe became friendly with Mr. Martin.

It was one of the first warm afternoons of summer and everyone was outside. Posthumus, Howe, Paul and Rhino had taken rugs and the gramophone down to the Meade House lawn. They had stripped to gym shorts and lay in the sun idly listening to records. All around them were the sounds of summer, but predominantly the thwack of leather cricket balls encased in long stockings on the oiled surface of new bats. No one had spoken for a long while and then Rhino said, "There goes old Martin." They raised themselves on their elbows and watched a man come out of the Cottage gate and push his bicycle across Meade House playing fields until he reached the road. He propped the bicycle against one of the high storm gutters and, with great care, mounted.

"One . . . two . . . three . . ." Posthumus counted as old Martin pedaled precisely three times before starting to freewheel. "That's it."

"The time is four o'clock and here is the news," Rhino said.

They watched Mr. Martin freewheel gently past them, the tires of his bicycle making a gentle hissing noise on the gravel surface. Posthumus was looking at his watch. "He's two minutes early," he said.

"It's the sun," Rhino said. "Makes him thirsty."

"I'm going up to the Tree for a smoke," Posthumus said.

Rhino said, "I'll come with you."

Paul shook his head. He was lying on his back watching the huge fleecy clouds sail across the blue sky. He watched them through the branches and light green leaves of a mimosa tree and if he focused hard on the clouds it appeared that the tree was floating away. The music from the gramophone seemed to come from infinite space.

"What do you think old Martin *does* every afternoon?" Howe asked.

"Imbibes," Paul said sleepily. "What else?"

"D'you really think so?"

"How the hell do I know? It's what they say."

"Who?"

"I dunno. Why else does he go to the club every day?"

"I feel sorry for him, don't you?"

"What?"

"Feel sorry for him."

"What for? Put on something else."

"Okay. What about one of mine?"

Paul turned over on his side. Howe had opened a green box containing twelve-inch records. "I didn't know you had any."

"Posthumus doesn't like them."

"Well, he's not here."

"What would you like?"

"I dunno. You choose."

"All right." He wound the gramophone and took a record from its sleeve. "It's the Rienzi Overture. Do you like it?"

"It's terrific," Paul lied. He lay back again cradling his head on his hands.

Why the hell should he feel sorry for old Martin? Martin was just old Martin and, anyway, you didn't feel sorry for masters.

Herbert Martin had come to King's at the beginning of the year to take senior English. Paul remembered his arrival for it coincided with the announcement at Assembly that during the long Christmas holidays five Old Boys had been killed and one had been awarded the Military Cross. The school had stood in silence as

L. Q. Pyke, the headmaster, had read out the names: "James Hildreth Adnell, killed in action in France. Brian Lionel Cutter, died of wounds in Florence. Morris Albert Herbstein, died in a prisoner-of-war camp in Germany. Pierre van der Merwe, killed in an air crash at Young's Field. Harold Maynard Roberts, killed in action in France. . . . I want you boys to stand for the customary two minutes' silence while we pay homage to our dead." They had stood, most of them looking covertly up at the platform where the school staff was ranged on either side of the headmaster, each man standing with bowed head. It was then that Paul noticed an unfamiliar figure in black gown at the end of the line. He, too, stood with head bowed, his right hand holding his left wrist so that the hand was turned to the front. All Paul could make out was the thinning grey hair on his head. "Now," L.Q. said as he raised his head. "Something rather more optimistic. I have just received notification that one of our boys has been awarded the Military Cross." There was a rustle of interest. "Many of you will remember him. I shall read what information I have." L.Q. had a way of making words like "notification" and "information" sound very important. "For outstanding bravery in the field, in that Sgt. George Marshall Dold without aid did destroy a machine gun nest which had already inflicted several casualties on his platoon while in action in Northern Italy on December 21, 1943, Sgt. Dold has been awarded the Military Cross." There was a gasp of surprise. At first Paul was as surprised as the rest of the school but then he remembered the upstairs bathroom and the work they had done on Dold's thumb and he realized that what Dold had lacked was not courage.

"These are sad times . . ." L.Q. was saying. "They are testing times. But they are also our days of glory and I want you boys to remember that. So now I want you to join with me in giving three hearty cheers for

George Dold. Hip, hip . . . hooray! Hip, hip . . . hooray! Hip, hip . . . hooray!" The school joined in thunderously.

"Now," L.Q. said, as the cheering died down. "I want to introduce to you a new member of my staff. . . ."

It had been the anticlimax, Paul realized now, that had sewn up old Martin. Here they were mourning their dead heroes and cheering a live one and suddenly there was Martin standing up at the end of the staff line, right hand clamped to left wrist, round plump grey face with the deep cleft in the chin turned towards them, the weak blinking eyes, the round shoulders. And then L.Q. going on and on about how difficult it was to run a school the size of King's when half the staff were in the army and how good it was of Mr. Martin to come out of retirement to help, etc. . . . etc. . . .

Paul had been standing three rows from Posthumus but he had heard him say quite loudly, "He's nothing but a wet fart," and there had been a subdued titter. There was a strange look on Posthumus's face and Paul smiled to himself; Posthumus hadn't liked the bit about Dold.

At first the school had decided to play with Mr. Martin; not very inventive play but enough to make his life unpleasant. In class they put small round pebbles in the aisles between the desks so he would turn an ankle. They hid the chalk. Knocked his books from the desk. Asked inane questions. Constantly wanted to go to the lavatories so that during one forty-minute period of English, ninety percent of a class might be absent for part of the time. Some went out and did not return. But after a while they simply ignored him. They talked in his class, read library books, wrote letters, slept. It was as though he did not exist.

He had been given the old cottage at the far end of the Meade playing field, a small brick building roofed with rusty corrugated iron that had served once as an

isolation ward for scarlet fever cases before the new
hospital was built. He lived there by himself. Paul only
saw him in class or occasionally free-wheeling down on
his bicycle. This had fascinated Meade House when
it first began, for Mr. Martin was as regular in his habits
as a bank manager. Each day at precisely four o'clock
he mounted his bicycle, pedaled three times and free-
wheeled down the gentle slope into town. At precisely
five-thirty he could be seen slowly pushing his cycle up
the road: bicycling down, walking up, day in, day out,
and always at the same time.

After the first few occasions when half of Meade
House had lined the fence to cheer him on, even this
habit lost its interest.

Perhaps he *was* sorry for old Martin, Paul thought
. . . perhaps . . . the clouds sailed past the tree. . . .

A voice broke through the layers of drowsiness. "Do
you like Schumann?" it said.

"Yes, sir."

Paul woke with a start. Mr. Martin was standing at
the fence. He had propped up the bicycle and was
holding his left wrist in that characteristic way. For a
moment Paul was confused, then he realized that Mr.
Martin had been talking to Howe and must have been
talking to him for some time for Howe was standing
at the fence and the record on the gramophone had
ended. It must be 5:30 precisely and Mr. Martin had
stopped on his way back from the club.

"I have also got 'Scenes of Childhood,'" Mr. Martin
said gently to Howe. "Who is playing yours?"

"Schnabel, sir."

"I have Giesking."

There was a long and awkward pause and Paul
watched them through half-shut eyes. Howe came
away from the fence and began to put the record back
in its sleeve and old Martin stood there, a half-smile

on his grey face, and Paul could hear that his breathing was labored.

"What else have you got, Howe? It's so unusual, you know . . . I mean here . . . to find a boy. . . ."

Howe shuffled through his records. "'The Siegfried Idyll,'" he said. "'Carnival,' 'Rienzi,' the Schumann piano concerto, 'Romeo and Juliet,' 'The Pines of Rome.' . . ."

"Oh," said Mr. Martin, raising his eyebrows. "Who is playing yours?"

"The Orchestra of the Augusteo, Rome," Howe said without looking at the label.

"Good," said Mr. Martin, nodding. "That is the best, I think. De Sabata. Mine is Mengelberg and the Concertgebouw. But yours is the better." He coughed, clutching more tightly to his wrist. "Would you like to borrow mine and compare them?"

"Thank you, sir," Howe said, flushing.

Mr. Martin stared at him for a moment, the shy half-smile still on his lips. "Or perhaps . . . if you had the time . . . perhaps you'd consider visiting me and bringing your copy and then . . . and then we could. . . ." He checked as though realizing that what he was saying was not coming out well at all. ". . . And you, too, Thompson," he said suddenly. "Of course. It's so refreshing. I had no idea. Perhaps tea one day."

"Yes, sir," Paul said, scrambling to his feet. "Thank you, sir."

"Very refreshing indeed," Mr. Martin said. "I won't forget." He nodded to them and began to wheel his bicycle up the gentle slope towards the cottage.

"BAND! B-A-A-N-D! 'SHUN! ! Six-eight rolls B-Y the left QUICK MARCH!"

CRASH! CRASH! CRASH! Pause, CRASH! CRASH! CRASH! Pause, CRASH! CRASH! CRASH! CRASH! CRASH! CRASH! CRASH!

Tumpty-tarradiddle . . . tumpty-tarradiddle. . . .

The King's College cadet band shattered the silence of the summer morning. With drums rapping and bugles howling it marched smartly up the Meade House playing field, right-wheeled past the tennis courts, blasted its way past the girls' school where some windows banged up briefly and were banged down again, and made its way, with less energy, out onto the Commonage road where the town ended. They went on for half a mile, the pace noticeably slower, the blowing and rapping increasingly ragged in the hot morning sun, before Rhino gave the double-beat on the bass drum and the band came to a halt.

"All right, fall out," he said, unhooking the big drum from the leather cross-piece on his chest. He wore a leopard skin over his shoulders and his shirt, where it could be seen, was black with sweat.

Acting-Sergeant Leslie Stokes and Acting-Corporal Paul Thompson, bass and solo drummers respectively, had joined the band eighteen months before when they discovered that practicing was held outside the aural limits of both school and town populations. It had not taken Paul more than a few seconds to realize that this meant a safe period during the morning in which they could smoke. Now Rhino, who could not tell one bugle solo from another, was in charge of the band and Paul was his second-in-command.

"Did you bring the smokes?" Rhino said as they sprawled under a mimosa tree.

Paul nodded. "You got the slatch?" Rhino produced a tiny piece of matchbox striking surface and Paul pulled out a bent Auriac and a match and they lit up. The rest of the band lay in the shade with their instruments.

"You! Peters!" Rhino shouted to a young bugler. "Start blowing! And Laubscher! You start banging." He turned to Paul. "You never know, someone may be listening for us."

"Brilliant."

"Well . . . with the Governor-General coming. . . ."

"Oh, Christ, I'd forgotten that!"

"What'll we play when he comes?"

"The usual. We only have to march to the Rec and back, then we play when his car arrives. Same as when Smuts came. We do the three-fours marching and the six-eights for the car."

They passed the cigarette backwards and forwards. "Laubscher, you bastard!" Rhino shouted. "Hit that fucking drum!" He turned back to Paul. "What if he drives all the way round the Rec? That six-eight thing doesn't last long, and the whole town'll be there."

"Then we play it again. Or the three-four if you like. Doesn't matter how we do it. Anyway, we don't know more than the two so they're all we *can* play."

"Someone's going to ask us one day why we always play the same things."

"Just say we love them."

"Horse was shitty about our 'noble repertoire' the other day. He's in charge of arrangements."

"Horse can get stuffed. He wouldn't know a drumroll from his arse-hole."

They smoked in silence for a while, then Rhino said, "L.Q. spoke about the anthem again last week."

"What'd you say?"

"I said we didn't know it yet."

"Christ, how the hell are we ever going to play it! Look at Peters. . . ." He indicated the perspiring bugler who was coaxing drain-like noises from his instrument. "How can you teach 'God Save the King' to someone like him? He only joined the band because he's scared of rifles."

"But what'll we do if L.Q. says we've got to play it for the visit?"

"Don't talk crap. The Governor-General's coming in three weeks; we couldn't learn it in that time even if we were capable and anyway they're putting the rugby piano in the grandstand. Flash told me, because L.Q. asked him to play it."

"What?"

"'God Save the King,' you fool."

Rhino looked relieved. "You'll go over it just before . . . ?"

"Of course. You don't think I'd leave it to an ungulate, do you?"

"Three-four going over and back. Six-eight when his car arrives."

"Oh, Christ, I'll write it out for you. Jesus! *You* in charge of the band!"

"And what about you!"

"At least I know *some* music."

"Is that what you call it?"

"Now don't be boring, Leslie. I've told you we only listen to music."

"Ya, with your pants down."

"You're jealous!"

"Me! Old Martin with his pants down. Christ, it makes me feel sick."

"Well, don't think about it, then."

"You take sugar, don't you, Thompson?" Mr. Martin said.

"Yes, sir."

"Yes, of course you do, I should have remembered. All boys do. It's only when you get to my age . . . help yourself . . . please. . . ."

"Thank you, sir."

"And you. . . ."

"Yes, sir. Thank you, sir," Howe said.

"Enough? Some cake?"

"Thank you, sir."

"Thompson. . . ."

"Thank you, sir." Paul had been eyeing the cake since they'd come in. Old Martin usually only produced one thing with tea, buns or bread and butter and strawberry jam but it was usually good. Today it was fruitcake; rich and dark and sticky.

"Is it all right . . . uh . . . ?"

"Yes, sir," Howe said with his mouth full. Paul always knew when Mr. Martin was addressing Howe. He felt the old man would have liked to have called him Hugh but couldn't, but equally didn't want to call him formally by his surname, so he called him neither.

This was the third time Paul had been to Mr. Martin's for afternoon tea. Howe had been two or three times by himself. The room was tiny and very hot under the corrugated iron roof. The furniture was sparse, a round table badly stained, three or four wooden chairs with initials carved in the seats, a morris chair with torn leather cushions, and a desk. It seemed to Paul it must have been the same furniture as when the cottage was an isolation hospital. The only difference was that two complete walls had been covered by built-in shelves and the shelves themselves contained neat rows of twelve-inch records, hundreds, perhaps thousands, all standing vertically in light brown covers. Each cover was marked with the name of the composer, the work, the orchestra, the conductor, the soloist and a series of identifying numbers. Each shelf was marked with serial numbers on small squares of cardboard. The only new piece of furniture in the room was a massive radiogram which stood near the shelves. It could take up to six records at a time and change them automatically. The first time Paul had seen it he had been more fascinated by the automatic change than the music. The only gramophones he had known before were those you wound, and although he would never have admitted it, the music played on the radiogram was somewhat over

217

his head. He had never heard of Berlioz or Mussorgsky or Sibelius, and although there were occasional patches of music that came through to him as heart-stopping melodies that he could have listened to over and over, Mr. Martin did not play them very often. Once he had registered that Howe's great interest was the piano he would spend an hour or so after they'd finished tea playing piano solos or concertos. Sometimes he only played one work but played it by four different pianists and orchestras and he and Howe would sit in the hot room listening to one section over and over to see how the four interpretations differed one from the other. Then he would ask Howe which he liked and why and they would argue and Flash would get quite excited and so would old Martin and he would stand there holding his left wrist in his right hand and breathing raggedly and beam down at Flash and tell him he should not be taken in by the too-sentimental approach or that he should beware of pure technique or something like that. He never asked Paul, in fact he seemed to forget he was there at all, which suited Paul well enough.

After a couple of hours they would leave and old Martin would stand in the door saying how nice it was of them to come and they would say, "Thank you, sir. Thank you very much," and you could see old Martin was sad that the afternoon was over.

"He's a homo," Rhino said to Paul.

"How the hell do you know?"

"Well, he's not married, is he?"

"Neither is L.Q. and you couldn't say he was."

They were lying on a grassy bank near the practice nets eating a mixture of dry cocoa and sugar out of a tin.

"What about when Flash goes by himself? How d'you know what happens then?"

"Oh, Jesus, I'm tired of this. For Christ's sake shut up about it and don't guts all the cocoa."

Paul knew that old Martin had grown fond of Howe. Dimly he perceived that in Howe Mr. Martin must have seen a green oasis in the desert of King's College. Paul did not pretend to himself that his own presence at the tea-and-music afternoons was important. He went because of the food and because in the beginning Flash had wanted him to go. On the first occasion he had been unable to attend Flash had not decided to go himself until the last minute. At first Paul had wondered about this hesitation but from one or two things Flash had said he'd realized that the boy's beautiful face and curly hair had brought him occasional encounters which had frightened him. Not that old Martin had ever tried anything; Paul would have been the first to hear. And slowly the doubt seemed to leave Howe's mind.

"If Posthumus finds out he'll break Howe's neck," Rhino said, scraping up the last of the cocoa and sugar.

"Finds out what?"

"That they listen to music."

"So now you *believe* it!"

"I'm just telling you."

"Well, then, finds out *what?* What's wrong with listening to music?"

"Nothing, except that he thinks Flash is having extra piano lessons downtown."

"Extra lessons?"

"That's what Flash told him. And Posthumus doesn't like it. He was shouting for him the other day, something about his laundry not being sent. And you know how he is about that bloody piano. He looks for Howe every day and then has to go by himself." Paul nodded. "He'll murder him."

But Posthumus did not find out, not at that point, anyway, and Howe's visits to Mr. Martin's cottage became more frequent. In fact, Howe seemed to disappear altogether now between the ending of school and supper time. A week or so later Paul discovered the reason.

He had been unable, because of band practice which now took place every afternoon, to accompany Howe to Mr. Martin's. At least, that's what he told Rhino. The fact was that he was no longer invited. And so it was only by chance that one evening before prep as he and Rhino were hurrying up to the Tree on the Top Fields for a smoke that he discovered what was going on. The cottage stood in its own yard at the end of Meade field and they had to pass it on their way to the Tree. As they drew level with it Paul heard the sound of a piano. This was not unusual, for it was known that Mr. Martin played his radiogram almost every evening and well into the night. But there was something about this particular piece of music that Paul recognized. He had heard it before, frequently. An image of the room off the Minor Hall rose in his mind, a memory of the rugby piano. And then he realized he was listening to a piece which Flash had been studying.

He stopped, holding Rhino back. "That's Flash playing," he said.

They circled the cottage and came in on one side which was hidden from view by a thick privet hedge. Cautiously they pushed their way through a break in the hedge and slipped along the wall to the window of the sitting-room. In the early dusk the light in the room was on and the curtains had been drawn—but not sufficiently well, for Paul was able to see through a gap where they did not quite meet. The furniture had been rearranged. The table had been moved to one side and the desk was no longer in the room. In its place stood a new upright piano at which Howe sat on one of the kitchen chairs. By his side, in another straight-backed chair, sat Mr. Martin. He sat very close to Howe and occasionally would lean forward and turn a page. On top of the piano, which shone brightly in its coat of new French polish, stood an equally shiny metronome, the arm of which swung left, right, left, right, hypnotically.

"Jesus," Paul whispered, more to himself than Rhino, "he's bought him a piano."

All through prep that night Paul watched Howe, but there was nothing unusual in his demeanor. After a while Paul began to wonder what he was looking for. Old Martin had bought a piano and Howe was playing it. That was all. But Paul had a feeling he should be warned about Posthumus. After prep he looked for Howe, but he was showering in East Bathroom with a dozen other fags and when Paul went in search of him later he was told that Howe was putting Posthumus's clothes away.

The school was preparing for the Governor-General's visit so his opportunity did not come for several days, and by that time it was too late.

Paul heard the sounds as far away as Middle Dormitory. He began to run towards Posthumus's room. The sound of the thrashing increased and he had counted at least six strokes—the maximum anyone had ever been caned at King's—before he reached the door, and still the thrashing continued.

"You little shit!" he heard Posthumus say in a soft voice, then once more came the sound of the cane.

The door was locked and the whole top floor of Meade was deserted.

"Posthumus!" he shouted.

The noise stopped abruptly. "Who's that?"

"Me. Thompson."

"What d'you want?"

"For Christ's sake let me in!"

"Fuck off!"

"Let me in." Paul gave the door a kick.

"If you don't bugger off I'll mess you up properly."

There was a short silence. Paul could hear his own breath, and from the other side of the door a curious subdued bubbling. A feeling of nausea gave way to one of fright. Then he heard Posthumus say softly, "Shut up, you bastard."

Paul began to kick the door. He kicked hard and loud and at the same time began to shout, "Posthumus! Posthumus! Posthumus!"

The door was flung open and he fell forward into the room. Just as Posthumus hit him he saw Flash Howe. He was tied over the bed end and his face had been thrust into a pillow. His trousers had been lowered and the swagger stick which Posthumus had been using had left purple-pink ridges on the white flesh of his buttocks. Paul had taken the swagger stick on his elbow and the sharp pain brought tears to his eyes.

"I told you," Posthumus said, and his face was bright red with effort and rage. "I told you to bugger off!" There was a look in his eyes which Paul had never seen before. He had a feeling that in that moment something in Posthumus might easily give way.

"Christ, don't be a bloody fool," Paul said, rubbing his elbow. "I came to warn you, man."

The hand holding the swagger stick slowly dropped. "Warn me?"

"L.Q.'s on his way with Horse. I saw them crossing Meade field."

"L.Q.!"

"Yes," Paul lied. He knew that L.Q. was the only person in the school whom Posthumus feared, for L.Q. was a headmaster who expelled and expulsion would do Posthumus out of a farm. "He's on house inspection. He's already been to Napier. We're next."

Some of the madness left Posthumus's eyes. "You sure?"

"That's why I came."

"Christ, thanks, Thompson. Help me with this bastard."

They untied Howe's hands. "What'd he do?"

"He's been bloody lying to me."

They raised Howe's face from the pillow and it left a damp patch of saliva and tears.

"I'll take him," Paul said.

"Where?" There was a moment of suspicion.

"Sick-room shithouse. No one ever goes there."

"Okay. I'll go out the other way."

Paul helped Howe down the stairs at the end of East corridor. "You all right, Hughie?" He felt rather than saw Howe nod. "It'll be okay in a little while. You'll see." He stayed with Howe in the sick-room lavatory for nearly half an hour. Howe seemed dazed by the beating. When Paul asked him how Posthumus had found out he could only mutter, "I don't know." When he was certain that Howe had finished crying he made him wash his face and told him to go and lie down, then he went in search of Rhino.

"'Course I didn't tell him," Rhino said, incensed.

"Well, someone did."

"I wouldn't tell Posthumus something like that!"

"Who then?"

"How the bloody hell should I know." They had been standing near the reading room when Peters, the bugler, came past. Rhino grabbed him by the back of the neck and pushed him into the reading room. Paul followed and closed the door.

"Oh, please, Rhino! Let me go!"

"I'm going to kill you," Rhino said dispassionately.

"What for? I haven't. . . ."

"If you don't. . . ."

". . . done anything!"

". . . tell me something. You understand?"

"Oh, leave him," Paul said. "You're as bad as Posthumus."

He turned to Peters. "D'you know where Flash Howe goes to in the afternoons?" Peters looked puzzled. "Come on. No one's going to hurt you. We just want to know."

"But everybody knows," Peters said. "He goes to old Martin's place and plays the piano."

"*How* do you know?" Paul said, irritated.

"The other day . . . we were playing tip-and-run . . . and Simpson hit a ball into Martin's garden . . . and Christie went to fetch it . . . and . . . and he saw Flash inside. . . ."

"Did you tell Posthumus?" Rhino said, taking him by the back of the neck and squeezing.

"Ow! Take my dying oath, Rhino!"

"Anyone could've," Paul said. "Okay, you can go." Peters scampered from the room.

"I told you Posthumus would get wild," Rhino said.

"I've a bloody good mind to tell Horse."

"Tell him what? That Posthumus striped Howe? What the hell would *he* do? Probably try to gate him, that's all. Howe's just a fag. Everybody knows that fags get striped."

"This was more than a striping. He really hurt Flash."

That evening in prep Paul again watched Howe but the pretty face gave nothing away. At break Paul tried to talk to him but Howe said he had to go upstairs to wash Posthumus's socks. Paul saw sick apprehension in his eyes.

"Oh, Thompson! Could you spare me a moment?"

Paul had been coming up from school, a pile of books on his arm, when Mr. Martin called.

"Afternoon, sir."

"Afternoon, Thompson. I was wondering . . . eh . . . you haven't seen . . . Howe by any chance?"

"No, sir."

"Yes, I see." Mr. Martin seemed undecided as to what to do next and he stood peering down at his shoes, the left wrist clutched in the right hand. Paul was surprised at how sick and exhausted he looked. He seemed to have lost weight and the skin hung in small folds from his grey cheeks. "I haven't . . ." he said softly, the breath wheezing in and out of the lungs. "That is . . . he was supposed to visit me. I haven't seen him for a week and I was wondering . . . I thought he might be ill."

"No, sir," Paul said. "I don't think so." For a moment he had been tempted to make up some story about Howe but he had felt a sudden distaste for Mr. Martin.

"Oh . . . oh, well, would you tell him . . . tell him I shall expect him tomorrow afternoon?"

"Yes, sir," he said, woodenly.

"Oh, and you, too, Thompson. A little surprise. Something special, you know. . . ."

"Yes, sir. Thank you, sir."

"You're sure he's not . . . No? Well . . . it's unlike him. Tomorrow, then." He turned away and began walking slowly up to the cottage.

Paul shifted the pile of books to his other arm and turned into the Meade gate. He was met by Horse, who came flying down the corridor towards him, his black gown billowing out behind. "Ah, Thompson, I've been looking for Stokes but he seems to have disappeared. You're second-in-command of the band, aren't you?" Paul nodded. "Well, you'll have to do. Come into my study."

Paul dumped his books in his locker and hurried after him. "Those who ordain these things," Horse began, giving him a wolfish smile, "have seen fit at the eleventh hour to change their arrangements. The Governor-General will no longer be arriving by train but will descend upon us by air the day after tomorrow, two hours earlier than planned. Is that clear, Thompson? Ten A.M. instead of noon?"

"Yes, sir."

"So that you fall-in straight after breakfast and our rendezvous with the Catiline conspiracy is postponed. For which I have no doubt you are thankful."

"Yes, sir."

"There is an added complication," Horse said. "Brigadier-General something-or-other, O.C. Eastern Cape Command, is joining His Excellency for the visit and Dr. Pyke has decreed that both anthems shall be performed."

"Sir?"

"You have heard the word 'anthems' before?"

"Both anthems, sir?"

"Both anthems."

Paul stared at him. "You mean . . . ?"

"I mean *both* anthems. Well? I am waiting, Thompson, to know whether these can be rendered by your good selves."

"Dr. Pyke said Howe was to play 'God Save the King' on the piano, sir."

"Dr. Pyke also told me that you had been practicing it. We can't have both played on the piano while the band stands idle. It would look grotesque. If you play 'God Save the King' first and then Howe plays 'Uit die Bleu' . . . then we shall have a balance."

"Sir. . . ."

"Well?"

"Sir, we haven't got it right yet."

"You've been practicing it for how long?"

"Six months, sir."

"Six months? And you haven't got it right yet?"

"No, sir."

"You perplex me, Thompson. Sometimes I think you are not totally devoid of intellect and then I find that the very word has no significance when attached to you." He lit a cigarette and puffed at it furiously, then his eyes began to swivel violently. "All right . . . as you were. We shall have to extemporize. Let me see, now. . . . Howe will play 'The King' and instead of the other we'll have 'The Last Post' for the Brigadier."

"'The Last Post,' sir?"

"Yes, Thompson. 'The Last Post.' There is not a single band in the whole Christian world—including the band of King's College—that cannot, during a major international conflagration, find someone to play 'The Last Post.'" He loosed his lips and brought his vulpine face close to Paul's. "Do you understand what I'm saying, Thompson?" The cigarette waved. "No . . . ! No . . . ! Not a word. I don't want to hear. I simply assume, Thompson. Do you understand? I *assume* that after His Excellency has addressed us and after Howe has played 'The King' that someone in the King's College band will honor the Brigadier—thus honoring our nation—with 'The Last Post.' Do I make myself clear?"

Paul hurried off in search of Rhino and found him boiling a tin of condensed milk to make soft toffee.

"'The Last Post'?" Rhino said vaguely, his interest centered on the boiling water.

"Yes," Paul said savagely. "'The Last Post.'"

"I don't know it."

"You don't say. Look, for Christ's sake leave that bloody thing alone and listen. You're supposed to be in charge of the band. What're you going to do?"

"What about Hofmeyer?" Rhino said, mentioning the only bugler of any merit.

"Hoffie's got mumps."

"Oh yes, I forgot."

"It'll have to be Peters."

"He'd never know 'The Last Post.'"

"Then we'll have to teach him. D-a-a, d-i-; da, di. . . . It's not all that difficult. He'll just have to learn."

They took Peters to the Commonage for the remainder of the afternoon and by supper time, through reddened lips, he was able to give a recognizable rendering of the first section of "The Last Post."

"Okay," Paul said wearily, dismissing him. "Tomorrow straight after lunch." As Peters staggered off into the dusk clutching his warm and gurgling bugle, Paul said, "We'll get the first part right, anyway, then he can just play it over again. No one'll notice except the General."

The following day Paul raced through lunch and was one of the first out of the dining hall after closing grace. He stood on the grass searching for Peters in the emerging crush. Then he saw Howe, moving even more slowly than usual, and recalled, with a start, the invitation. He ran over and took his arm and felt the sudden jerk of fear. "Listen, old Martin wants you at the cottage for tea."

"I can't. . . ." Howe began.

"He asked me, too, but. . . ." They were swept along in a tide of blazers.

Howe shook his head. "Posthumus. . . ."

At that moment Paul spotted Peters. "Hey, Peters!" he called, but the bugler did not seem to hear. Paul loosened his grip on Howe's arm. "Hey . . . !" He turned over his shoulder to Howe. "Well, you tell him, then. Tell him I can't, either. . . . Hey, Peters!"

"I mustn't," Howe shouted. "Posthumus said he'd . . ."

"Peters! Wait!" Paul dived through the crowd and caught up with Rhino. "That little bugger's trying to give us the slip!" They raced after Peters and caught him as he was going into Meade gate.

"I was only going to get my bugle, Thompson, take my oath."

"Never mind your oath, we're coming with you."

By supper time the first section of "The Last Post" had been played nearly fifty times. They were all exhausted. "If I play any more now I won't be able to in the morning," Peters mumbled through lips that were not only red but slightly swollen. "I've gone deaf," he said, shaking his head. "There's a sort of singing noise in my ears."

"There'll be a sort of singing feeling in your backside if you play it badly tomorrow," Paul said unsympathetically.

During the night Mr. Martin killed himself. The whole school knew something had happened by breakfast time, for the early risers who trapped moles on the Top Fields had seen the police entering the cottage. At breakfast the rumors were flying from table to table. He'd been caught exposing himself at the convent . . . he'd fallen down drunk in the main street . . . he'd pinched the petty cash from the club's till . . . he'd knocked down a kaffir-boy on his bicycle. . . .

"I'll bet he's kicked the bucket," Rhino said with a nervous giggle.

Paul, who like everyone else was already dressed in his khaki uniform, looked angrily across the table.

Then Dr. Pyke came in the door and went up to the masters' platform. He stood beside his own table, his face somber. At first there was a subdued murmuring, then silence.

"Something tragic has happened," L.Q. began, "and I wish you all to know what facts are available to me at this time before you invent your own." He paused and looked at a piece of paper in his hand.

"I told you," Rhino whispered to Paul.

"Some of you will have already seen members of the police entering Mr. Martin's cottage and I have to tell you that during the night Mr. Martin took his own life." Paul felt his stomach cramp into a tight ball. "It appears that Mr. Martin hanged himself from the shower in his bathroom." The silence in the dining hall was almost

229

tangible. "Mr. Martin left a note, a copy of which I have here." He lifted the paper and six hundred eyes strained to see it. "I shall not read you the entire letter, which is addressed to me, but I shall tell you the salient points." Dr. Pyke glanced down at the letter again, and continued. "I gather from Mr. Martin that he is one of four brothers and sisters. Each died of heart disease in their fiftieth year. It seems that Mr. Martin had been suffering from this disease for some time and that it had been preying on his mind. Yesterday was his birthday, his fiftieth birthday." The knot in Paul's stomach twisted. L.Q. folded the letter and placed it in his inside pocket. "I don't need to tell you how sorry we are as a school for what has happened. It might interest you to know that Mr. Martin is . . . was thought to have the largest private record collection in the country. He has asked that this be sent to his only relative, a cousin who lives in Rhodesia. Arrangements are being made to comply with this request. I have also instructed that a telegram of sympathy from the school as a whole be sent." He buttoned up his jacket and nodded at the master-in-charge. "I should like to see Howe after breakfast," he said and walked quickly from the dining hall. The silence followed him out, lasted for perhaps twenty seconds and then the hubbub burst.

Paul sat quite still. The food, congealed and cold, lay untouched in front of him. Rhino said something that he didn't hear. Fifty . . . fifty . . . the number was going round and round in his head. ". . . A little surprise . . . something special . . . 'The Last Post' . . . a little surprise . . . fifty."

"You've gone white," Rhino said. "You're not going to puke, are you?"

Slowly the present reasserted itself. "What?" Paul said.

"Puke. You're not going to, are you?"

"Don't be a bloody fool." He tried to focus on Rhino.

Rhino looked at the dining hall clock. "Jesus, it's after nine! We've got to get the drums."

Paul was in the armory tightening the snare on his drum when Howe came in. The armory was a dark and shadowy place. The only light that entered from the half-open safety door glinted on the muzzles of the machine guns and the stocks of the carbines, giving the place an air of menace. In the half-light Howe looked like a ghost. His eyes were red and tears had left dirty smudges on his cheeks where he'd rubbed them. His hair was unkempt and his clothes awry.

"It's because of yesterday," Howe said. Paul did not look up. "Isn't it?" It was as though Howe had come to hear him deny it.

"Didn't you tell him?" Paul said.

"No." It wasn't more than a whisper.

"I told you to."

"I know. But I couldn't. Posthumus said . . . he said that if I went near the cottage again he'd write to his father telling him that Mr. Martin was . . . well, you know, that we were. . . ."

"Pulling each other's wires," Paul said brutally.

"Yes."

"Well, were you?"

"Of course not. You don't understand!"

"He bought a piano for you, didn't he?"

"That doesn't mean. . . ."

"What the hell could Posthumus do, anyway?"

"He said his father hates homos like he hates kaffirs and when he got the letter he'd phone L.Q. and then Mr. Martin would be dismissed and I'd be expelled."

"And you believed him?" Even as he said it Paul remembered Howe after the beating and realized the depths of his fear. "All right, Hughie," he said, pushing down the leather grips that stretched the vellum. "It wasn't your fault. You heard L.Q. There was something wrong with his heart." For a second he had been about to extend the blame to himself, but something in him shied away. He picked up the drum and tapped it lightly with his fingers. He wasn't going to think about it.

"You don't know how kind he was," Flash said. "He was going to get me a music bursary. He said I'd go to university." And then, abruptly, "You don't understand! No one does!"

"All right, I don't understand. What'd L.Q. want you for?"

"The piano," Howe said, and the tears came again. "He wrote it in the letter. He wanted me to have it. And about the bursary. . . ."

A shadow darkened the door and Horse shouted, "Thompson! Are you in there?"

"Yes, sir."

"I am reliably informed that nothing is ever played after 'The King.' So 'The Last Post' first and then 'The King.' Is that clear?"

"Yes, sir."

"Well, come along, Thompson, they're falling in!"

Since early morning trails of dust had been converging on Kingston from every direction as farmers drove in to see the Governor-General. The whole recreation ground had been decorated. At one side of the grandstand flew the Union Jack, at the other the South African flag. Strings of smaller Allied flags and bunting had been tied to the rafters so that they looped in and out of the covered area. The grandstand was large for a small country town and an hour before His Excellency was due to arrive it was full. So was the open stand which had been erected alongside. At the far end of the Rec a wire enclosure had been built for kaffirs but only a handful had turned up. In front of the grandstand was a small platform with four chairs, a microphone and a colored umbrella. To the rear of the platform the King's College cadet corps was drawn up in ranks, to its left stood the band, bugles and drums shining. At precisely ten o'clock, clapping and cheering was heard from a small crowd near the gate.

"P-A-R-A-D-E! PARADE! 'Shun!" CRASH! CRASH! CRASH! The drumrolls smashed the silence. A 1935 open Packard came sedately through the gate and drove around the cinder track that circled the two rugby fields. Everyone on the grandstand began the cheer.

As the rhythm changed to a six-eight drum-beat Paul managed to pick out the Packard on the extreme fringe of his vision. It hove slowly into view, stopped just past the long-jump pit and someone sitting next to the driver ran around to open the back door. The Governor-General, his aide, the Brigadier-General and the Mayor went up the two steps onto the platform, the band stopped more or less together and the parade was stood easy. In the intense morning heat Paul could feel the sweat trickling down the side of his chest; both the drumsticks were wet.

The Mayor stepped up to the microphone and began a long speech about how good it was to have the Governor-General in Kingston, etc. . . . and the Brigadier-General, etc. . . . and how pleased he was to see the ground so full, etc. . . . and there'd be a silver collection for war funds at the gate on the way out and Kingston had always dug deep into its pockets for our boys up North, etc. . . .

Then the Governor-General spoke and then the Brigadier-General, and Paul and the others stood in the hot sun and pretty soon he began to hear the familiar noises: the rattle of a carbine and the thump as someone in the ranks behind him fainted. It was always the same on hot days and Paul's mind wandered back to Dold and the blotting paper he had wanted to put in his shoes and suddenly he realized that they had stopped making speeches and were just standing on the platform, waiting.

"Peters!" he hissed. Peters was two rows back and was supposed to come to attention, march to the flagpole and play "The Last Post."

"*Peters!*" he hissed louder. A second later he half turned. Peters had gone a sort of chalky color and was swaying on his feet.

"PETERS!" This time it was Rhino's voice. It seemed to get through for Peters came to attention and marched slowly to the flagpole. With great care he brought the bugle to his lips. "Daa-a-, d-i-i-, da, di. . . ." The opening phrase of "The Last Post" floated insecurely through the hot air. Peters managed the second set of phrases and then the bugle began to sound as though it was being blown under water. Peters blew harder, the chalky color of his skin turned a dangerous pink. All of a sudden he drew himself upright and fell slowly forward, a small, rigid figure, the bugle still at his lips.

Paul's drum was unclipped and lying on the grass. He remembered to come to attention, turn left and take three paces before running forward to Peters. As he did so he noticed that the four faces on the platform were turned towards him with expressions of mild curiosity.

The fall had driven the bugle into Peters's mouth and now as Paul helped him across the cinder track to the shade of the stand it was making a hollow mooing sound.

Paul looked up for assistance but only a few of the nearest spectators were interested in a fainting bugler. Something of greater significance was happening near the piano. Paul saw Horse as he placed the still-comatose Peters on one of the wooden seats, and went up towards him. Horse was holding Flash Howe by the sleeve of his blazer and Howe was tugging and struggling and crying and blubbering in a voice loud enough for those in the surrounding seats to hear, "I won't! You can't make me! No! Leave me! No!"

And Horse was saying, "They're waiting, Howe! You've got to! Oh, God! Sit down and *play!* Don't you realize no one can move until 'The King'. . . . !"

"Never . . . ! I'll never play here again . . . !" Howe shouted and with a jerk freed himself from his jacket and came stumbling down the grandstand steps.

Horse, still holding the blazer, looked around, bewildered. Then he saw Paul. "Can you play?" he asked, desperately.

"No, sir, it's about Peters. . . ."

"Can he play?"

"No, sir."

"Well, don't stand there arguing! Who *can* play? There must be *some*one!"

At that moment, a moment Paul was to remember all his life, he saw the figure of Posthumus standing near the piano and, without thinking, he said, "Posthumus, sir." Horse wheeled and saw Posthumus. He fought his way through the standing crowd. "Posthumus," he called and then Paul could no longer hear him. But he could see. Horse spoke for perhaps thirty seconds, and then there was a bulge in the crowd as Posthumus stepped down towards the piano. His big face was flushed but Paul saw that it was not caused by the heat. There was an expression of almost holy satisfaction in his eyes. He sat down at the piano. Horse raised his hand to the school. The rustling and murmuring died. And then slowly and clearly Posthumus began to play. The school started to sing on the downbeat of Horse's arm. "God save our gracious King, Long live our noble King, God save our King. . . ." The anthem was taken up by the nearest citizens and quickly the whole stand was singing and so was the temporary stand and the cadet corps. Everybody was singing. Except for those nearest the piano.

They had sung the first few bars and then had faltered. So had Horse. He stood there, his mouth slightly open, staring at Posthumus. But Posthumus was oblivious. His head was bent towards the keyboard, his lips were drawn back with concentration. Above the ragged singing of the spectators Paul heard the tinkle of the piano as Posthumus moved into the third verse of "Red Sails in the Sunset." But that was not what held his shocked attention, it was the unremitting thud of a deep bass beat. As he listened he could hear it more distinctly. It throbbed up the scale and then descended, over and over again, filling his head with a primitive tribal rhythm.

As "Red Sails in the Sunset" drew to its conclusion Paul realized that Posthumus had finally mastered the crawling bass.

YEHUDI MENUHIN

The virtuoso violinist Yehudi Menuhin was born in New York City in 1916. At age seven he made his solo debut with the San Francisco Orchestra; his first Carnegie Hall recital was at the age of ten. He has expanded vastly the repertoire of violin concert music. This is his introduction to *Violin: Six Lessons with Yehudi Menuhin* which The Viking Press, Inc. will publish in early 1972.

VIOLIN: SIX LESSONS WITH YEHUDI MENUHIN

To whomever this may concern, be he teacher or beginner, advanced student or performer, I would like to address these few words about an instrument which I have known intimately for nearly fifty years, an instrument which must surely be one of the most beautiful artifacts ever created by man and one of the most capricious to handle. It is perhaps this very elusiveness that adds to its magic, for unless one is willing to become its slave, to resign oneself voluntarily and with all one's heart, the violin will take its revenge, withhold its manifold voices, withdraw its infinite range of subtleties, and you will be left holding a lovely piece of musical furniture, offended and inert.

No one violin is like another; each is as separate and particular as a human being and as differing in its re-

From *Violin: Six Lessons with Yehudi Menuhin* to be published by the Viking Press, Inc.

sponse to the bow which touches its strings as a variety of people would be to one opinion.

It is in the conquering of its moods and endless modulations, in the manipulation of its voices from the most delicate of whispers to a hearty bellow, that the whole vocation of violin playing lies. For the player is an independent being: no alien hand has set an arbitrary pitch, no ear but his own will dictate the tuning. He alone is master and servant, and as soon as his bow touches the instrument the marvelous battle has begun, the challenge and the response are joined and the achievement is wholly his.

It is this wonderful relationship between the violin and its player that makes it and its other stringed relations unique, and it is with the understanding of this quality that the violinist should approach his task. In this way he can never be bored, even though he may despair; never feel imposed upon, even though like the captain of a ship he will learn the infinity of horizons and know the patience and endurance this recognition exacts. The violin is indeed the very foundation of our musical culture without which none of our chamber music ensembles or symphonic repertoire could exist.

The violin is an instrument inseparable from time, having taken thousands of years of search and refinement to evolve from the applied principle of setting a tightened and taut string vibrating against a hollow background. In fact, both the violin and the bow are derived from the bow and arrow—from the quiver of the string, just audible as it is released, pizzicato, to send the arrow on its path. The violin bow gradually changed shape to become more malleable and was strung with a hundred prickly horsehairs to rub the strings out of their tense and immobile expectancy—but essentially it remained a flexible length of wood. The body of the violin itself was evolved from a hollowed-out length of wood; resonant, no longer as flexible as the bow, but able to trap, amplify, and prolong vibrations. Strung with four strings which initiate these vibrations, it transmits them by means of the bridge to the body of the instrument.

The universality of the violin as an instrument of music is illustrated by the fact that our own violin, perfected in Italy in the seventeenth century, has been altogether successfully adopted into cultures as alien as the Indian, where the player squats on the ground with the violin base pressed against his ribs and the violin head pointing diagonally downwards, resting on a toe. Again, the violin is equally at home among the nomadic, intuitive gypsy peoples, fulfilling yet another, altogether different expressive requirement—wild, natural and nostalgic.

From the fiddlers of the Hardanger plateau in Norway to the Highlands of Scotland, from the urbanized Jews of European Russia to the quaint fiddlers of the Blue Ridge Mountains of the Carolinas, and now on a vast scale to the people of Japan, the violin has succeeded in suiting every style and fulfilling every need.

Let us now consider the peculiar difficulties and requirements of the violin as an instrument to master.

There is no fixed or immovable point of support for the instrument, nor is there any—except for those parts of the feet touching and balancing on the floor—for the violinist himself. The violin must become one with the fluid movement of the whole person, responding visibly to the undulant flow, to the swing, pendulum or circle, never blocking this flow at any of the joints of the body or at any of the points of contact with the violin and bow, and directing it into the very last muscle and finger joint, which must be trained to move in all directions and to control while in motion, as the violinist himself must respond visibly to that inner surge which is born of the music itself and of his thoughts and feelings about it.

Unlike most other instruments and most other activities in general (and unlike, incidentally, the Indian way of playing the violin) the hands, which must be extremely flexible, strong, and resilient, are employed well-nigh continually on or around shoulder level, that is, above the heart. As they must be continually supplied with blood, the heart must be in good condition and under no strain (or minimal strain) from any causes of anxiety or tension. The problem of maintaining circulation by the follow-up and alternating of movements, efforts, pressures, and relaxation; the problem of training the correct reflexes; the problem of warming up each time one sets out to play—in violin playing these become of crucial importance.

The accuracy and precision, the lightninglike adjustment of pitch, sound, and stroke, the switch from the minutest, invisible "inside" motion to the broad sweep of a golfer's swing, require a degree of mastery allowing of almost no margin whatsoever. In addition to this, an intellectual and "emotional" grasp of the musical work in hand is necessary; and finally, with the quality of grace or inspiration, you have a good performance.

Have I made it all sound unreasonably difficult, the controlling of an instrument so intractable and so infinitely subtle as to be a kind of Untamable Shrew? I hope not, for although the violinist's is a very challenging profession, good violin playing is by no means impossible, and can in fact be a long and deep satisfaction to teach, to learn and to conquer.

To prepare oneself properly for this task, I think it is necessary not only to concentrate on the playing of the violin, but to cultivate an attitude of mind and heart, as well as certain habits of hygiene and general physical condition, so as to burden the playing itself as little as humanly possible with impediments of any kind.

I would like to say a few words about the moral attitude. I look on this as a kind of bridge between the past and the future and between oneself and the outside world. In working, one is investing effort and consolidating memory for the reward of future performance; the better and more precise, the more complete and dedicated the effort, the greater will be the reward. With the equation between oneself and the world at large, we receive as much inspiration from both the music we play and the audience we play to, as we give of ourselves. This conception of a personal budget is valuable for living in general, and underlines the importance of conscience, of example, and of integrity and honesty; when we are working on the violin we are alone, and yet what happens during these hours of isolation is crucial to what will happen on the stage before an audience.

Even that cold and clammy word *hygiene* has its place in the approach to the violin, for health is a very necessary concomitant, and cleanliness, stimulation of the circulation by contrasting temperatures such as hot and cold water, rubbing the skin with a rough glove, as well as certain exertion in sport and other activities alternating with rest, all add to the general toning of muscle and circulation. These are good maxims to bear in mind. Even though violin playing demands infinite subtlety, it also demands great resistance and strength. It is useful to swim, to play tennis even, provided one can relax completely and recapture the subtlest sensations of violin playing; provided—and this is so personal and individual a reaction that it cannot be made an arbitrary law—it in no way alienates one from the center of one's being as a violinist, either mentally or physically.

Again, diet is obviously a very important element and one which must be left to the individual in his infinite variety of metabolism and body chemistry; but I would recommend a balanced diet, with plenty of raw fruit and vegetables, and a minimum of fried foods. It is well to avoid foods made with refined flour and refined sugar, especially sweets of the artificial kind, those insidious energizers which together with cigarettes and alcohol give with one hand and take away plus an additional discount with the other. (For the medical support of this principle, see *Nutrition and Physical Degeneration* by Walter D. Price. Also, for additional reading I recommend *The Saccharine Diseases* by T. Cleave.) It is also important never to eat too much food at any time, especially prior to playing.

Ideally violin playing should begin at the age of three or four as in Russia and more recently in Japan. Two lessons a week—the instruments remaining with the teacher—are sufficient. At that stage the child learns, as all fledglings do, by example and challenge. In my experience, however, by the time a child is eight or nine he or she can grasp the mechanical analyses and explanations quite clearly.

Though this book is organized in six lessons, I do not recommend that the student or the teacher should work through them steadily page by page. Sometimes the analysis and the exercises may appear didactic and too specific in their deliberate application to those minute movements, those inner feelings of parts of the fingers which become, as it were, antennae. My purpose is to develop the utmost sensitivity to the subtlest movements, and to guide the teacher in awakening the pupil to these sensations.

In violin playing it would be wrong to stop at that point, however; for the technique is but the means without which you are helpless, unable to convey your musical conception, however clear it may be, in all its color and spontaneity. Those movements which I have so carefully classified will ultimately merge into each other and overlap in a manner that not only defies analysis (which at that stage is anyway useless) but will also inevitably contradict one or another of our carefully enunciated dicta. This process, resembling that of digestion, depends largely on the physical characteristics of each individual violinist; therefore the teacher like the gifted doctor must know how to temper and adjust these exercises according to the physical, psychological, and emotional attributes of the pupil in front of him.

A violinist's work is never done; but having worked for some fifty years on the instrument, I feel that the time is ripe, for better or worse, to put into words the approach I have evolved. I have tried in these pages to cover what I believe to be the material means essential to violin playing. I hope that this book will be useful, that it will encourage the study of the violin, and that it will help others to experience the inner joys and satisfactions that the violin has brought to me.

LORE SEGAL

Lore Segal lives in New York with her two children. She has written a novel, *Other People's Houses,* and a children's story, *Tell Me a Mitzi.* *The Quarter Turn* is taken from a novel she is working on now which Farrar, Straus & Giroux, Inc. will publish.

THE QUARTER TURN

"Lucinella! Come in!" cries Ulla. "You're looking fabulous!" (That's what William said, but he doesn't count. He even wants to marry me.)

I'm trying to get a glimpse, in Ulla's hall mirror, of myself looking fabulous.

Ulla is wearing her harem pants and she looks terrific. She says William is looking good but there I *know* she's fibbing. "Dump your coats inside on the bed. Cilena! Come in!" says Ulla to a woman with serious eyes and a sweet, sexless figure like an English schoolgirl. "You're looking fabulous!"

And here comes Maurie; his polished, fat face reflects light. He puts an arm around my shoulder. I like Maurie. But don't, Maurie, *please* don't ignore William. Now look what you've done!

Maurie's snub has uncovered Will's underground and let out his company of little black familiars with their barbed and poisonous tails. One crawls out of the bottom of his trouser leg and says, "So! Maurie won't publish your play!" Another falls out of his sleeve and says, "And at Betterwheatling's, Thursday, J. D. Winterneet didn't remember who you were." There's one that clings to Will's lapel like a boutonniere saying, "Remember Lila who put out for the whole eighth grade except you and that kid with the adenoids?" adding, "and Lucinella doesn't want to marry you!" One, a meany, sits astride William's nose and looks into his eyes with the precise slant of eye Miss Coleman in kindergarten wore when she saw the pee seeping down his trouser leg, and William groans out loud, "Arrrrh."

"The trouble with Maurie," William says, "is he doesn't have the first idea what publishing is all about; he runs that magazine like a shoe business."

Now that is not true but I clasp my hands around William's arm and keep silent. And I add, "Also he picks his nose in public and eats the snot." (So does William except only in private. So do I, but I don't eat it.)

William removes my hands from around his arm and stalks after Maurie.

What I cannot forgive is the meagerness of the back of William's neck. Tomorrow I tell him I'm through. Tonight, while I'm looking fabulous, I'll practice operating solo again and there's Meyers in the doorway.

Fondly we embrace. Ridiculous, we say, that we never get together; New York is impossible! We figure the year and month to the day when we did the Sunday crossword, at Yaddo, walked into the village, saw the Chinese lady's tiny shoe in the museum, drank beer in the pub all afternoon and talked. "You watched football," I say. "We ate peanuts," he says, "and the next day I went home."

We get drinks and sit down on the couch and herein lies our downfall.

"I saw Winterneet at Betterwheatling's, Thursday," I say.

"Cilena said Roundling is coming," says Meyers.

"Bert," I say.

"Pavlovenka," he says.

"So?" I say. "What are you writing?"

"I'm not," he says. "You?"

"I'm writing a story about parties," I say, but the prospect of telling him about it brings on an extreme lassitude and I close my mouth.

Meyers's mouth is closed. He fingers his drooping blond mustache with trembling hands. I do like Meyers! I want to frame a question to which his answer will be something true, preferably intimate, but a thin, glutinous film is growing between my lips; if I don't part them my mouth will be sealed up forever.

(Over by the bar, at a tremendous distance, I see William talking to Maurie. From the way Maurie is leaning backward I know William is telling him what publishing is all about.)

Meyers's lips have parted. He says, "Have you seen Winterneet?"

"At Betterwheatling's, Thursday," I say.

(Maurie turns his back on William and walks away.)

"There *is* Winterneet," says Meyers. Here comes Maurie to greet his famous guest. I know Meyers wants to go and talk to Winterneet but he cannot get up from the couch because he doesn't want to hurt my feelings. I want to go to William who stands alone, holding his glass, but I cannot get up because I don't want to hurt Meyers's feelings. Now it is too late. Our rumps have put roots down into the couch; and here Meyers and I will sit in mutual silence through eternity.

A hundred years pass. Ben, that princely man, is working his way across the thickly growing crowd toward me; his eyes are friendly. He bends his beautiful, intelligent head, and kisses me on the cheek. I arise. Meyers has risen. My unsealed lips say, "Hi, Ben! So? I thought you were going to Yale. You know Meyers, of course?" I turn to my right but Meyers is gone. In

247

his place stands a young girl with glasses whose face needs a good wash. Her hungry nose is pointed into the space between Ben and me.

Ben says, "They offered me a chair, as a matter of fact, but here I am, as you see. What's new with you?"

"I'm writing a story about parties," I tell Ben and the bespectacled girl. "It asks the question, Why do people go?"

"I never go to parties," says an elderly woman on my left.

"I always throw up at parties," says the bespectacled girl.

"I come to have conversation with you," I think is what Ben is saying; his lips move but a swell in the nice noise of the growing crowd carries the sound away.

"That's what I come for," says the bespectacled girl. "I want to have conversations and get to know people, only I never talk to anybody I don't know and I don't know anybody so I never have any conversations or get to know anybody."

"At the next party you will," I say meaning to address myself also to the elderly woman.

Ben says, "That's why I don't go to Yale! I'd miss the next party."

The bespectacled girl looks at Ben, smiling, and turns expectantly toward me: She has lighted upon a conversation.

"You can't leave New York," I say, "although the Bomb will get you if you stay." I keep trying to keep my shoulders turned so as to include the elderly woman, but Ben's lips are moving.

"What?" I ask.

He says, "I said what *is* it that's going to happen at the next party?"

"It," I say, "the Great Orgasm."

"The *what?*" Ben asks leaning down his ear.

"The GREAT ORGASM," I yell, raising up my chin. And here is where I have my first intimation of *déjà vu* only it is a false *déjà vu*: Ben and I really *have* been here before, at Betterwheatling's, Thursday, and Ben's eyes quicken as he recognizes himself yelling, "What is the use of that, the morning after?"

"There *is* no morning after, dum dum, not after the Great One," I shout familiarly back.

"Damn!" Ben yells familiarly, comfortably, "I must have been to all the wrong parties again."

"Of course, you have!" I yell. "It's the *next* party that's going to be the *right* one," and notice the guilty chill on my left side, where the old woman's bulk no longer displaces air.

Will's voice at the back of my head says, "I've never seen anyone who enjoys the exercise of power as much as your friend Maurie." I turn toward him. "What fun," he says, "for him to be an editor, accepting, rejecting. . . ."

Now this is probably partly true.

"His trouble," says William, "is he has to keep checking his position by standing on someone's shoulder or with his foot on someone's neck."

I turn back to Ben who is gone. The bespectacled girl is gone.

"Lucinella!" says Winterneet, and takes my hand.

"J. D. Winterneet," I say, pleased.

"How do you do, sir," says William.

"You remember William," I say anxiously, but Winterneet puts out his hand and says, "Winterneet. Pleased to meet you. I'm too old for these parties, Lucinella, come sit on the couch with me."

"Better not," I say, "because then, when we've run out of things to say, we'll be stuck with each other for eternity."

I've made J. D. Winterneet smile. On my right William's underground gapes.

"We can always go and freshen up our drinks," says Winterneet.

"That's what I mean! And there's always the john, but that means going clear out of the room and *staying* out, and God knows what we might miss!"

I've made Winterneet laugh.

"I'm writing a story about parties," I tell him. "Doesn't it strike you as peculiar that we don't simply tell each other, 'Thank you, now I've had enough of you and want to talk to someone else'? I think it is a sort of sympathetic magic: if I don't rip the rug out from under your feet you won't rip out mine because that uncovers our underground where we keep all the other people who've thought us less than perfectly charming and interesting, reinforcing our suspicion that they're right. What I haven't figured out is why that panics people."

I'm talking too much but Winterneet is looking so kindly at me that from somewhere I haven't figured out floats up my rainbow-hued, transparent, and highly unstable company of people who have liked me, reinforcing my suspicion that I'm charming and interesting: I feel myself taken delicately under the armpits and borne upward; three-quarters of an inch above the rug, I float.

"And now that you have closed every avenue of escape," says Winterneet, smiling, "we're stuck with each other for eternity."

"Not if we keep standing up," I explain, "because in another half hour the room will have filled to capacity and we can maneuver the Quarter Turn: you will accidentally turn an angle of ninety degrees and find yourself in the middle of the adjacent conversation."

I demonstrate and find myself looking into the clever eyes of the girl with the unwashed face, looking back at me with hungry hopelessness from behind her glasses.

"I read everything you write," she says to me. "It's exactly my cup of tea."

My eyes cross and focus on the bridge of her nose. I put on a falsely sweet, discouraging face and say, "Thank you. How nice of you."

She reddens. She says, "I don't suppose praise gives you any fun any more."

Now I look at her. Her rounded back and forward thrusting belly describe the letter S inside her beautifully tailored dress of rich black wool. Her palpable misery makes me mean. I say, "Remember somewhere in *A Moveable Feast* Hemingway says they could always tell an outsider because he praised them to their faces. It's just that there's no way to handle it."

"I can't see you being at a loss," she says smiling, her face scarlet.

"Are you kidding!" I say.

"You know everybody," she says.

"So will you when you've done the party bit for ten years."

She shakes her head. "I don't get to go to parties much. I don't know anybody."

"What brought you to this one?"

"Ten wild horses," she says. "No. I sent Mr. Maurie some poems which he didn't publish. He invited me."

"Then you're probably going to be good," I say.

She can't handle that. Her eyes cross and focus on the bridge of my nose. She says, "Anyway, so for three weeks I fixate on tonight as if it were the start of the New Life, but I put off getting dressed, figuring I'd come late, at ten, and leave at eleven thirty; I figured I could live through an hour and a half."

"What's your name?"

"Lucinella," she says.

"How old are you?"

"Twenty," she says.

"Hang on, Lucinella, it gets better from here on," I

promise her. "You'll publish a book (she shakes her head) and marry a man (she grimaces; she looks as if she's going to cry). When you make a *faux pas* you won't toss all night trying to unsay it. (She laughs out.) You'll get handsomer as you get older: you'll learn how to wear your hair. Give it ten years. . . ."

"Ten years!" she howls. To her this decade, to which I cling by the fingernails with my legs streaming horizontally behind me, feels like a drafty waiting room with no clocks.

"For godsake, get yourself a drink," I tell her.

"Alcohol makes me throw up," she says.

"Well," I say, "I think I'll go freshen up mine."

I pass William talking to Maurie. William is saying, "But J. D. Winterneet hasn't had a new thought in fifteen years," and Maurie answers, "Don't be a ninny, William," and walks away.

There's the elderly woman standing in a clearing in the crowd. She holds a glass. I will go talk to her and by sympathetic magic next time I'm in a hole at a party someone will come and talk to me. I'm working up something to say when Cilena smiles at me and says, "You met Roundling at Yaddo. He's my husband. I'm no good at parties."

"There's a story I was going to write once," I tell her, "called 'The Bottomless Bucket,' about a party where everybody carries buckets. The game is to collect the odds and ends of love like attention, flattery, a proposition or two, a little rape, so's to have your bucket brimful at all times."

"I know," says Cilena Roundling, and holds up her arm to show me hers. I show her mine.

"The catch is that the buckets have no bottoms. Say there's someone who wants to marry you; in the act of sticking him in your bucket he's already fallen out the other end."

"So you have to keep collecting in perpetuity. It's so *tiring!*" says Cilena.

"I never wrote the story because I don't know why we need a bucket in the first place."

"Ah," says Cilena, "I've been reading Erich Fromm where he says how we experience separateness as anxiety."

"Wow!" I say.

"Exactly," she says, "and not only anxiety but as 'shame and guilt.'"

"The shame of not being loved! Jesus. . . ." I'm very excited. I tell her about the Great Orgasm. "You have it once and for all and never need another bucket."

"The Millennium!" says Cilena Roundling.

I tell the rather elegant, very black man who stands near us about the buckets. He thinks I am flirting with him, which is true.

He says this is precisely what he's working on. "I'm doing a piece for Maurie on the parallel uses of female desirability and male power."

"Are you really!" I say. "That's what I never get the point of. Or do you think power is a different sort of bucket?" I ask Cilena, but she is gone.

"Power is the point," he says excitedly. "In the social animal it is the powerful male who has the selective advantage in attracting the desirable female at the peak of her oestrus."

"Erich Fromm says we experience separateness as shame," I tell him, very excited too.

"It's a matter of genetic survival," he says, "because the weak am ale ad oes an otap ass aona his a genes."

I say, "I at hink awe a ar eal la loo kin ga fo rat hea mill ennium."

He says his name's James Winslow. He will send me his article and writes down my address. I promise to send him my story. We will have lunch and continue our discussion. There's Roundling. He comes toward me. Roundling is very large.

"By the way," I say, "who is the elderly woman in the frizzy hair putting on her coat?"

"That's Lucinella," says Roundling, "the poet, didn't you know? She hasn't written much in the last years but she used to be good in a minor way."

"How can she bear it!" I say. "God! To be minor, and old!"

We watch the old woman get into her coat. Maurie and Ulla have both come to make a small fuss at her leaving.

James Winslow is gone. Roundling is silent. He stands beside me.

"How's Thomas Mann coming?" I ask. The last time, at Yaddo, we started talking about Mann and ended kissing on the stair.

Roundling explains the fuck-up with his publisher in detail. It is not very interesting and my mind wanders: his proximity moves me. It's Roundling I could really be in love with.

"Your wife and I had a conversation," I say.

"Yes?" says Roundling.

"I like her," I say.

"So do I," says Roundling.

Still he stands beside me.

"Have you got an English publisher?" I ask him.

Roundling explains in detail the fuck-up with his English publisher.

Maurie joins us. I say, "Listen, Maurie, I'm just drunk enough to give you hell about William." Roundling has disappeared.

"Jesus," says Maurie, "let me get myself a drink first."

"Me too," I say. "Doesn't Ulla look terrific?"

"She does," Maurie says in a voice detective fiction writers used to describe as "dry." Ulla is sitting straight-backed on the couch receiving what Meyers, who squats before her, is saying into her mouth. She sees Maurie and me looking, and smiles at us.

"Maurie, why did you turn down William's play? He's not a bad poet, you know."

"I know he's not," says Maurie looking irritable and unhappy, "but he writes lousy verse plays. I'd rather talk about your story. I'm going to take it."

"You are!" I say. The world has stopped spinning; only my head continues to revolve. I suspect a hoax.

"I have a couple of quibbles, of course," says Maurie.

"Of course," I quickly say. "It's getting to be awfully coy for writers to be writing their stories in their stories."

"Yes," says Maurie, "but. . . ."

"And the metaphors don't dovetail. . . ."

"Shut up a moment, Lucinella," says Maurie, "so I can think. What I think I mean is this: it's OK for your narrator to mock herself, if that's her nature; it's not OK for the writer to mock her narrator. You are mean to her!"

"I know, I know!" I say intensely elated. "Maurie, you're really *very* good." I really like Maurie! "You're absolutely right. It's *not* OK. It's going illegitimately round the outside of the story and flirting with the reader, like saying 'I'll tell you mine because it is the same as yours,' which isn't even necessarily so. And anyway nobody'll love me any the better!"

"There you go," says Maurie. "Why 'illegitimately'? Why 'flirting'?"

"To say it first, so you won't," I say. "Hi, Betterwheatling. Come over here. Did you just arrive?"

"No," says Betterwheatling.

"What's the matter?" I ask him.

"I don't know. What *is* the matter?"

"You look sort of . . . Maurie is taking a story of mine," I say, but Maurie is gone. "It's about parties," I tell Betterwheatling, "and how when you feel crappy

255

all your abject memories crawl out of your underground, but when you feel good all the good ones fly out of . . . Goddamn, I've just dovetailed two metaphors! Out of the goddamn brimful bucket! Of course!"

When I say damn a lot I know I'm high, but not so high I couldn't climb down if I chose. I could stop talking only I can't seem to choose to. I'm telling Betterwheatling about the bottomless bucket. He says, yes, lovers tend to fall out the bottom, but a lot of friends stay in.

"That's perfectly true, Betterwheatling," I say, "but it bloody undermines my story." I tell him about Erich Fromm. He says if only Fromm didn't write such rotten English.

I tell him about the Great Orgasm and about my theory that we go to parties millennium hunting. "I mean, why do *you* go, Betterwheatling?"

Betterwheatling says he likes parties.

"So do I! I love them," I say, "but *why* do we? What do we promise ourselves is going to happen? Why aren't we in the library reading, at home cooking, or out horseback riding?"

Betterwheatling says he was at the library all afternoon and is no good at cooking. Horseback riding he doesn't like. He says he likes parties.

"Betterwheatling," I say, "you're no damn use to me."

There *is* something about the way Betterwheatling stands, talking with me. I can't diagnose it. He avoids my eye, refrains from looking at his watch, I don't think in impatience with me, which I can always tell the look of that but why doesn't he take off his coat? That's the clue. Of course! I know! Betterwheatling should be leaving for another party but can't because he doesn't know if *I'm* invited.

And here is William. He says for me to get my coat;

we're going on to the Friendlings'; Maurie and Ulla will come as soon as they turf everybody out.

In the bedroom the younger Lucinella is digging in the mound of coats. I avoid her eye; I don't know if she's invited to the Friendlings'.

"Well . . . goodbye!" she says, but still stands, giving it another moment to happen.

I could invite her to come to the Friendlings' with us.

"Well," she says, "goodbye!"

"Goodbye," I say. "Come and see me in ten years and we will talk."

On the way Will, who is high, gets pesty and keeps saying *why* won't I marry him.

"I will," I say, "probably."

"You don't *love* me," Will whines, craning his neck in a U like Chagall's birthday lover, to stick his outraged face into mine.

"I do," I say, "I love you," which is probably true. "It's only that there must be more to love than love!"

We're dumping our coats on the mound in the Friendlings' bedroom. In the mirror I see Meyers coming from the john. By tacit covenant sealed in the silence on Maurie's couch I do not turn, and he tiptoes out behind my back.

Winterneet walks in, takes his coat off, and seeing William says, "I meant to drop you a note. I liked your play!"

William's eyes cross. "I shouldn't have sent it and bothered you, sir."

"I like it." Winterneet is thoughtful. "Nobody's done anything like it since Fry, who was too much in love with words. It's a good play," he says. He walks into the living room.

"I thought his bit was not to know who you are," I say, and Will, unsnubbed, looking amused and charming, says, "Sh, that was at another party."

Out in the living room Ben comes toward me through the crowd, his lips moving.

"Go away, Ben," I say, "you are too tall for me to talk to."

"I said 'Saul Mailer's supposed to be here,'" Ben shouts into a split second of total silence. "Why do we *come* to the bloody things?" he asks, his eyes quickening in recognition even as I have that *déjà vu* feeling of *déjà vu* answering, "Because if we stayed home, we might miss the right one."

Will is bringing me a drink and says, "There's Saul Mailer!" And, really, there in a small clearing of homage, aging, with a small pot, white, curly hair, rather beautiful, stands Saul Mailer talking to a furiously pretty girl.

I refuse to add my attention and turn my back. Now my back gives him my attention.

William says he remembers a sign in the Uffizi translated into funny English; it explained why visitors must not touch famous paintings: It is bad for the painting; it costs a fine and finally, it is useless.

Though compared with Saul Mailer Winterneet is merely eminent, I pull his sleeve and tell him William's story about the famous painting.

Winterneet can't handle my mentioning his fame to his face and says, "I don't know what you mean."

"Yes you do," I say. He looks startled. "It's because fame looks as if it has one foot in the millennium," I explain. "We want to touch it and connect ourselves."

"Don't be silly," says Winterneet, looks right, left, begins to walk away, but I keep beside him craning my neck in a U to oblige him to look me in the eye: "Of *course*, it's silly. That's what I mean. 'Finally it is useless.'"

Winterneet says he's going to freshen up his drink.

I look for William.

William is talking with Saul Mailer. I walk over and

stick my nose into the space between them. Will sees me all right but he's approaching the denouement of his funny Blackmur story and Saul Mailer laughs, and launches into a funny story about Edmund Wilson.

I turn ninety degrees right and James Winslow smiles and says, "Fra hog higo na mo."

I say, "Fra hog not mu pen," and he frowns. What have I said!

"Fra hog me," he says and adds he is surprised I would fall into that particular, and if he may say, not uncommon liberal trap, and walks off.

There's William over there talking into Ulla's open mouth. I'm always surprised when someone flirts with William till I remember I'm even in love with him.

Maurie's by the bar, laughing with the furiously pretty girl.

I see Betterwheatling in the door with his coat on.

"Saul Mailer's here," I tell him. Betterwheatling says he knows. "Are you leaving?" I ask him.

He says the Bernards are having people over for Harry's birthday.

Betterwheatling has gone.

I perform a Quarter Turn right, but there's no one there. There's nobody on my left. I look into my empty bucket and feel ashamed. Where's William? There is Roundling who would be so much easier to love walking toward me. Roundling stands beside me.

"Talking of your wife," I say, "why is it I endow all wives I don't know of men I know with an unearthly glamor. When I meet them they always turn out to be girls."

Roundling's eyes behind his glasses have an odd black cast. He says, "If you could choose between a feeling and a joke, which would you take?"

"Are you joking?" I say. I'm upset. "Is that how it looks? I just laugh quickly so you won't." Where's William!

There, on the couch, Winterneet is talking with Maurie.

By the bar stands Cilena with the Friendlings.

James Winslow is talking into Ulla's open face. "Have you seen William?" I ask her.

"Try the bedroom," she says.

There's no one in the bedroom except Meyers putting on his coat. The john is empty.

In the foyer Ben and the furiously pretty girl are laughing.

In the kitchen a man is getting ice out of a tray. He turns around. It is Saul Mailer.

"Hello," he says.

"Have you seen William?" I ask.

"Have you tried the dining room?" he asks. "There's an impressive buffet. Paté from Zabar's." His aggressively blue eyes smile and that does it.

I want to go home!

William is eating Zabar paté.

"Let's go home," I say.

"What, now? Just as it's beginning to be fun?"

"I'm drunk and sleepy and probably going to cry."

"Have something to eat," says William. He feeds me a marinated mushroom.

"William! Do you know the Bernards are having people over and didn't invite us?" I drop a tear.

"Who are the Bernards?" asks William.

"I don't know. They don't even know us and already they've decided we're not charming or interesting enough to invite to Harry's birthday and I know that's where everything is going to happen."

"*I* think *you* are charming and interesting," says William feeding me another mushroom.

"That's because you love me, so it's like one's mother saying it. It doesn't *prove* anything."

"J. D. Winterneet thinks you're very bright," says William.

"Ah, but he doesn't love me!" I cry.

"And Ulla said you are looking fabulous."

"Oh William! She says that to all the girls, so we'll forgive *her* for being beautiful. Do you know the two-some from Dylan Thomas, 'Always one, pert and pretty, and always one with glasses'? That's Ulla and me, ever since high school. And so I became a poet."

"Maurie loves your story!"

"It's no use, William! Praise doesn't feed into the part of me that's hungry. The two systems aren't connected. It's a matter of plumbing. Why are you taking my hand out of your pocket?"

"It tickles," says William.

I shake my head. "At Maurie's you took my hands off your arm and you walked away."

William wipes my tears with his handkerchief. "You can put your hand in my pocket," he says. "You can tickle me any time. Have a mushroom."

"It isn't just my hand," I say. "Did you ever read a Chekhov story about this little servant girl who runs errands all day and rocks the baby all night and runs errands all next morning and she's cleaning the master's boot and yearns to crawl inside where it's dark and sleep."

"You can crawl in," says William. He feeds me mushrooms. As I diminish the room distends headlong. William picks me up and puts me in his pocket.

"I've thought of a joke," I say poking my head out.

"What?" he says.

"What do you do if the Great Orgasm doesn't bring on the Millennium?"

"What?" he says.

"Wait till the Second Coming."

"Go to sleep," says William.

And now, on their giant legs, Maurie, the Friendlings, Saul Mailer, Roundling and Cilena, James Winslow and

Ulla, J. D. Winterneet and Ben with the furiously pretty girl are coming to the feast.

Before I curl up I fold my hands neatly: "Forgive me my vanities as I forgive all of you your vanities."

JAMES LANDIS–NICHOLAS DELBANCO

James Landis is a senior editor at William Morrow &
Company. Nicholas Delbanco, born in London,
teaches at Bennington and lives on a farm in Greenwich, New York. These letters were selected from
their extensive correspondence during the writing of
Delbanco's fifth novel, *In the Middle Distance*, which
William Morrow & Co., Inc. published in September, 1971.

LETTERS
JAMES LANDIS
NICHOLAS DELBANCO

The following snippets of correspondence between
Nicholas Delbanco and myself have been pulled from
letters written between the end of autumn 1970 and
May 1971, when Delbanco was living in the south of
France and traveling through Europe and Asia. All of
it is in reference in one way or another to his fifth novel,
In the Middle Distance, which he wrote in 1969–1970,
which we discussed at some length during the spring
and summer of 1970, and which he finished in November 1970, while living in France; it arrived in manuscript on my desk in early December.

Since Delbanco is an exceedingly careful and conscious writer, there was very little revision necessary.
Nevertheless, there are always questions an editor asks

concerning word usage, punctuation, sentence rhythms, clarity of sequence, and, in this particular case, possible anachronism (since Delbanco was writing in some detail about years that antedate his own birth). Ordinarily I would have phoned these questions to him or asked them in person, for we've seen a good deal of one another since we first began to work together in the summer of 1968. But because he was so far away, we began to correspond on matters relating directly to details of the manuscript. It is specifically from these letters (for we have always written to one another) that these samples have been drawn.

They were not originally put together for publication in *Works in Progress*.

In the Middle Distance is, in Delbanco's words, a "fictive autobiography." It is the story of a middle-aged man named Nicholas Delbanco, an architect, who during a time of crisis in his life retires to his farm in Cossayuna, New York, there to try to draw his past back into himself—to see his life backwards and so put together its pieces—and also to write a novel in the form of a journal, "as an act of explication and an act of penance," to quote the book itself. But the journal that's used in *In the Middle Distance* is one that was actually kept by Nicholas Delbanco the novelist, who is in fact not middle-aged but twenty-nine.

Obviously the novel contains its mirrors, personal and otherwise. When Delbanco thought of adding one more —pieces of our correspondence concerning our work on the manuscript—and wrote me to suggest as much, I avoided the question by simply not responding to that particular suggestion. But when he repeated it, I took him seriously enough to hurry home with our numerous letters and overnight made a selection from them, typed up my choices, and mailed them off to him; by that time, I was myself committed to the idea. A few weeks later, at his suggestion, I made further selections, and all these were set in type and so appeared in the galley proofs of the book. When he returned to the United States in May 1971, he picked out several more of our exchanges, and they were added to the book at the page-proof stage.

Since neither of us wanted terribly much of the correspondence to appear in the body of the book, we eliminated most of what we'd chosen once we had a chance to sit down together with the galleys. Of the selections that follow, a few do show up in the final printed version of *In the Middle Distance,* but most do not and so are being published here for the first time. I don't imagine they say all that much about how an author and an editor work together; but I do hope they give some feeling for how two good friends manage to talk on paper about a fine book that one of them has written.

—James Landis

(EDITOR'S NOTE: The following pagination refers to the typescript of *In the Middle Distance*.)

EDITOR: p. 254, line 14: Change "she said" to "she would say"?

AUTHOR: All right, if you prefer. I do it on purpose, attempting to put the fantasy past probability's bounds, at this point. So that Nicholas is completely *within* his imaginings here.

AUTHOR: Would "ball" as slang expression for fornicatrix major, etc., esq., have been plausible for Nicholas in 1951? Line 1. He should wash his mouth with soap.

EDITOR: p. 180: It may very well be that "ball" wasn't current in 1951, but I suspect balling itself was (being only nine at the time and having lost my plum—girls have cherries, boys, plums—only the year previous—to a chambermaid employed on my parents' estate, out in the stable, it was, the rain pelting down and I out there to tend to Pablum, our champion roan, to keep him steady amidst the lightning and the thunder, and as I bent to take in my hand some hay for food and comfort, who should I uncover but the naked chambermaid, Yika, whose affair with Pablum we had all known of for several months but whose affections for me—remember, I was not a thin boy and just nine and not very talkative for fear of my double chin being noticed—were until that moment hidden, to say the least, though, to my credit, I hope, I appeared to accept her advances nonchalantly enough to pass as experienced and gave up my plum with no little pleasure, pleasure for me, certainly, and for Yika too, I have no doubt, if one can judge by the way her cries of "Ball me! Ball me!" soon —but not too soon, for I was a steady boy—dwindled into gasps of affection and, soon, tears), and if balling itself was, and if Yika, in fact, knew and used the term (though I like to think that I inspired its first entrance into language), then I see no reason why—I shall try to say this modestly—we can't let my personal experience stand as universal and allow into your book, "ball."

EDITOR: p. 131, line 5: "Michael was nine" (actually, "just turned nine"—p. 156, line 7). Just checking to make sure this is correct. Nicholas is at this point forty, which puts this about eight years prior to time present, or 1962–63. Michael was born in 1955, which means he might more likely be eight (or even seven) than nine, though I'm not at all sure my calculations are right.

AUTHOR: Nicholas is not quite forty yet. And it's the summer of his turning age, and when he buys the farm. Which is, I believe, 1964, one year after Simon dies. Argal Michael is just turned nine. The real problem here is that I didn't imagine I'd get the book done this quickly, and computed it all for publication in 1972. What to do? Shoot for immortality, or make it Michael had just turned eight, and have Simon, p. 19, die in '62. Let's do it that way, & hope the whole comes out right.

Disregard. Make him forty-one.

EDITOR: I will admit to a sudden inordinate hunger to know more about this new book of yours and to know how you fare in relation to it, how much you love it.

AUTHOR: Sorry as to silence re *Plague Year:* I'm not holding anything purposively back; it's just that, short of a volume or voluminous letter, I can't yet tell you a whole hell of a lot more. Perhaps you thought I was joking re Oedipus and his analogues. If so, not so. But I'm at a hiatus with the thing right now, and trying to decide what to do; think I've done a draft of a half, and that already eighty thousand words. The problem being, of course, what of Oedipus at Colonus, and Antigone. . . .

The book continues apace, though at a snail's. Have, somewhat, a sense of having rushed it, compiling all the verbiage I could muster in those silent months. Want to think a bit about it now, and will report the thinking's fruit come May. If not, interminably loquacious as I by letter am, before.

AUTHOR: Listen, Landis, and not that this ain't explicable, but it dawns you haven't much mentioned how you are. Nor Patty. Except with a strain of rush and frenzy and scattering. As apology. Which shifts my paranoia to flat-out fear. That you're in some sort of trouble, the world too much with, getting and spending, so forth. Wastelaid in olde Eliot's landscape. Thank you for the date of the Quartets. Which a happy one (with little Sara fluting as quintet) I insist we'll as of the soon springtime be. The only pretty ringtime. Tell me, Friend, that it's Morrow that mires you, or the subway system, or the price of beans. Not worse.

EDITOR: Ah. So you sensed trouble in the domestic pantry. Very perceptive. In my silences you must have gleaned at least traces of the following course of events. Sara Cass was one day bouncing down Central Park West, her fair mother in tow, when she came upon a dog of middling size but most fascinating demeanor, eyes blue and wide and moist, beard neat, tongue of no great length but, more important, rarely to be seen, as if this dog had an almost human sense of decorum. "Doug, doug!" (pronounced Doog, doog), said Sara Cass. Then both she and her mother crept their eyes up along the leash and came upon a most unusual man, a fellow of middle age with bulldog jowls and slavering mouth and wet nose (with just the slightest tinge of brown at its tip). He introduced himself. "I am Doug." Introductions from the other side followed quickly, and soon this man, Doug, had not only offered coffee in his apartment to both the ladies but his dog to Sara Cass. The coffee was served and accepted gratefully, for this was a nippy day in the very belly of December. The dog —the offer of it, that is—was a more delicate problem, for though the dog and Sara were getting along famously in the corner of the man's livingroom (a hard, cold place, for even the furniture was made of bone china, and he had, of his own admittance, a terrible problem with breakage), Patty could see neither taking a gift from a stranger nor depriving any man, friend or stranger, of so good and faithful a friend as his dog. Nevertheless, the man was persistent, and through Patty he vigorously pressed the dog upon Sara Cass; Patty, however (and this I scarce need tell you), is of strong will, and the more the man forced his offer upon and through her, the more she resisted. Things began to feel a little tense, for the man, Doug, was clearly offended at this rejection of his generosity, and Patty was getting pretty peeved at his inability to take a simple no for an answer. Well, to make the story short —in fact, the afternoon did drag on for my wife and daughter—around dusk Patty began to put her things —cigarettes (filthy habit, I wish I'd made her stop when I still had some power over such things), matches, notebooks (just scraps of paper, really, but she never was able to call things by their true names), hash marks (fake German currency made from rolled and pressed hashish, very good for getting and spending, as you say)—away and to move her eyes around the room in search of her coat. Now, I don't think I have to tell you that neither the man nor his dog wanted Patty and Sara to leave, nor that, to press their point, the man announced that he was in fact a dog—and turned to one on the spot—and the dog announced that he was in fact a man—and turned to one on the spot. I don't even think that Patty was startled in any profound way by their transformations; and as for Sara, when she saw her new friend the dog change to a man, her eyes took on a distinct look of disappointment, and she backed away just slightly, and she smiled again only when she glimpsed behind her the man Doug now a dog, whom she approached with all good speed, saying, "Doug, doug!" (pronounced Doog, doog)—and they went off into a corner. The dog-turned-man walked slowly up to Patty, motioned for her to sit down again, said, "I am Doug," and proceeded to offer his dog to Sara, for her to keep. Patty, of course, being firm in her decisions, still refused, and continued to refuse; and at somewhere near dawn, man turned to dog, dog to man, and the whole process recommenced (as you would say). And it continues to this day. Which accounts, I hope, for my lack of news about my family, which is no longer mine—I must be honest—and which, I suspect, I shall never see again. Separation is, you can imagine, cruel. But to assuage the pain, I have taken into my home a pet—small concession to loneliness, small comfort but comfort nonetheless—a dog named James—curly hair, small hazel eyes, yellow teeth that give off a surprisingly sweet odor of tobacco—from whom I am trying to learn the gift and tactics of transformation, in the hope that one day I, as dog, shall be able to make my way up to that apartment on CPW, just south of my own home, and win back, if not my wife, then at least my daughter, Sara Cass.

(If that doesn't tell you all you need to know—that I love my wife and daughter and that both of them are steady—then you'll just have to ask again.)

AUTHOR: Ah I never told you of my theatrical self's demise. Asked to play the lead in an experimental effort by yes Auden & Isherwood, I accepts. Grabbed whereat I'm vulnerablessed, by flattery's balls. The play being Dog Beneath the Skin, the role being naught but Top Dog. So your excursus as to Doug delights. Sith I spent a month, then being very method, in the Cambridge Dog Pound, learning how to woof. From Chihuahua to Weimaraner & back. Wherefore let me at him, old curly-headed kid in the third row. A funny tale you tell. And the play was in full-dress, except I had to wear a raccoon coat atop mine plus-fours, and I sweat as per usual and under the arc lights as per Pavlov. What.

EDITOR: As for scheduling, we may have a problem here. I've asked that the novel be published on September 12, which happens to be your first anniversary and so, it seemed to me, a fit and mirroring occasion; the fact that September 12 is a Sunday in 1971 and that books are almost never published on Sunday seemed to me more distinctive than of concern. Now, if you'd rather the book weren't published on the day of your first, then just let me know and I'll move it to a later date.

AUTHOR: Yes I love the notion of September 12 publication. Let's shoot for it, and thank you for keeping the book on the fall list, and of course I can guarantee return by middle May, and of course you can't guarantee the publication date—but no harm in trying, and it's a fine notion willy-nilly.

EDITOR: p. 91, line 14: Change "as" to "like"? (Oh, screw it, forget I asked. There is so little of this sort of rhetoric in your writing now that your popish editor must grant this indulgence.)

AUTHOR: Thankee, sir, sez he, tugging his forelock. You're too kined.

EDITOR: p. 6, line 16: The song "Oh! My Pa-pa" came out in 1953. Would it have lasted so long for Michael to be singing it here? (I know that you and I still sing it, but Michael wasn't born until 1955, so he wasn't even alive when Eddie Fisherman (which he shortened to Fisher for shame of being known as a Jewish person [which, by the way, is not the same thing as being known as a person of the Jewish faith, of which more never])). I think you'll have to come up with a new song title, perhaps that great 1963 hit, "I Picked My Nose in the Body Lottery."

AUTHOR: Hard to answer. I'd like to keep it, withal. Or take some time to replace. Howzabout the classic, "My Boy Bill."

EDITOR: p. 43, lines 7–8: "about eighteen hundred worth of equipment about. . . ." That's okay, I think, and it's too innocent to be rootsey-cutesy-tootsey; but I pass on the copyeditor's query (her name is Rita Tushingham, and, would you believe it, after all these years, she still lives with a query, which may be why she became a copyeditor, since, after all, God shaped our ears in the form of a questionmark, and the ears are at least a secondary sexual orifice aside from being music's vessel, and vassal, and music is the sacred art, with apologies to you, good novelist and, now, screened-autobiographer).

AUTHOR: Don't understand the problem, nor does Rita Tushingham clarify it much; it was meant to be innocent, factual, not "rootsey-cutesy-tootsey."

EDITOR: p. 11, bottom: I wish there were some way to establish immediately that the Greenwich you mention here and of this novel is in upstate New York and is not the Greenwich I think most people think of, the rich, commuter Greenwich. *Of course* any careful reader will eventually clarify things for himself. Nevertheless, the novel has enough valuable confusions to make the elimination of this one no great shakes. Perhaps you might, in giving details of the direction in which he drives, hitch the reader right.

AUTHOR: It hadn't occurred to me that this might prove a problem, since I've gotten used to considering it "my" Greenwich, not the Conn's. How would the simple addition of "New York" do? Argal. "Nicholas left Beacon Hill for Greenwich, New York, on June fifth." But I'm not averse, if you can get the copyeditor to do it, to changing the whole thing. "Eagleville," for instance, is a community near by, which could be substituted for Greenwich in every instance. Or "Cossayuna." Maybe that would make the best sense. It would do no violence, might do some good. Rispondimi. (Cossayuna preferred.)

AUTHOR: Have been reading too much Freud. Ain't sure I want to credit the notion of art as socially validated daydreaming, nor to think of it as therapy for loss. What of this book? I've had a drink since page number one, and feel a deal less cheerful; write me, sweetheart, that you think it OK. OK? OK.

EDITOR: Freud? Drink? I don't care what you think of your art in this book. Fact is, it's not therapy, it's art, and the only way I can really see the two coming together is for a man to write (paint, etc.) something, realize that what he's done is *good*, and say, "Shit, I feel much better." Art. Therapy. Psychophilosophy (therapy, analysis, etc.) I now and then think of as basically a creator of excuses, either excuses to do something one wants to do or excuses to stop doing something one no longer wants to do ("I'm divorcing my parents"—the negative-positive act—an example of one, I mean—perhaps the most common sort of act in human behavior) or excuses merely to *think about* (i.e., allow into consciousness) doing or not doing. I suspect

273

—shit, I may be way off here, but let me say it—that your concern in that little paragraph about art/therapy is not whether or how the two go together, nothing so abstract as that, but that you *put down*, you wrote right out on the page (for publication), so much about yourself (so much from your life), and you didn't *feel* it, you don't feel it (and I mean deeply), either the loss of a part of yourself or the pulling of something new into yourself through revelation and sharing (like what one gains through giving to another as gift a possession one much values for himself). In speaking of feeling here, I'm not really talking about weeping over a passage in the midst of writing it or planning it, or even of trembling with the ongoing act of personal revelation (trembling over writing well, and of being frightened of writing well, is something else again); I'm speaking of your saying, in a sense, Here is my life (saying it to the reader and so telling a bit of a lie, but, more important, saying it to yourself) and sensing that it *is* your life (There's more than that, you fuckers) and ending up feeling various things but nothing more intensely than emptiness. And incompleteness—that the book is incomplete (it isn't) and that you are incomplete (you are). (I get the feeling all that sounds pessimistic and presumptuous. I find it working up from sadness to reality to, at the very end, a real kind of optimism. And it would be presumptuous if I weren't writing about myself through you.)

EDITOR: p. 54, line 9: Despite Patty's urgings to the contrary concerning not only my health but my exalted position in business and culture and life in general, I do eat turkey TV dinners and know very well that *my* brand (Swanson—the best, by the way, at least in the moderate price range) never have and hopefully never will contained (contain) yams. I question whether others do either (though it wouldn't surprise me—the

Morton people, for instance, turn out the most execrable products). However, if you're writing here out of personal experience, then, by all means, leave the yams in. If you're just guessing, though, why not change "the yams were bad" to, maybe, "the sauce was sour."

AUTHOR: Hullo, Patty. Yes yr position is exalted; no I hain't never et no Thanksgiving preprepared Turkey. Come next november from Springfield to Greenwich. Springfield to Eagleville. Springfield to Cossayuna. Substitute "sauce" for "yams." "The sauce was bad."

EDITOR: p. 11, bottom: Well, Nick, I remain confused about the time-scheme in this book (which isn't to say that you need change anything, for my mind has been particularly cheesy lately and may well be jumping when it ought to rest and resting when it ought to hump). Explanation will, I guess, have to wait until we're talking (since your letter of 12/12 didn't help much, your saying that "he starts at the summer's end, ends, three hundred pages later, at its shut"). (On p. 28, the first entry in the journal is dated July 1, and its first words are "March 23"—no simplicity here either.) Here, on p. 11, you have him leaving for Greenwich on June fifth, and Barbara is to join him with Eve in ten days. She doesn't, does she? And he stays there more than a month (which is, isn't it, the amount of vacation he's taking?). (If I didn't know how carefully you put books together, I'd probably think there were some fault of yours in the confusion I feel; knowing, I feel the fault is mine and apologize and place my inadequate mind before you out of some dumb sense of honesty, willing to appear foolish rather than silently hip to your workings.)

AUTHOR: About the central time-problem: the experimental thing about this book is that—with the exception of the closing, parenthetical moments, and the errant forward progress of that arrant journal, there is no chronological progression. So that what might be taken as the "action" of the novel simply does not exist, and whatever tension or development there be must be retroactive. I hope I'm not too cute or ardent in the defense, but I purposively didn't want to make it clear.

AUTHOR: There's one page absent from the draft I send you, and for obvious reasons; I'd like you to insert, as dedication page, the following. For Elena, my wife/ With all my love. 'Tis, quotha, a surprise. Reply by code.

EDITOR: This being (should the mood hold) a brief *Essay on Dedication,* written not for obscurity's sake but secrecy's, since my mood, while I hope it is not obscure, is surely secret, no new thing, since I—like, or unlike, you (who can be sure, which may answer the question in the following mark?),?—(there's a combination of punctuation I've spent my life waiting to use, so am I then a writer, O Muss—which lady is the sloppy writer's Muse)—pick up here, but I'll repeat, since I am a secret sort of guy, as wouldn't you be if you had my dedication? Or your own. For surely you are dedicated too, and make a secrecy of dedication, or, a dedication of, to, secrecy. Writers are like that, husbanding their talent, time, even their affection, love, since writing is difficult and loving is difficult, and the two together have proved impossible for less dedicated men than you, for the scribblers in the ink and the dabblers in the quim who end up writing nothing and feeling nothing and putting down on paper, grey with rejection, their despair (false, but true withal) at feeling nothing felt. What greater proof of your dedication to your work and your love than an almost finished new book, merely now to be spruced up, receipt in my hands here on Madison Avenue to be swiftly acknowledged, and your dedication to your love? Love, after all, is demanding (and hopefully not demanning), and marriage moreso or less, depending on the love and the marriage and how they remain in balance, the former constantly overweighing and so informing the latter, for best effect. Once this new book is in galleys, you will be able to see, right in type, in that weird permanent (but not permanent) form, the fruits of your dedication, but perhaps not your dedication itself, for some say that best appears in page proof, not for your eyes, it is true, but then, not for any other's, a sort of publishing house secret (the chief copyeditor's, really), kept by us so that you can be on with other work and not so taken with your dedication in a finished book that dedication to the past beauty created keeps you from the new pain and freedom of continued work. And don't think that I'm writing of seeing dedication in your galleys or whatever simply because I was in the mood to write an essay on the subject of dedication; I mean truly that you mustn't sell short the feeling of accomplishment and past struggle (in other words, dedication) when you lay eyes on a work of yours in type or print—therein is, if not permanence (not a word or concept I much care for), the past come to life, your own past, the hours spent at writing, the hours of love among the writing, and your self (remember?: "a book about his self and his house"), especially in the case of *In the Middle Distance*. Forgive the coded quality of all this. My mood takes strange directions. All my love to you and Elena.

EDITOR: I dreamt that you and I were in a store in the Village, resembling Gyro West on Bleeker off Sixth, to buy some pants. We each picked out a pair and went off to the dressing rooms. I pulled mine on, felt that they fit, maybe did a knee-bend or two to test, and then wondered what you were up to. I called you over the partition between us. You didn't respond. So I chinned myself up on the partition, there being a space between its top and the ceiling, and I, still smiling at my acrobatics, gazed down at you, crumpled against the far wall, your throat slit, blood around. My dream must have created its own defense, because it immediately shifted to a future time in which it was clear that your wound was not fatal. But the only other picture I had in the dream was of myself, walking down a dark street, near a corner, a razor in my own hand to ward off attackers.

AUTHOR: I too (and probably concurrent with yours) had a strange sorry dream. Having to do with lunch with you at Le Pavillon (at long last, though I was there in sweater and corduroy only) and suddenly delivering you a lecture on the evils of intemperance; get, good friend, neither too drunk nor too often. A plywood soapbox, at best, but my dream's message: Hide Park.

THEODORE WEESNER

The Car Thief, of which pieces have appeared in *Audience, Esquire* and *The New Yorker,* is Mr. Weesner's first novel. Random House, Inc. will publish it sometime early in 1972.

A HOME IN THE COUNTRY

A buzzer started the day. In darkness, at five-thirty A.M., along the second floor corridor, the buzzer sounded for a full thirty seconds. It buzzed only here, *Upstairs,* where serious offenders were confined in separate rooms, and not *Downstairs,* where children abandoned to the county for various reasons slept in dormitories. Known by the inmates as the Lincoln Hotel, after the two-lane rural highway passing in front, this small complex of old red brick buildings was otherwise called the Shiwasee County Juvenile Detention Home.

Alex Housman, a sixteen-year-old, was sitting on the edge of his cot by now. The buzzer was continuing to echo, lightly, in his ears. He remained partially asleep, and it remained dark in his room, but in a moment, rising, he began pulling his cot together, tightening the sheets and blankets as he had been instructed. He then put on his clothes, the detention home uniform of beltless bluejeans and a powder-blue ex-navy work shirt. A towel hung over the bar at the foot of his cot, and when he had dressed his feet, sitting on the cot again, he placed the towel over his shoulder and stood up to wait. He revolved his neck a couple of times, for the pleasant stretching sensation, and he then reached his hands over his head, merely to stretch further, but in the reaching he was taken by a yawn and he stood a moment with his muscles and arms pleasantly doubled.

The sky remained dark but there was light enough to mark the new day, to reveal, however darkly, the illustrated and autographed walls of the room. His window was not barred but covered with heavy-mesh wire, and he stood, as always, to the side of the window, to look out. The detention home stood within its own fenced and uncultivated fields, the surrounding fields were also uncultivated, and only the lights, but not the buildings, of a single farmhouse could be seen from the second floor. The lights were not on now in the farmhouse; there was only the black silhouette of the horizon, the deep purple sky above, the salting of stars overhead. Beyond the fields, perhaps ten miles away, was the city. Looking down now, he saw that the ground, some thirty feet below, was just visible in the purple light.

Someone coughed, not far away, and the sound was startling for a moment. He stretched pleasantly again and turned back into his room, to walk its short distance. For the first time since he had been here, over four weeks now, he saw a simple difference between freedom and confinement: he could not go, he had to wait to be taken. How long must he wait? Breakfast was only minutes away, but beyond that he did not know. He had been charged with what a detective called UDAA, *Unlawfully Driving Away an Automobile*. He had driven away between twelve and fifteen, keeping them a few days and leaving them parked somewhere, out of gas. At the time he was questioned he had been unable to recall the exact number, but now, this morning, he felt he could get his memory to recall nearly every detail. He was also hungry; ever so faintly the odor of breakfast being cooked in the large kitchen below was making its way upstairs.

The lights came on in the corridor then, yellow lighting the hole in his door, preceding any noise. Then came the key sound of the corridor door being unlocked, and locked again, and then the footsteps of Mr. Kelly. Alex looked to his door, watching the hole. Close by, next door, came, as always, the long and insistent knocking: *kunk-knuk-knuk-knuk-knuk-kunk-knuk-knuk.* Alex readied himself, waiting for his door to be rapped with the wooden paddle and unlocked, but then, a small break in routine, the knocking did not come. He heard the boy next door, a twelve-year-old Negro who called himself The King, whispering to Mr. Kelly. The King was always begging to be transferred downstairs and he was at it again, whispering fiercely, *"Please, Mista Kelly, please, I gotta move downstairs today!"*

Mister Kelly said no, not today, as he always said, but then The King, sounding like he was trying to force tears, said, *"But I got to! I got to! They gonna get me! They say they gonna whop me! They kill me!"*

Alex heard Mr. Kelly half-whisper then, "Who said that?"

"Oh, Mista Kelly," The King said. *"I cain't tell you that! You know I cain't tell—"*

"Who said what?" Mr. Kelly said.

"Oh, man—don't make me tell you that. They gonna whop me for sure! They mean, Mista Kelly. They really mean! They gonna get me!"

Alex knew what was worrying The King—a new boy who had been admitted the previous evening. Stocky, almost charcoal black, the new boy had frightened all of them. They usually played shuffleboard along the corridor with their shoes to pass the time—their individual rooms were unlocked only at night for sleeping—but with the new boy there, no one suggested the game.

The King had merely asked him who he was and what he was in for, and the new boy, as if he were insane, had snapped at him in a shrill voice, *"Don't talk to me! I don't want you talk to me! Who you, punk?"* Later, rising from the corridor floor, where they all sat most of the time, and walking along, the new boy had suddenly weaved his shoulders and shadow-boxed wildly for several steps.

Mr. Kelly came on then, knocking and unlocking the doors, shouting *Let's go!* as always. In and out of the washroom, Alex, and the others, looked at The King, silently, but The King kept his eyes elsewhere. The new boy was last in line.

Downstairs, when they filed into the dining room and over to the "Upstairs Table," Mr. Kelly kept The King back and directed him to a seat at a table of younger children. When they were settled and all was silent, Mr. Kelly called on The King to give the blessing. The King, withdrawing his legs from under the table and standing, did not look down as the others had, he looked up, almost straight up at the ceiling, and placed his hands together under his chin. He said:

> For every cup and plateful,
> God make us truly grateful.

Red Eye, across from Alex, snorted, not to laugh; Alex looked down at his bowl, bit his lip and sat shaking through most of the breakfast, and shed tears, not to laugh out loud.

After breakfast, upstairs again, they lay along the corridor. It was still no more than six or six-fifteen, and as always, the half dozen of them sat on the floor and soon began lying over on their sides to sleep. They spent most days this way. Occasionally one of them was called out by Mr. Kelly, to be interviewed by a detective or a probation officer, or visited by a parent, but most hours, most days, they either stood or sat or lay on the floor waiting. They were especially quiet this morning; no one mentioned anything of The King making it downstairs, all of them perhaps aware that the new boy was not yet aware of what had happened.

In a partial dream, lying on his side facing the wall, Alex seemed to smell the odors of a cafeteria. They were odors of meatloaf or noodles or macaroni and cheese casserole, or of the heavy steam which rose from a cafeteria. He seemed to be in junior high school where his room had been opposite the cafeteria and the odors had been there throughout every morning. Then he was moving quickly through the school corridor, and as he passed through the locker room door he was already unbuttoning his shirt, then he was unbuttoning his pants with one hand and simultaneously working his lock combination with the other, pulling off his clothes and kicking off his shoes, pulling off his socks inside out, and slipping quickly into the straps, finger-straightening them, of a manila-colored jockstrap. Reaching down, he pushed his feet into white wool socks, and his legs into satin trunks, and pulling on his white basketball shoes, tying them quickly, grabbing a green sleeveless jersey and slamming the tinny locker door, he was moving again, goose-bumped, slipping into the jersey on the way, through the cool tile tunnel entrance which opened into the expanse of cool gym, walking under the netting, the high wire-covered windows, over the glaring honey-colored floor, among the hollow *thud-thud-thud* of so many basketballs, the squeak of rubber soles— Then he was coming out of the dream, looking around, until, waking, he sat up and sat against the wall. There was the key in the door; the others were also sitting up.

Mr. Kelly pointed at him, and then at Red Eye, who was a Negro Alex's age, and then at a boy called Billy Noname, who was white, who was either afraid or unwilling to give, or did not know, his last name. "You, you, and you," Mr. Kelly said to them. "Let's go."

They rose and followed him out. It was another break in routine. Downstairs in the kitchen he put them to work washing the baseboards under the stainless steel sinks and counters. By the clock in the dining room, which they had passed through, it was still only ten minutes to seven. The steamy air of the kitchen, the people working there, the sweat and labor—these were no small change after the dirt and sloth of upstairs; the noise alone of pots and pans and faucets running was almost exciting. On their hands and knees they looked at each other. They also looked at each other and looked at a pair of raw legs coming from a beltless cotton dress, knowing they belonged to a big-boned girl of about thirteen. In a few minutes, when Mr. Kelly came back and called them from under the counters, Alex could hardly stop thinking of what was up under the sack dress, however homely the girl. He was learning something else about confinement. With the others he followed Mr. Kelly into the hall. Mr. Kelly said, "I got a nice dirty job for you boys." Glancing at each other now, they knew what had happened.

Still there was something joyous over the break in routine. Whatever it was, it was different, a small adventure. They were also spending some time with Mr. Kelly himself, like pupils with the teacher. In the locker room, Mr. Kelly rummaged through a cardboard box, coming up with three jackets, laundered but greatly wrinkled, which he gave them to put on. Alex recalled that he had changed clothes in this room when he was first admitted, but it seemed now to have happened long ago, in a past year, to another person.

Wearing the jackets they followed Mr. Kelly along a hallway in a direction they had never taken before. Red Eye, behind Mr. Kelly, gave a middle finger to the ceiling. Down a narrow flight of stairs, they passed the laundry works and entered a cool tunnel-shaped corridor, which grew darker along its length. At the other end, Mr. Kelly, in almost full darkness, unlocked a door and opened it, and there was the light, a sudden air on their faces, in their noses, the chill of outdoors. A gray spreading of chrome was over the sky, spreading into gray-blue. The breeze raised a little tuft of Mr. Kelly's hair, as he told them to come along. They followed. It was cold this morning. The air was startling and Red Eye raised no fingers.

They crossed an open space of thirty or forty feet, walking near the red brick wall of a building, and came to a smaller brick building, windowless, from whose side a red brick chimney rose narrowing far into the sky. Mr. Kelly opened a green, copper-looking door with a small wire-meshed window in its upper half, and they entered. The building was partially dark and instantly warm. They were on a metal landing, and below, hollowing down, was a space twice as deep as the above-ground part of the building. Mr. Kelly said, "Down we go," and they filed down metal stairs, turned at a landing and followed down another flight, where they saw two black furnaces which filled one side of the room, shedding orange-white light downward from their door edges.

A man in khaki pants and shirt appeared from under the stairs. Standing before him, Mr. Kelly outlined their job. They were first to clean up the coal and coal dust which lay along a coal chute, then, when the coal trucks came, they were to push the coal back into the bins—there were two bins, like large stalls—filling the space to the ceiling, then they were to sweep up whatever coal had been spilled, and then they were to help load the ashes, and finally they were to sweep and swab down the furnace room, furnaces, walls, and the steps. If they worked fast, they could finish by lunch. They were to work without talking, and they were to obey "this gentleman, Mr. Hamson."

Mr. Kelly climbed the stairs then and left. Mr. Hamson said, "Don't make no difference to me if you boys talk, just so you keep it down."

They stood waiting. Mr. Hamson, a man in his fifties, partially bald and paunchy, said, "Fact, you might as well take it easy for a while. Those boys won't be here with the coal anyway before eight or later, and it don't take but twenty-thirty minutes at the most to clear that chute there. You fellas keep a secret?"

He looked at them. "Smoke?" he said.

They all three took cigarettes, Pall Malls, like Alex's father smoked, and lit up. Mr. Hamson said, "Heck, I like to get along with the boys they send me over here to work. No reason not to, is there? That's the way I see it. What you boys in here for?"

They stood smoking, as if waiting for someone else to answer.

"Well, I guess you don't much care to talk about it. That's okay. I generally don't ask the boys anyway, ya know."

They stood smoking the long cigarettes, the smoke as strange and as strong as cigar smoke. Alex was feeling a little woozy.

Mr. Hamson said, "Well. I'm going to sit at my place over here. You fellas take it easy for a while. Unless," he whispered, "that door up there opens. You get on the brooms and get to looking busy if it does."

He returned to the space under the stairway, where there was a table and a chair, and removed a newspaper from a wastebasket. A lunch bucket was on the table, next to a Thermos bottle and cup, and a lighted light bulb hung from a heavy wire overhead. On the wall above the desk, behind a glass face and wire mask, was a large clock with a sweeping second hand.

Red Eye lowered to a seat on the floor first, then

Alex and Billy Noname followed. They had sat there only a moment when Mr. Hamson said, "Well, fellas, ya know, maybe you better not sit down. Case somebody comes in."

They stood up; he returned to his paper.

When they began to talk, speaking of The King, laughing a little loudly over really whooping his ass, Mr. Hamson said, "Ya know, fellas, I think I'd keep it down pretty much if I was you. No telling if somebody ain't listening, ya know, like the man said."

And after only a couple more minutes, when they were coming to the ends of their cigarettes, he rose and stepped over and said, "Shoot, boys. I guess you might as well get started cleaning up the coal there. No telling who ain't gonna just walk in here on us, ya know? Might as well be working anyway. That's the way I look at it. Get it done now, don't have to do it later, ya know?" He looked at them, and added, "Don't have to kill yourselves now. Just work along steady like, and you better flip your butts in that bucket there."

They did so, stepped over to a black bucket near the glowing furnace doors, dropped their cigarette butts in black water, and glanced at each other again, worried over this man who seemed afraid of everything, including them.

Pointing to Alex and Billy Noname, Mr. Hamson said, "You two work the chute here. Throw the coal back into the bins. And you," he said to Red Eye. "I guess you better get back in the bin there and when they throw the coal in, you get it and pile it as high back there as you can, cause we got a lot of coal coming and we'll need all the room we got."

Alex and Billy worked along under the chute. The job was easy. They scooped the coal into coal shovels and pitched it back into the bin, where Red Eye had to shovel it up again and carry it several steps to the rear of the bin. Mr. Hamson whispered, puckering his lips to keep a straight face, "Hope you can see that boy back there not to hit him."

Still he could not check himself and laughed as he returned to his chair and newspaper. And a moment later, when Red Eye called to them to throw it to one side where it was easier to scoop, the man said, "Keep it down now, boys. Like the man said."

Mr. Hamson seemed part of the punishment. He had spoiled whatever of the adventure remained, and now the work was becoming work. Alex felt remotely sour over the arrangement, but it was Billy Noname who moved. Saying nothing, he edged along the chute back into the bin, where two of the three should have been stationed in the first place. Alex felt left in the taint of Mr. Hamson, and disliked the man all the more. He heard Billy Noname laugh over something Red Eye had said, and wished he could join them.

It was impossible to finish in four hours. The first coal truck did not come until after eight and at ten o'clock and eleven o'clock they were still driving up, one every hour or so. Much of the coal tumbling and sliding down the chute kicked over onto the floor, and several times through each unloading the coal filled the chute and stopped sliding so Alex had to reach with his shovel to unclog it and push it down, as Red Eye worked to clean the end of the chute. Billy Noname tried to maintain room by shoveling the coal to the rear of the bin, piling it up.

The coal dust rose and fell with each release from above, three or four clankings of the truck's mechanism for each load, and they were all three soon black with coal dust, their nostrils full, squinting and turning away when the clouds rose from the tumblings down. Alex coughed often, trying to clear his throat, and spat peppered saliva into the coal itself. Simple breathing made his throat wheeze, and he tried before long to do most of his breathing through his nose, until the insides of his nose, at the roof of his nostrils, also began to feel the irritation. He could have simply quit, whatever it might cost him, as if his life were in question, as if he were going to suffocate from inhalation of coal dust. But the others kept working inside the bin, and he kept hoping this load, this tumbling of coal down the chute, this braying of the truck's motor, was the last. He was hit a good many times by flying pieces of coal—they were no larger than wood chips—but this was nothing next to the difficulty of breathing. He worked on, shoveling, walking shovelfuls over to pitch them in, clearing the chute, playing games of looking and not looking at the clock, of believing this load had to be the last load, for the time was running on, then not glancing at the clock for another twenty or thirty minutes, until the end of another load.

Close to noon, he thought they had to be near the end. Mr. Kelly could not have been that far off in the hours, and he could not really deny them their lunch. He must have known in the first place that they were innocent. Still he did not show. Alex seemed to pick up a second wind, but every time he thought they were cleaning up the last of the last load, another truck pulled up, braying again, raising its rear, and the coal came tumbling and sliding down.

They worked through the lunch hour. Alex kept looking at the clock now, thinking they would still be called to lunch before the food was put away and the kitchen closed. Then at one o'clock, Mr. Kelly appeared in the furnace room, but fifteen minutes later, after eating a lunch of remains in the cafeteria, they were back in their places, shoveling coal, several truck loads still tumbling down the long chute.

When they finished, when they had the chute completely cleared again and still no truck came, when they had swept up the spilled remains and the dust, and there was no room left to stand in either bin, and still no truck came, it was exactly, by a jump of the clock's long black hand, twenty-one minutes to three. They paused then, their chins on their broom and shovel handles.

Mr. Hamson had been in and out during the morning, had eaten his wax-papered lunch and his two apples from his lunch bucket at the table, and now, as they stood leaning, he came over, sucking a toothpick.

They did not move.

As if blind to their accomplishment, and to their finishing, and to their exhaustion, to the chute which had been swept clean enough to reveal its scratched steel surface, to the coal stacked ceiling high in the bins, he said that he'd move the chute back himself but they had better get the rest of the dust by the edge of the bins. Red Eye pivoted around on his handle away from the man, rocked his head back and forth, and did not look at him.

Then as they swept up the black dust, no more than a cup on one of the shovels, Red Eye called out, "Hey, man! Hey, you got any more cigarettes?" He seemed loose enough to use the shovel broadside on the man's head.

They met in the center of the room and the man threw up Pall Malls again from his package. He avoided looking at them. Alex felt bold himself, felt an absence of fear, a presence of humorous cruelty. He laughed for no reason as he accepted a light from Mr. Hamson's hand. Then the man retreated to his table, left them smoking, and the feeling settled.

For the ashes job, Alex worked on the truck outside, as instructed, and Red Eye and Billy Noname worked inside. Alex went up the metal stairway and outside again, carrying a shovel, and walked around the building to a lower side. He was alone for the passage of perhaps fifty feet, and coughing as an excuse to stop. Bending over to spit peppered gobs of saliva, he scrutinized the fence, some two hundred feet away, along Lincoln Road. He wondered if he was being watched. He had no real intention of trying to escape, but as if the role had been forced upon him, he acted it out in part, assumed the sense of a prisoner in a penitentiary movie, where escape was nearly always the issue. But then he caught a glimpse of himself, and where he was in fact, and that he had no idea when he was going to get out of here, and he laughed weakly at the joke of himself.

The truck stood, braked, on a steep ramp with walls close on both sides. The man behind the wheel was asleep. His head was slumped to one side, his ear on his shoulder, his mouth slightly open. Feeling high and angry and sad, Alex kicked the tire under the cab, to wake the man, but it made no noise. So he pitched his shovel up, clanging it into the bed of the truck, and climbed up as noisily as he could, kicking and stomping, then stomping the bed of the truck as if to clean his shoes. He saw Red Eye's face at a small window overhead, almost filling the window. It did not look like Red Eye could hear him through the glass, but he roared, "LET'S GO! LET'S GO! LET'S GO!" in imitation of Mr. Kelly, feeling crazy enough to run or to sit down and cry.

The door of the cab opened then and the man stood on the running board to look around at him. "Hey, what's going on?" he said.

"We're loadin' this truck, man!" Alex shouted at him, laughing, feeling mean. "We're loadin' this truck. Let's go! Let's go!"

The man stared at him for a moment, then withdrew into the cab again, closed the door.

Ashes. They came sliding down an outside chute. The coal had been coated with dust, but the ashes, with the exception of occasional clinkers, were entirely dust. The chute, apparently loaded inside, overhead, by

Red Eye and Billy Noname, directed the ashes into the rear of the truck bed, and it was Alex's job to spread them around so they would continue to flow. He pushed the ashes forward at first, but the wind was wrong and a cloud of gray rose immediately and he stepped to the front himself where the air was more clear. But then the hill of ashes around the chute became so high it covered the end, spilling over the sides, and blocked the flow. He closed his mouth, squinted his eyes nearly closed, and stepped back into the side of the loose hill to push the ashes around. Now, perhaps from the break and from the change to cold air, his muscles seemed wound tight, and he shoveled more slowly, with less strength.

Before long the powder cloud had puffed up overall, and there was no way to escape but to try for footing on the ashes at the side of the truck, to stick his head out of the cloud. When he had gotten some air into his lungs, and blinked his eyes a few times, he tightened his face again and waded back in.

The ashes kept flowing in. He worked with his mouth and eyes completely shut now, as a blind man, and finally, when all at once it seemed he was losing his breath, in anger and in something of a panic, he quit. He dropped his shovel over the side, climbed blindly over the side himself, feeling his way, and dropped to the ground. He moved up the ramp past the front of the truck, into the clear air, bending his head and neck as low as his waist, trying to contain the gritting irritation in his eyes. His eyes watered and as he forced them open, he saw only a blur of liquid. Stopping, he blew his nose, coughed the powder from his throat. He was before the truck in the clear air this way for some time, a full four or five minutes, getting his eyes to where he could see shapes and colors through the blur, when the truck driver called out, "Hey—you! Where you going? You better get back here."

Alex gave him a wild finger, coming up from the waist, although he barely saw him. He looked down again, fingering the water and grit from the corners of his eyes. The man said no more and Alex did not look to see if he had moved or not. He was sure he had had it, and did not care.

He stood there. After a couple minutes, in less of a blur, he saw Mr. Kelly, without his coat, half-running towards him from the main building. He looked down, continued working on his eyes.

"What are you doing?" Mr. Kelly said. "Why aren't you working?"

"I couldn't see," Alex said. "I was blinded. I couldn't see."

Mr. Kelly said nothing for a moment.

Then, edging toward concern, he said, "Are you all right?"

"Yeah, I'll be all right," Alex said.

"What happened to you?"

"Nothing. I was just pushing the ashes around and the stuff got in my eyes. I couldn't breathe."

Mr. Kelly stood by him for a moment without speaking. Then he left, walking quickly over to the truck, and Alex heard him call up to the driver, "Didn't you know you're supposed to hose these ashes?"

Alex did not hear the man's answer. Mr. Kelly was mad, and that was a surprise. Squinting in that direction, he saw Mr. Kelly walking around the truck to the ramp, pointing, still talking to the man.

Then Mr. Kelly came back to him. "You sure you're all right?" he said.

"Yeah, I'll be okay," Alex said.

"Well, brush yourself off," Mr. Kelly said.

Alex slapped himself, turning away from the puffing dust.

"You better come with me," Mr. Kelly said, starting away.

Alex followed, pleased. He walked behind Mr. Kelly back across the open space, into the building and through the tunnel and upstairs to the first floor again. Mr. Kelly spoke once, when they were upstairs. "I wanted to punish you," he said. "But I didn't intend to torture you."

Alex followed him through a pair of swinging doors, into rooms he had never seen before. There, suddenly, on the right, in the rest of a large warm room they were passing through, two or three dozen children, the younger ones, up to seven or eight, were playing as children play in a kindergarten room, with blocks and games and torn books, a couple scratching on a black chalk slate which covered four or five feet of wall space. The scene, the children, passed like a horrible and wonderful moment in a dream. He wanted to stop and look, and watch, for it seemed he was about to see something—but he walked on, drawn by Mr. Kelly through another set of double swinging doors and turning left, into a bathroom.

There was not a single sink here, but a line of seven or eight. And these were shining clean, the chrome polished, and there was a mirror on the wall. Mr. Kelly was telling him to rinse his eyes out with water, and he was bending over, cupping water in his hand from the running faucet, splashing it into one eye at a time, but the room he had just seen remained with him, moved through him, so he did not want to open his eyes.

"Is that better?" Mr. Kelly said.

Alex nodded that it was, although his eyes felt cold but not much better.

"Here, let's have a look," Mr. Kelly said.

Alex held his head up and Mr. Kelly used his hands and fingers to spread open his eyes to look in. "You still got some specks in there," he said. "Does it hurt?"

"Not too much," Alex said.

"You can see all right?"

"Yes."

"I think you'll be all right. You go back now and finish up. I don't have to take you back, do I?"

"No," Alex said.

He walked back through the room of children, still behind Mr. Kelly, and he glanced again as he had before, and again it was as if he had come close to seeing something. But he was no longer sure if he wanted to see it. In the corridor, Mr. Kelly went on, and he turned down the stairs, and walked back across the open space alone. For the first time since coming here, he felt partially at home.

The driver was on the bank opposite the truck, spraying water from a hose over the ashes in the truck. There was little dust now, only that which escaped when the coating of wet muck was peeled off in shoveling. Alex felt no fear of the man, and did not look at him as he worked. Nor did he feel much strength. He shoveled, one shovel after another, slipping them to the front. Another truck had pulled up to wait its turn.

They worked on through the afternoon and then through the dinner hour. In the afternoon, while Alex worked outside on the trucks, Mr. Hamson was replaced by a man coming on another shift, a man whose name he did not learn and who said little to them. They slacked off when they saw they had missed supper. Then, inside again, under the dim hanging lights, when they had finished sweeping and washing down the walls and the furnaces and it was dark outside, they hosed the floor and swept the water into a drain in the center, and hosed it again, and then again, until the water began to wash partially clean. The floor dried quickly in spots from the heat of the furnace. Then, once again, they stood waiting on their broom handles while the new man telephoned Mr. Kelly. They were too tired to talk very much. By the wall clock, it was past their bedtime; it was five minutes past eight.

Mr. Kelly wore a navy pea jacket. Going back, they crossed ahead of him through the darkness, through the chilling air, and back into the warm building. Mr. Kelly seemed sleepy, and said nothing. But then, in the quiet and nearly dark first floor hallway, he said to them, "Tired?"

They were, but no one spoke.

"Want something to eat? You hungry?"

They nodded, surprised, and he told them to go wash up and he'd see if he could find something. Alex led them through the swinging doors to the shining bathroom he had used earlier, which was lighted, as if for night use, with a single light. They used the urinals, commodes, sinks. In the mirror they looked like coal miners. Red Eye said to the mirror, softly, "Who is that? I don't know him." Strangely happy, they combed their hair with their hands, and whispered when they talked as if close to someone sleeping. Alex said, "I think that's where they sleep," pointing toward the unknown end of the building.

One door to the dining room stood opened. Inside, a couple of overhead globes were lighted. They walked in cautiously. A half-gallon tin tub without a label was on the table nearest the kitchen opening, under one of the lights. Mr. Kelly was in the kitchen, standing, slicing bread with a knife. They stood waiting until he came in, carrying a tray with the sliced bread in one hand and one of the metal pitchers in the other, and told them to sit down. They reached their legs in under the table and sat down, and as always in the dining room, they did not speak.

In a moment Mr. Kelly returned with a table knife and four of the clear plastic glasses which always looked dirty. "Okay, dig in," he said, slipping into a seat on the bench himself.

He poured himself a glass of milk and passed the pitcher on. The tin tub, whose top he unscrewed, was half-filled with peanut butter, with oil puddles in its knifed terrain. They followed Mr. Kelly, taking up two slices of bread, spreading on a thickness of oily peanut butter, biting through their sandwiches, swallowing milk, reaching for the pitcher again.

Mr. Kelly said, "Go ahead, drink all you want. There's plenty of milk, plenty of bread."

Alex was surprised that Mr. Kelly was eating with them. Then it occurred to him, with a small shock, that Mr. Kelly lived here, that this was his home, that he seemed never to leave.

They sat together as a momentary family, although little was said. Almost nothing was said. Mr. Kelly, as always, was distant. But he sat there; he was present. At one point he said, "You eat like you've been working," and they laughed loudly, and with pride, and the man could not help smiling himself. Alex saw his reflection in the tin tub. But he felt completely safe for the moment, safe from something not quite known, something outside the lighted table itself, something as large and as complicated as the city, which lay as if in waiting, beyond the cold fields.

SOL YURICK

Sol Yurick is a New Yorker who has written three novels, including *The Warriors, Fertig* and *The Bag*. Harper & Row will publish *Sound Money Kill*. Mr. Yurick says of his new novel, "It began when I reviewed *In Cold Blood* for *The Nation*. Something about the way Capote handled the book irritated me. A certain haunting ambiguity . . . an evasion . . . an inability to get to the facts . . . traditional, surreal. It ended when Capote threw his great party. What are they celebrating, I asked, and from that point I conceived the idea of *Sound Money Kill*, the Marxist detective novel, in which the real killers will be exposed once and for all. Add this: Legal insanity is when you kill for any motive other than money; and, there is no legal category for political crime as such. Maybe, after all, the execution of the Clutters was a sentence, legally executed and the killing of Perry Smith and Dick Hickock the crime . . . and maybe, after all, the killer was . . . well, that's what will emerge, won't it?"

SOUND MONEY KILL

Did Justice Triumph?

Sometimes a corpse comes into the detective agency crying for justice.

Jorge Ubico said: first the execution, then the trial. This, it seems to us, is the first principle of bourgeois justice.

Certain kinds of cases interest me, cases in the

American grain: Lizzie Borden, Albert Fish, Charley
Starkweather, Carryl Chessman, Charles Manson, The
Bender Family of Kansas, who *really* kidnapped the
Lindbergh baby . . . cases that linger in the popular
imagination, cases which will not be expunged from
consciousness, cases of which we keep asking . . . why?
Cases like these, it seems to me, provide true grist for
a Marxist detective's mill. . . . But it's more of a
hobby: the agency doesn't take on this kind of case.
The Party admits that *every* case is political, certainly
economic, but. . . .

For instance: I have never been satisfied with the
resolution of the Clutter case. On the surface it was all
so simple: A (bleeding) Kansas family of four (who
owned a house with canvas walls out on the plains)
named Clutter (Bender), simple farming folks (the
kind who settled the West, who) are kill(murder)ed
one night by those who come to steal (yield up) money
by the hammer(of shotguns)ing through tent walls
(smashing in the heads) of the unwary.

No money taken: none in the house. Therefore no
motive. Crazy. Nasty crime. Husband, wife, daughter,
and son (named Bender) all in one night. . . . Insanity. Jobian motif, of course. Test of faith. Clutter,
one of those old-fashioned and virtuous, stern, sons-of-
the-pioneer types who settled the West, locked in his
strategic *agroville*, protected by hymns, diligence, and
goodness-on-the-plains; religious, perfect, upright,
feared God, wagons, combines, reapers, self-denial,
prayer and revival and mortification of the flesh (qual-
ities called up by dry farming on the Great American
Desert), eschewed evil and walked in the ways of God
all of his days (which is what got him where he was in
the last place), the kind who fought drought, dust,
wind, plagues of grasshoppers, and had it made, when,
then, one night, because History always progresses by
its bad side. . . .

Now God collars Satan in the form of Perry Smith and Dick Hickcock, and says, "Sees't thou my favorite servant, Herb Clutter there?" And so it begins. A kind of one-night compression of the plagues, the illnesses, the boils, the destruct, the doubts and testings, all those seeds in one night. . . . Now nothing was stolen . . . nothing to steal. Yet, of Job, we see that everything was stolen. . . . So then the *real* dialogue of Why? The motivation is carried out in Truman Capote's book, *In Cold Blood* . . . continues there and in the popular press, on television, on the radio . . . always with the whining lament, Why Did They Kill? It was a very popular case: why should it bother me? Not our kind of case at all. Yet, to a Marxist detective there are no "accidents of fate." Admitted. And what have we said, saying this? Cases like these hint at the contradictions in society. And we *do* solve crimes by the scientific use of dialectical materialism. But is it the sign of a major contradiction? No: no political significance.

The book. *In Cold Blood.* It's typical of its kind. Capote. Class thinking. I remember that face: blond hair over the young, sensitive brow, the limp body lounging on the couch, wearing a checkered vest. . . . Now he's grown older, grosser, this epicene-masked blackglassed face, this "I know a secret" smirk. The whole production irritated me. No, not so much the book, not so much the simple-minded analysis, the childish bragging about the almost perfect memory, the talk about the "criminal mind," not even the publicity and the money that came out of it, and the pseudo-expertise, and those liberal fools, those *intellectuals* vaporing about the shocking rise of violence, the climate of violence which is conducive to. . . . Not so much any of those things . . . but then what? *The public's response* to it. Why respond? Who was Clutter to them? Why did they *feel* the terror personally?

The Party ought to identify with the public's need

for mystery-solution. The criminology of everyday life. We have paid too little attention to that vital chapter in the *Manual of Marxist Detection*. Stories in the papers; *The New Yorker* writes . . . *Time* explores, *The New York Times* dwells on, endlessly, *Esquire* reinvestigates . . . and so on. . . . The product, the fear, swallowed, and the speculation market stimulated. . . .

Why go on about it at such length, why the empathetic terror-response if it was, after all, a *marginal* killing by a pair of psychopaths? They cannot bear the area of the unresolved Why, the unassimilated mystery, just cannot bear it . . . and yet need it. They will pick over this case for a hundred years as they have over the other persistent cases. . . . How many times have we solved and resolved the mystery of Lizzie Borden? Marginal? Irrational? Marxists, after all, have a different theory of psychology and motivation. *We* don't have to give the Perry Smiths unconscious dreams cribbed from a Flaubert . . . *we* know the true content of dreams.

And isn't it the master criminologist of all time, Marx himself, who says, *"The criminal breaks the monotony and everyday security of bourgeois life. In this way he keeps it from stagnation and gives rise to that uneasy tension and agility without which even the spur of competition would get blunted. Thus he gives a stimulus to the productive forces."* The public, roaring out its fear and feeding off its surplus anxiety and trembling. . . .

And the anger sets me to trembling too, sets the detective to feeling, wanting to rush out and tell the fools, no, no, you're not paying attention to the right crimes . . . if they're even crimes.

I send the Party Detective Bureau no memos . . . they would reject one anyhow. Better to be alone, untroubled in my small office on Union Square. Live in it. Live in the building. No rent. The Party pays that. Anyway, we own it. A couch. I sleep on it. A desk.

Coffee and pastry in the morning. Not very healthy. Role calls for me to be a drinking man, so there is always a drawer with a half-empty bottle in it. A filing cabinet full of small and unimportant case dossiers. A ham sandwich at lunch. Sometimes, early, just before and during lunch, I go to the movies. Loew's Union Square. Ornate Depression movie palazzo . . . which is in the building. Take the whole afternoon off. No, that was a long time ago. The theater-space's been converted into offices. . . . All except for about six feet of it on the upper part of where the movie used to be. Or: a walk in the Square park below in Union Square. Walk up and down the walks and stop, sometimes, to listen to the disputatious clumps stationed at the strategic crosspaths of the Square, stirring up and renegotiating the problems of the world. Practicing Free Speech and Democracy. Still, I'm always shocked at how much the seedy contenders (and they are not always seedy . . . why there's even a Wall Street broker who comes up some evenings) know. What streams of information and invective, statistics and hatred come out of those mouths. Passersby bent on shopping, or with their minds work-drained, think them mad, stupid, idle, parasites, irrelevant. If they were *really* smart, what are they doing here? How come they're not great legislators, statesmen, lawyers, even doctors? Join in it myself sometimes . . . it's been so long . . . I shouldn't argue business, but . . . there hasn't been a conference since, I think, 1953. . . . And then, back to the office, to . . . unfaithful husbands, wives, that kind of thing, collect unpaid bills: appear seedy, menacing, big, squat, with ham hands, and do the system's dirty work to keep it running and to keep myself alive. . . . Sometimes screw some woman who comes in not wanting anything real done, but who has read too many detective novels.

It blunts your deductive tools to solve little crimes

the bourgeois way. Console myself by solving cases in the head, like chess problems, to keep alert, solve them the Marxist way. Console myself by thinking that this is a cover for the real work of detection . . . which no longer goes on, for the Party's really dead and therefore, I am dead. . . . Well, they used to say that a Communist was a dead man on leave. No. No. Sometimes one eats shit for us and tastes death for the Party, death and loneliness extended for many years. . . . No. For the office is an isolated outpost for the farflung and wideworld Marxist Detective Bureau upon whose manifest windows the world over (high over Union Square one can see) in gold letters, the sign (appearing in many languages), "Strictly Confidential, tracing, shadowing, locating, low rates—quick results, lie detection specialists—electronic equipment (which was untrue because we have no budget for it and anyway, better methods), when the first man reaches the moon, we could be the first to *follow* him, marital problems"; and the picture of a badge, and an eye in a clock, and a Sherlock Holmes decal, standard figure bent over a footprint with a magnifying glass (which was real). But the *real* sign that identifies us is: in one corner a little scrawl saying The Private Eye with the Public Vision, and in the other corner, Founded, 1917. But matrimonials was what it was all about; surprise the husband (wife) *in flagrante delicto* as defined by the law, not necessarily the act.

Our real function is to solve political cases, cases the ruling classes have an interest in distorting: frameups, miscarriages of justice, executions in the guise of trials; we cry justice for the oppressed, expose corruption, expose the hollow lie that is American Justice, *etc. etc. etc. etc. etc.* Oh yes, we've solved and exposed a lot of cases; old victories: Sacco and Vanzetti, the Scottsboro boys, Tom Mooney and Warren Billings, the Joe Hill frameup, the Haymarket affair, the Rosenberg case.

. . . But nothing big for a long long time. Isolation and emptiness can burn you out just as much as too much work. You can feel the juices evaporating into space, sparkling there, shining in the darkness, going black slowly with the blackness as it all finally overwhelms you. . . .

Still, maybe those were the wrong kinds of cases to work on. A waste of energy. No one's mind is changed. Without a real police force, without a real court, without some place of redress . . . other than the future which vindicates our history . . . those sessions going on in the sweet by and by at this very moment, in *our* future time to come. . . . Think of the greatest detective of all time, Karl Marx (with his trusty assistant, Fred Engels) staked out in the British Museum Library, cut off from his base of operations which does not in fact yet exist (but *will*, rest assured, *will*), still tracking down . . . surrounded everywhere by the enemy. . . . In the popular imagination Sherlock Holmes was the greatest detective of all time, but the popular mind imagines what the ruling class wants it to imagine. . . . Marx found the crime; discovered the crime was, in fact, still going on, *found the victim*, enlisted his aid in fighting the crime. . . . The first principle of Marxist detection is . . . find the crime.

Still; would it do to initiate a new tendency? Write a report to the central committee of the detective bureau on this Clutter/4-Hickock & Smith case? Not at all. Still, it kept bothering me. Something was wrong about the whole thing. All this energy and space in print, all this attention paid to this petit-bourgeois dilettante's analysis of . . . what? Coming to what? Two sets of feet dangling, hanging (I knew how that sort of thing felt) in Kansas, Bleeding Kansas. . . . More was involved than that. I felt it. Instinct for these things. A Marxist instinct. Everyone asks why? Why do they ask why? Sense stirs to grow alive again after such

305

a long while . . . a tingling in the head and in the body.
Restlessness and a feeling out towards . . . what? Sleep
and save it. The best I will sense is *their* binoculars
perpetually trained on me. And *hear* them listening in
on me perpetually. And find clumsy hand-signs that
they have been here again and again. The grand hum
of endless Union Square traffic and the perpetual blink
of lights. . . . Two sets of feet dangling . . . shot-in
heads, hammered-in heads, cut throats and bodies fry-
jerking in the electric chair, and a bullet in the back of
the head in some nameless cellar. . . . Think it out:
we don't have their apparatus. The Party doesn't perpetually film me sitting here and working out sterile
and intellectual and formalistic crime problems from
across the Square and the Party doesn't need to bug the
office so that every belch and fart is recorded for our
file. . . . Anyway, as I said, we just don't have the
funding. We use our heads . . . we deduce and we
have a dream of perfect deduction that from just a
few clues. . . .

Since we had no time or money to solve this case,
I did the next best thing: I wrote a review of Capote's
book for one of the Left publications. Purpose? To sort
of solve the case in print, to expose some of the contradictions and peculiarities in the book, to raise the
consciousness of the reader to an awareness that there
is another world he doesn't see yet. . . . As I wrote
the review, I got angrier and angrier. I denounced the
book's sentimentality, its intent to obscure the reality
of crime in America. Maybe it tended to run away with
me. But it's also part of our traditional style; we
heighten what *seems* the unimportant by underlining
with invective. Call it a report to the general public.
No, more than that. To take what was for America a
rare crime, but which was in reality a popular and sta-
tistically frequent crime, and to make it suffer the Job-
fate vicariously, gladly. . . .

Writing the review set my mind to rest. Everything subsided and I went back to solving those little cases, sordid, secret, popular kinds of cases, everyday cases, cases talked about in "The Criminology of Everyday Life."

Wake, dawn early in the morning, tingling and alive, listening, expecting. . . . Godstand at the window and watch the being-killed viscousing out of the subways and down from all the busses in Union Square, marching along the flanking streets, through the Union Square crosswalks, among the slices of crumblittered scurf, flowing as to war, into the office buildings to man their stations; see the aimless old, the crippled, the pensioned, the shocked, perch along the benches; and observe the winos flow out of their dollar-a-day caves. . . . And later the shoppers will come. And infer the slaughter going on in small acts, the constant robbery, and see the proofs code-locked in stones and brick and cement itself, and the disappeared binding-acts left only on the top-secret celluloid surfaces of time and motion studies locked away in high-security vaults. . . . War goes on all the time and strange treasures pile up in strange ways and the dead finally fall elsewhere in another space and in another time. . . . Each surface a vast layered record of crime, an Encyclopedia of American Suffering and each bloody moment fixed, locked into the rigid unmoving surfaces, a data-bank perpetual till the trump-all moment looses the bondage of adhesives, de-cements the disciplines, discoalesces, disaccumulates, *detentes* its incremented crime, shattering treasures into the street, an unlocking of plunder-bunds that only revolution can accomplish. . . . And try to remember, however vaguely (for the tired and burned-out mind will not work) those little days of glory, those days of protest when we took Union Square for our own; when we thought . . . no, *knew* that we were close to bringing the whole thing down around their heads. . . .

An amusement, really: that was what it was. We are all broken men now. Alone, when not on a case, I appear to be a medium-sized man, slim, but fudged around the edges with puffy fat. . . . I have grey hair and varicose veins, a chubby lumpface and I smoke too much. You get beaten down and beaten up being an organizer, a worker, a teacher, a detective, oh, many things . . . dead eyes, dead and burned out from having seen too much . . . with a little cunning left in them. Only discipline to sustain me, Party discipline. Waiting. Waiting. For what? The Party's dead. Its only feeble life is the rent for the bureau which they don't collect. Admit it; there's no one left but me at a post from which there is no communicating and even the eyes and ears which watch us perpetually are tired and record only onto some enormous tape which no one bothers to scan anymore. We have a joke: the FBI *is* the Party, or at least sixty percent of it; and when they want to know the secret and sinister world dominating plans of the Party, *they* initiate it. What can my face, in the face of such circumstances, look like, other than dead? Nothing at all like the passionate and alive face in the photograph of myself (in a gilded and overflowered frame bought from Woolworth's) I keep in one of my drawers. From time to time (then I was almost twenty, going to City College, passionate and burning with the sense of the world's injustice that had to be set right; what we were going to do in those days; I used to wear glasses in those days . . . and a small mustache to make me look older) I come across it in the course of business, when opening drawers, looking for something, a note-pad, a pencil sharpener, an eraser, seeming myself like a flash of sudden face on some unexpected curve-flawed surface, an image I have not had the time to prepare for . . . like a face like one's self shining in the plate glass of doors leading into ornate movie theaters (Loew's Union Square was always our favorite), or the lip and mustache segment bowed out, rounded, and the rest of the head, top and chin ovalled, distorted in the brasswork of guideposts that line up maroon plush ropes corralling customers waiting to escape The Depression into the movies, and we stop and look at one another and give one another one of those where-have-I-seen-you-before smiles . . . for in the unity of our looks, the similarity, there is a terrifying disparity, a vast contradiction, a terrible and irreconcilable revisionism that age has brought about . . . but nodding sets it right, a remembrance of the historical situation reunites . . . or seeing one's face hovering in darkness, a dim image in the great glass plate which separates the customers-waiting-for-the-newsreel-to-end-and-the-show-to-change from the great audience pit, seeing my face-image somewhere in the midst of a crowd watching Great Stalin, watching the paraders march by on May Day in time to the Fox Movietone March . . . floating even next to him on the reviewing stand (when was it? '24, '34, '36, '50, '53, '56, '6? . . .) among the heroic presidial images . . . those sweet days in Loew's Union Square. They don't build movie houses like that anymore. Used to be in this very building but they tore it down and turned the space into office space. . . .

There was no reply to my article for months: a ravening critique tossed into righthanded deaf space.

Spring became summer and summer autumn and dry leaves skittered up and down the walks of Union Square. The nights came on earlier and the red of the great sign, Klein's On The Square (a gnomen in the shape of a carpenter's right angle, neon-calibrated) shone redly on wet streets partitioned with fan-bars of headlight. In winter the great Greco-Roman cap of the Con Edison building was lit up and its insolent

circle of lights arranged into a clock shone and domi-
nated not only the whole Square, but the whole Lower
East Side, as it used to when I was young. . . . And
on the southeast corner of the Square, the little old
lady who sold peanuts seemed to accrete substance
into a monstrous bundle of woolcovered winterflesh out
of which peered an old and wrinkle-lipped face. She
was there when I first came to the Square many years
ago, looking exactly as she does now, and was there in
a green sweater-coat and knit cap in the hard blind-
ing May sunlight when I got out of Loew's Union
Square, and I wonder now if perhaps it was her mother,
or even grandmother; possibly it was a hereditary position.

Of course there's to be no answer to the article.
Who cared about it? Even the Party, if such there
was, didn't care. The case was dead now; the furor died
down, Clutter and company buried, the killed/ers forgotten, the world satisfied that they were mad, or
evil. . . . And I understood then that it wasn't so much
a message to the world at large as a message to detective headquarters . . . maybe even the Politbureau
itself.

These things come when you least expect it. Or
when your attention is turned elsewhere. And when
you look back in the right direction, you see what you
finally saw. . . . A tendency as subtle as the first cell
defecting into cancer itself, turning to its neighbor, in-
doctrinating with its Revisionist Negativistic Attitudes
into a Defecting Narodniki Annunciation. . . . I had
indeed fallen into petit-bourgeois ways and smug com-
placency and accepting of under-capitalism, my Marxist instinct leached out by all the years of routine work
. . . the loneliness. . . .

One day an envelope came with the new replacement sheets for *The Manual of Marxist Detection*
which is kept in a huge, thick looseleaf book. The re-

placement sheets indicate that there have been changes in operational policy . . . what kinds of cases we're going to concentrate on. One of the directives which came along with the replacement sheets informed me that the chapter, "The Criminology of Everyday Life," was obsolete: it's the chapter most heavily annotated in my manual and, along with the notes, I have been sticking in sheets—a sort of personal supplement—on which are pasted clippings from the newspapers, especially about those crimes which interest me the most, which are indicative of the system as a whole. Procedure is to burn the replaced sheets, burn and crumple the ashes into dust. I couldn't bring myself to do that. I put the sheets into an envelope and put it into one of the drawers in the filing cabinet. A deviation, to be sure . . . but who cared?

A letter of praise came from a reporter assigned to follow in Capote's footsteps for *Esquire:* expose Capote's lies, distortions, and revisions of truth. These things spring out of the publicity and are, indeed, as Marx pointed out, occasioned by the ". . . stimulus to the *productive forces* . . ." So the revisionist analyses of the case have already begun: there would be a large canon of criticism in time. . . . The ultimate purpose of the followup was not to disprove (and how do you disprove, for the issue was never in doubt: the Clutters *were* killed), but to carp in some way, to denigrate the motives of the little author-detective, to imply that in some ways he distorted, to hint that his very self-interest was involved with the execution of the killers. One point fascinates me: It wasn't one man, Perry Smith, who killed all four in the family, as Capote asserts . . . they *both* killed two apiece. And calmly at that. *What was there to hide?*

Any detective, literary or otherwise, working within *their* canon, accepting *their* ideology, can only operate in a distorted manner: of course Capote lies . . . !

How can a man who uses such metaphysical and idealist and bourgeois, such obscurantist humanist twaddle as "ninety-five percent perfect memory" or "criminal mind" begin to understand what he's doing, and more, does he want to, does he dare? But I detected a sense of pleasure at receiving the letter: I was not unread, I was not unappreciated in the world. I read the letter two or three times: I forbore from scorn at the shallow analysis. The Marxist detective had methods that outdid all other methods: we were a match, after all, for all their technology . . . indeed, in their technology is their defeat. Still, he hadn't seen it: he was defeated by it: there was no questioning the fact that the two had committed the murder. Their time sequence defeats us. What was he objecting to, after all? A few distortions for the sake of bourgeois dramatic arrangement? A few lies for the sake of suspense? Yet, something was there. I didn't know what yet. Something was there. A contradiction in the book which expresses itself in tone, in nuance; Capote's muted hatred for Herbert Clutter and his family . . . a timid flirtation with the outrageous . . . a contradiction hiding greater contradictions . . . an inversion . . . a sense of . . . what? Glee? Glee about the killings . . . lipsmacking enjoyment, a stirring of the organs. . . .

There was an announcement in *The Times:* Capote was to throw a big party at the Plaza in celebration of his book's success. There was a partial guest list . . . rumors of an obscene scrambling to be invited . . . a masked ball: black or white masks . . . What were they celebrating?

A second letter came. The Party, after all, did not sleep.

"Hillrose. . . ." No comrade? "The Bureau doesn't expect its members to appropriate Party time and invest it for themselves. . . ."

Yes. Even the tone, that cold old tone, the very anger, the scorn, brought, with the sense of dread, joy. The Party . . . we were not dead. I was not alone. Even after all these years I could feel a sense of aliveness now. . . .

"Don't enough political prisoners rot in the jails of the world?

"Aren't the frameups and railroadings enough for you, the obvious lies . . .

"Or has Hillrose suddenly become the champion of perverts and psychotics? Has Hillrose fallen into Left-Wing Communism and joined the infantile New Left with its celebration of Mansonism and Bonnie and Clydism? Does Hillrose fight for the petit-bourgeois's heroes because they and they alone permit the full exhibition of Hillrose's considerable talents? Talents, we might add, raised to an art in the Party Detection Schools . . . talents belonging to the Party without whom there would be no Hillrose, the Marxist Detective, but rather . . . Who? What dregs of the capitalist world? I needn't remind you that your very name is a Party name. Without us you are nothing but a shabby snoop.

"No, Hillrose has forgotten old comrades rotting in their capitalist prisons.

"Hillrose has forgotten his world historical mission.

"And how do they go about buying Hillrose off? A piece of flattery about exposing Party talents perverted into mere cleverness. . . . Praise at which he feels himself swoon with pleasure—revealing deep rooted bourgeois feelings—instead of asking, objectively, what does that letter mean? No. *I* did it, Hillrose thinks; *I*, not the Party.

"Consider how the tone implicit in your critical article—which, incidentally, you air in public before discussion has ensued in a democratic fashion with a collective of detectives, certainly an elitist form of expression reeking of opportunism. And then, then the individualistic joy with which you receive the letter from what is, after all, a bourgeois reporter with a bourgeois outlook, who is unable, after all, to begin to understand the political economy of crimes—and how you revel and grovel among the bones thrown to you by the hirelings of the capitalist press, who, by their very worryings over such miniscule crimes, obscure, as the Party well knows, the nature of the great crimes of capitalism itself. Consider, Hillrose, how you add to the bourgeois mystification of that crime by joining the orgy of speculation, implying, as it were, approval and alliance with irresponsible narodnik terrorists who have mounted an attack on potential allies, those also oppressed victims of American capitalism, the midwestern populists. More, giving the impression that the Party itself approves terrorism, adventurism, sectarianism, anarchism, random purposeless killing, or the random purposeless killer. WE ARE RESPONSIBLE REVOLUTIONARIES!

"This is an old story with you, Hillrose. Haven't we seen this personalistic and professionalistic tendency in you before? Haven't you tried to direct Party priorities into Hillrose's personal area, an area in which he can shine? Persisting in arguing when you've been outvoted?

"That you decide to go off on an adventure and indulge yourself in *this* case at a time when there is a profound economic crisis, when capitalism itself is in crisis, when capitalism can only preserve itself by becoming fascism, when capitalism has embarked on a wide offensive—to whose nature *you*, Hillrose, who should know it best, choose to deaden yourself—indicates that Hillrose is on the verge of a sellout, if this hasn't in fact already taken place. How are we to view this letter from this lackey of the press other than as a kind of compact? How is the Party to understand your joy other than as a confirmation of that devil's bargain?

"Firstly, it is a truism that every case has political and economic implications. This is elementary. The burning question is, do all cases have implications for the Party significant enough that we should step in to solve them? In short, do such cases reveal major contradictions in that system called capitalism?

"Secondly, granted the small increment of political residue in this case, what are these killers other than, *at best* (and this is to stretch a point) social bandits, Robin Hoodists: probably mere psychotics involved in primitive capital accumulation without social content.

"Thirdly, it smacks of dangers, political irresponsibility, to work so hard to offend a potential populist constituent-ally in a time when fascism is rising, to denigrate and doubt the nature and stature of the Farmer, Clutter, and his family. As you should remember, some of the most radical grass-roots, typically American, anti-monopolistic, anti-Wall Street, anti-imperialist actions and analyses came from the naturally downtrodden exploited farmers of the Midwest fighting the railroad and grain trusts. By your very attitude, by your very critique of Capote's book, you imply your support for this pair of psychopathic killers and work to alienate a potential ally in the broad-front struggle against the rising tide of fascism. Can one forget the Populist-Republican war of 1893 for the control of the Kansas House of Representatives, the heroic struggle and the armed repression of the Populists on the legislative stairs? Can we forget that 1893, a year of depression, was a year when the National Guard was called out to suppress laboring and farming masses, Americans?"

How did they know about the letter I had gotten?

"Certainly a letter of self-criticism is the order of the day. . . ."

That the Party knew about the letter was understandable. How did the Party know about my *feelings?* A good guess or . . . was I being watched by them too? And if so, why wasn't the *feeling different* than being watched by the FBI? I had become detached from we and my senses were dulling.

"Still, all is not yet lost. There are ways in which Hillrose can still redeem himself. The burning question is how can we find great tasks for Hillrose's great and special talents, tasks that will test those talents to the utmost?"

Send sense out to feel. Arouse, arouse. Eternal vigilance. The enemy is everywhere. *Feel* watched. The sense detectors lock into your energy output. But the senses are tired, lulled. Is it age? The useful paranoia . . . it will not work. Worn down. I cannot tell now if I live in benign space, hostile space, or neutral space. Wait. What's the line? Coexistence or conflict? Is there neutral space? What does the tone mean? I'd stick a pin in me to find out if I have feeling, but they'd see me doing it and know what it means . . . register the pain-energy-output. Have we then descended to buying *technology* . . . or. . . . I *know* that there are no taps, bug, or eyes except for the FBI vigil from across the Square.

"Has Hillrose considered applying that massive deductive talent to one of the great unsolved, *politically* important crimes of the day? For instance the killing of John F. Kennedy, Robert Kennedy, and Martin Luther King? Or is such a case perhaps not important enough for Hillrose? What's the meaning of this crime? What political tendency does it annunciate?

"The Control Commission thinks that it is the order of the day that you mount a massive reexamination of your attitudes, tendencies, accompanied by a reevaluation of the Clutter case, for our eyes, of course, which will accompany the analysis of the Kennedy Kennedy King liquidations. . . ." It was signed, however, Comrade Lovestone.

Comrade! So there was room for forgiveness.

Lovestone was alive after all these years . . . alive
and now working for the Detective Bureau. Alive and
back! Lovestone, who had brought me into the Party
in the first place, Lovestone who was a sponsor, father,
older brother. Lovestone with his intense and lean face
and his fine polemical tongue which could cut you to
ribbons, reveal the bourgeois rottenness at the basis of
your logic and destroy a fine piece of detective work
in an hour's working out of the contradictions raised by
your painstaking efforts. . . . Lovestone on a soapbox
in the local neighborhoods, daring tomatoes, hooligans,
rotten eggs, stones, even knives. Lovestone, whose eyes
detected Hillrose that May 1st so long ago, sneaking
out of the movie and knew, *knew* what Hillrose had
been doing; sneaking in, that moment of sin and weakness, spending Party money (but I was only seventeen
then! What difference? Lovestone was nineteen then),
when he should have been doing Party tasks, to come
out into that brightblinding thousandsun Mayday . . .
running out, in fact, running to his assignment, away
from that ball-feeling pervert's hand and that stench-
dropping behind as he moved to block the newsreel
shot of Moscow Mayday when Aura-ed Stalin looked
down, bathed in light, seeming to look into Hillrose's
eyes alone out of all those thousands massed in Red
Square, blocked by the tough silhouette with the broken
nose and the bullneck. . . . And Hillrose standing in
Mayday; seeing Lovestone on the reviewing stand in
Union Square, his voice assaulting the capitalist façades
all around, Browder beside him (he was a Kansas boy
too: Browder and Herbert Clutter), beaming on his
protégé; Lovestone setting the masses to moving and
elevating masses of sundrenched pigeons looking black
in the golden light; Lovestone bathed in light, bathed
in the *"Sun of the workers, Sun of the peasants, Sun
of the world . . ."* for, *"Stalin's greatness is a halo. . . ."*
The Party was out there, out there . . . after all

317

these years. But why didn't I feel of it, an extension, for surely the Party felt me, as a sick, a deviated outreacher. . . .

Lovestone had signed himself Comrade. All was not yet lost. He destroyed me, but preserved me, for we both had a certain investment in the old days.

The Party cared. Its very special kind of anger showed that it cared. Fascism? After long deadness, a sleep of twenty years wintering, it began to stir to life. Something was in the air. Fascism? Movement in the Detective Bureau indicated movement along a broad front.

Still. . . . How is the Bureau in a position to solve (and that means in a Marxist sense) cases like the Kennedy Kennedy King killings? *Wait a second.* The Party said crime. Singular. And if it came up with solutions, mere theoretical solutions, Holmesian solutions, what good would it do? *Who believes in us?* The masses are rich and besotted: the working class has sold out.

Why bother to so carefully negate, so scornfully destroy the analysis of the Clutter killings and the critique of Truman Capote's book? The Party knows. The Party cares. The Party sees into every facet. The Party watches like a mother. But its womb feels wrong: a still unborn sibling/contradiction lurking there. . . . Paranoia . . . a little mild yet, but it's a good Marxist feeling. Who had approved the killings? Peculiar question: where do correct questions come from? Who was not aware of the assassinations and their implication? Change in the usual regime. Different politics; same system. I felt resentment over the implications in Lovestone's letter. He did understand. . . . Lovestone understood the weakness of isolation that makes Hillrose a traitor in spirit. Get up. Test the air. Open the drawer (see young Hillrose's face—though he had a different name in those days—but this time be prepared for it. Seventeen; the glasses turned the burning eyes into something mild looking, studious, weak, not a revolutionary's face at all, but rather that of a student with his head full of chess problems and problems in dialectics with trick, unmaterialistic solutions, wearing a mustache to make him look older than he is, an intellectual's face, pick up the letter from the Capote-critic . . . and reread it and try to re-feel the feelings of glee and triumph and *feel* the being-watched and what sector does it come from? Read, Lovestone, read, for I assume you are, in a manner of speaking, glancing over my shoulder. . . . Or can they translate eye-movements into quantifications that indicate, by duration and intensity, what word is being read? Don't you see it?

—What?

I really don't know. Something big. Something looming very big, not even in the particular case, but in this type of case.

—Why defend it? Why the need? What tendency does it expose in you?

But consider the contradiction: When Lovestone requests(!) that the Clutter case be dropped from the agenda, he accepts the aberrational and accidental, in effect the single killer theory (or a form of it), the psychopath theory of assassination. Implicitly this contradicts the very foundations of Marxist detection and the Marxist world outlook. Which means one of two things: the *Party* has sold out, or has become expedient and is taking a calculated step backward, a move to the right. Which explains the assertion that Clutter was a populist (sheer historical distortion, of course, growing partly out of a political direction and out of the Party's refusal to involve itself with the day-to-day living of the masses and the grass roots, to understand American reality). Rise of American fascism? Line-change? Move to the right? Must rush off to the library and reread the news events of the last year as well as, most important, the financial sections of the last six months.

But what was the involvement with the royal assassinations of that politically important trio (why did the letter put it Kennedy Kennedy King rather than Kennedy King Kennedy?) but a form of speculation so removed from the Party's ability to do something about it that it entered the realm of abstract speculation, totally unreal: praxis in a vacuum: a game.

But. . . . Now when JFK was killed, the Party reacted defensively. Understandable. Oswald had been in Russia? His wife was Russian. He had been on the Fair Play for Cuba Committee. (Hadn't Truman Capote been on that committee too?) Oswald had asked for a progressive leftist lawyer immediately . . . but everything smacked of a provocation, a spy, a trap. The Party doesn't believe in assassination. Kill the person, revive the system. Oswald was a psychotic, was the line the Party took, even when, though we don't believe in bourgeois psychology, it is permissible now to let such thoughts surface.

Of Martin Luther King we said that he was the victim of: a racist, hired gunsel, a tool of a cabal of Southern whites: it was a plot and the people behind him were carefully shielded. Is a change in this theory indicated too? Why do we raise this question at this particular time? (I ask, why didn't we concentrate on Malcolm X's death?)

Of RFK, what was there to say other than it was palpably the work of a madman, Sirhan B. Sirhan, even though the assassination had political consequences, but the Party wasn't ready to go into those then.

A new line was demanded: new kinds of detective work: advance the solution-tendencies which, by the very way in which the letter was phrased, implies that the three killings fell into a pattern which the passage of history, the arrival of a new stage (fascism?)

revealed. Negate, now, adventurist motivations and smash single-killerism in every respect while dialectically accepting adventurism, economism, single-killerism as a motivating factor in the killing of the Clutter family. In short, Truman Capote was right.

Right?

Have they found me after all these years in order to destroy me? Can I bear these tensions? Did they have to do it this way? Was the letter necessary?

What are they trying to hide?

What has all this to do with Marxist detection?

Put Hillrose in their place. The Party lives and, hating it, I live too. Hillrose has lost his historical perspective entirely . . . he is a detached mote, alienated, fragmented, therefore bourgeois, a small and terrified shopkeeper, his psyche in the soul's cash register. . . .

But, to be alive after so many years . . . a positive resurrection. . . .

Be grateful then, not resentful. . . .

Why struggle with Lovestone, with the Control Commission, with the Line, with the Party, with the self?

What do they want?

Why was that letter of praise sent to me? A trap? How did they know of my *feelings?*

But to begin, to prepare, this means that one has to go through tons of material again, the Warren report, the rest of it, all those newspapers, to study those long-evolving tendencies, tendencies which began years ago . . . and, as always, resort to *The New York Times*, which considers itself to be living history, which excoriated the killers of the dream, Oswald, Sirhan, and Ray, and extolled the dreamer of the kill, Truman Capote. . . . Read, for the establishment in all its overt and covert forms, reveals *all*. . . .

Good detection begins with history: good detection begins with research and preparation: good detection begins with disputations against one's own inclinations which must be struggled against fiercely and defeated, of those inclinations have been in *their* hands, not a *them*, but a theyness of things and relations. . . .

Is the sense of being spied on real? Why realer than that of being reunited? Comrade Lovestone sits as a reflection in the from-inward-lit-against-a-from-outward-darkened window, his sardonically smiling image disappearing and reappearing, depending on the flashes of advertising and street lights, looming out of nightdarkened Union Square. —You've crossed over, he says.

I answer by going out into the hall and down the stairs and up elevators and outside the building, testing, sniffing, feeling out hostile space, and friendly and neutral space (though there is not very much of that . . . rather say less-committed space) and that space where contradictory clash-vibrations are set up to distort all aspects of being, wavering ordinary things like the world seen through heatwaves.

—Instinct is no substitute for a theory, Lovestone says. Instinct is *their* instinct, and I almost believe him.

I have a theory: If I went down to the Real Estate Bureau and checked out the title to the deed of Loew's Union Square Theater Building Corporation, it would be owned by . . . us *and* them, Party and FBI . . . joint ownership (with some wandering speculators who had bought into the stock, innocently, as it were, because it seemed like a good thing to invest in) of a public corporation which, through the years, changed hands many times, ownership appearing and disappearing in a maze of different hands and dummy corporations, its very walls solidifying and dissolving according to the dictates of the market itself (which has international implications involving the balance of payments and the struggle for raw materials and the resistance of revolutionary peoples of the Third World) according to the rise and fall of the business cycle. . . . But I don't dare. The researcher leaves his tracks. The hounds trace you down, following librarians who tell them what folios were requested and what library call slips mounted up.

Up a floor. Definitely *their* space. Electric tingling and hair standing on edge. Burn in it. Allergy to a kind of dirty police air they leave behind. Eye swims and skin crawls and a kind of panic . . . terrifying if we don't know what causes it. Go down the stairs through Party air. And then, through all that's left of the theater itself, Loew's Union Square, that old rococo empire, which is a long, low, flat room in which Hillrose has to stoop down, in which projected cloud images move steadily along the ceiling and stars twinkle even after all these years.

—Nonsense, says Lovestone. —The very sign of your deviation and backsliding is just these feelings I have been telling you about. Go back and think through the real motives . . . the politics of those killings.

But inner Party struggle is itself a beginning of understanding; but if there is nothing we can do politically it is a violation of the canons of Marxist detection and becomes a sterile exercise. There are those who have a dream of perfect detection, a dream of detection done in offices, or in rooms away from political life itself, away from praxis where, given a few facts, a few clues, one deduces the total crime. All this is a mistake, of course, mere Sherlock Holmesism, a perversion of the notion of scientific solutions done in a vacuum, a mere masturbatory action, a mystification of reality, a way of avoiding the dirt that reality casts on the slickest and most elegant theories, itself (*Holcomb, Kansas, where the Clutter family was killed*), a desire for solution merely to set the problem at rest, to avoid, to conceal, to negate understanding the whole, the real crime of which this is, is a revelatory twinkle on some dark surface (*used to be called* Sherlock, *Kansas*). What do you

323

think about that, Lovestone (*hinting at old county-seat war/contradictions-in-capitalist-time* . . . *though the headquarters of the Eden in the Great American Desert, east of the one hundredth parallel is in Garden City, Kansas where "Our soil so rich, our clime so pure,/ Sweet asylum for rich and poor . . ./ Poor did I say! Recall that word. . . .*)?

Lovestone doesn't answer. As of old, he smiles sardonically. Which is to say,—Why do you cling to your rotten personalistic bourgeois theories, Hillrose? Have they paid you off?

And behind him you sense the power of a crime commission, ranged around some old and battered table, its veneer flaking off in pieces, looking at you out of the dimness of an old, long, low, flat committee room . . . tables to the side piled high with stacks of Party literature, dusty, smelling dryly, causing Hillrose to sneeze, while overhead the identically shaped clouds progress evenly as they did on the crystal roof surmounting the theater. . . . —Adherence to the concept of social banditry as significant refers to a hidden political tendency in yourself . . . anarchic Bakuninism . . . worse, Nachayevism.

Two bodies cry out for justice.

—Four bodies, children of the pioneers and populists, who "To cultivated fields, the forest changed," call out for justice. And who did it? The *lumpen,* the drifters, the scum of society who are always for hire by the ruling class . . . it is these people who become the Brown Shirts, the Black Shirts, the Minute Men, the Birchers. . . .

—Comrade Hillrose has bourgeois dreams, they chant.

—Comrade Hillrose fails to recognize political priorities, they chant.

—Comrade Hillrose fails to understand the coming crisis in capitalism which calls for fascism, they chant.

We argue angrily, yet grow closer; the seasons change; history is run through like a film being speedily rewound. There is no way out. I begin to work on the assassinations of Kennedy, of Kennedy, of King.

Get it over with, solve the crime. Do your duty. The Commission's eyes are on you; weigh, as we always do, every word carefully.

Still, why is the social bandit theory, the single-killer theory unacceptable for the killings of two out of three, and why is it necessary for the killing of four? My analysis is perfunctory, dry, bureaucratic; the self-criticism is even more perfunctory: a tender provocation, a probe; where do correct thoughts come from and how will they emerge; who owns the Loew's Union Square Building now?

A cabal made up of southern racists, cuban *Gusanos* (working for the CIA) with an assist by the Mafia (who sometimes do domestic assassinations for the CIA) aided by Jack Ruby, who plays the peculiar part of the Cold War Jew harping on his patriotism, required for their obscure reasons which go beyond and deeper than mere logic . . . these are the forces that unite to assassinate JFK. A political assassination, a shift in power, and satisfies the first requirement of the proposition, "Capitalism is in crisis and fascism has embarked on a wide offensive." (Question: Did the succession of Lyndon Baines Johnson satisfy that proposition? Answer: Look at the economic base. But nothing's changed. It's *still* capitalism.)

Sit idly and shake up my consciousness; snip their pictures free from any possible ideological context: John F. Kennedy, Robert Kennedy, Martin Luther King, Sirhan B. Sirhan, James Earl Ray, Lee Harvey Oswald, Herbert Clutter, Mrs. Clutter, Nancy Clutter, Kenyon Clutter, Perry Smith, Dick Hickcock . . . Pin them floating on a black board without writing. No change. Then reconcile them in a black box till the fullness of time makes them faces without titles, without names, without assumptions. . . .

Has capitalism changed since the assassinations? Has there been a new regime? Was something larger at stake? Fascism indeed? My first emotion about the Kennedy killing was, let the capitalist pigs kill one another. Gut reaction. Very unpolitical, very undialectic, anti-united front. But challenging to the Commission which simply did not respond to its constituency, the detective in the field.

And to annoy them further, and to point up the validity of what I am trying to do, I find it hard to focus on this piece of dead history. Fascism indeed? Fascism pivots, they will tell me, around a singular crime which they succeed on pinning on the wrong people . . . a sacrifice, as it were, like the burning of the Reichstag . . . a propitiary sacrifice sanctifying *what has already taken place.*

Throw out something wild, something really nasty. . . . Clutter and his family get assassinated in November of 1959 when it becomes clear that Kennedy will become elected . . . what's the connection? Next year will annunciate the New Frontier and Clutter's on the Old Frontier. . . . Is Kennedy killed in the name of Clutter? Is *this* the significant crime?

A joke, really.

You hear laughter somewhere and there, in the bowels of the building, the Commission in its deliberations says that Comrade Hillrose. . . . No. Hillrose has sold out and will not accept discipline. Why deny the importance of social banditry which points more at the social contradictions in society than those crimes which we can readily apprehend, crimes that fasten to the popular imagination, that gets into their dreams and there, dialectically transformed into a synthesis of two irreconcilable logics, are an overdetermination of political contradictions. . . . Sirhan then becomes the overseas arm of the Palestine Liberation Front which strikes down Robert Kennedy for his potential acts protecting the Jews of Israel, and for making his bargains with the Jews of America, from whom he will deduct a certain soul-tax. Of the logic of his act and its historical motivating factors, what does Sirhan know? Pronounce him mad and bury the case, even though he acts out that logic, that inexorable *political* force, pronounce him mad for sitting in his room and priming himself to do the act by invoking the name of the victim and acting out the killing again and again as if the repetition of writing acts as theory which, in true revolutionary fashion, finds its ultimate resolution in praxis . . . and these very incantations work (futilely) to negate the logic of *this* world which would have him protect himself, to risk nothing, to live like some mouse. Social banditry? Possibly. Madness? No. What they dare not understand, they call madness . . . as they called the murderers of the Clutter family mad because there was no money transaction. . . .

Ah then. There are times when the detection comes to a halt. Possibly the very refusal to push to the limits is to retain forms of old sanity, to realize that it is to venture into areas appearing to the rest of the world mad, to talk to the world about a politics they don't understand, that they will understand only when they have moments of insanity, or when they are drugged or drunk. . . . I knew a man who had studied Marxism for years and years and couldn't make that final leap into understanding until he was under the influence of the expansive drugs . . . very like the logic of a crime which remained veiled to Sherlock Holmes until he took cocaine . . . a mind contractor which kept his solutions within the bounds of the greater crime, capitalism. Without the proper training it takes some little twist. . . .

After a week, take the box containing the clipped

pictures, shake them onto the cleared top of the desk, and play around with them. I know the Kennedys have committed their crimes, family crimes, for have they not babbled about Greek tragedy and family curses. And I know that there are crimes in King's background. That begins it. Oswald is not even so much a hero as just a face . . . a kid wearing a sweater, a veritable Gavrilo Prinkip . . . and Ray, he could be a face seen in the sports magazines, a hunter, and Sirhan, a serious-faced exchange student at some university who will go back someday to Palestine to make the land flower . . . possibly an agriculturalist. As for the Clutters. . . . It's hard. A lifetime of conditioning works against it and I look for ways that will shake my consciousness. The Clutters stand cheering in the crowds in Dallas as JFK drives by. Or I see them, not quite caught in the scan of Zapruder's camera. The Clutters stand looking up, full of hate, smiling smugly when King gets shot down. The Clutters are among the throng in the kitchen in Los Angeles when. . . . I mean take their cutout faces and actively superimpose them on other faces in the crowd. . . .

It doesn't quite work. . . .

Because. At night the clock of the Consolidated Edison building dominates the Square. I used to see it in the autumn dusks falling over the East Side tenement windows, over Suffolk and Norfolk streets, its gleaming numbers and high position forcing this world to fall into their way of seeing time . . . capitalist time. I hate it. Accumulative time. Empire-building time. *Their* one minute accreting to one minute, *their* sequence, *their* cause/effect, *their* general building and growth and accumulation, *their* compounded hoard of minutes which then becomes *their* history and which sucks away our time and renders us alone, and in that aloneness I am defeated for only the Bankers of Time can reverse *their* great laws of the universe, or alter them for a little while, laws like the law of compound interest growth which is the manifestation, the Cainmark of their crime. . . .

And soon the phone will ring, for months have gone by, and Lovestone is going to tell me to get going on it, or tell me, worse, that I am out of the Party . . . and I realize that even the dream of ideal deduction depends on *their* notions of crime and time and we have to believe what they tell us, for traditionally powerless to prove our respectability, our scientificness, we have learned to work with *their* statistics, newspapers, *their* science, *their* economics, *their* times and *their* contradiction-ridden history . . . and for this we have paid a terrible price . . . which makes it hard to deny what they have told us. . . .

What can break it?

Begin with this assumption then. You are being watched. Check it out. Listen to a creak. Check its ownership and creakmakingness in the library and the control of the means of production of creakmakingness. This space . . . it is no longer benign or neutral. Have I forgotten after all these years?

Thirdly, shuffle their pictures again and detach my preconceptions further. Pictures of people: some are murderers and others are not. Some are madmen. Look at the pious, thin lips shaped by hymnsinging, face of the man who lives in Charles Grandison Finney county in Bleeding Kansas, who stands, with some anonymous hired hand in front of a grim reaper, wearing a pith helmet.

Or look at the slightly hysterical face of Clutter's wife.

Or the girl, and of her legendary 4-H Club goodness and innocence and of her care for others and of her champion cherry pie baking . . . a churchgoer, like Katie Bender of the good Kansas Benders, Katie the spiritualist and Christian Kansas murderer was. . . .

And write these contradictions on two pieces of paper:

Nancy Clutter	H. Rap Brown
". . . and seeing as how you're a champion cherry pie maker, always winning prizes . . ."	"Violence is as American as cherry pie."

and clear the desk and then take the two statements and put them far enough apart so that the eyes can barely see both of them at the same time . . . and go between the field of cognition . . . the feelings trying to hold the two thoughts together, till it becomes a kind of dialogue and then a kind of dialectic and you begin to feel between both thoughts, reworking them in the head and the psyche until. . . .

Look again at the picture of Clutter standing in front of the reaper wearing the pith helmet like some kind of colonial lord and think that the roots of wheat and alfalfa and soybeans and cotton and beets are the roots of American imperialism. He wears coveralls, but I don't let that fool me; Americans are not afraid to put their hands to dirty work. The caption beneath the picture refers the reader to an article written about Clutter to be found in the Sunday *Times* magazine section of May 1, 1954. . . .

1954! The year the Party was finally shattered.

May 1! Irony. The worker's holiday. The revolutionist's holiday. The Marxist's holiday. Holiday that originated in America itself and celebrated all over the world.

I rushed to telephone the New York Public Library, the great branch at Forty-Second Street, to ask them to set the Sunday magazine section of May 1, 1954 aside for me. After a long while the librarian told me that I must be mistaken, for there was no magazine section for May 1, 1954.

"Where is it?"

"There's no section for that day, because. . . ."

"Was it mislaid?"

"No, no, I mean. . . ."

"Was it stolen?" Have they stolen some piece of incriminating evidence?

"No, no, you don't understand . . . May 1, 1954 was not a Sunday."

But the caption under the picture of Clutter said . . . had the day itself been stolen, or, was it another time, another space, socialist time/space? A clue. A hint. Their slip: a caption. The elementary police question: Where were you on the day of May 1, 1954, becomes . . . in *which* where were you on. . . . I had to get up there quickly. She, hearing nothing, kept on saying, "Hello? Hello? Hello? . . ." and then she hung up.

I had to go up North to the library when . . . Lovestone's voice said over the dead phone, "Do you presume to investigate the Party, Hillrose?"

I dropped the phone and got out of there fast.

ELAINE FEINSTEIN

Elaine Feinstein is an English poet and novelist. She lives in Cambridge with her family. Among her published works is *The Circle*, a novel which came out in England in 1971. *Strangers* is from a collection of her short stories.

Out of Touch

Now west down George Street a
star red as charred coal
blocks the line of the traffic

so that all the waiting cars
are made into shadows and
the street walls are red stained

and into that March sun   you
move off lost   another shadow
against the stones of

a spectral city: love
don't be lonely   don't let us
always be leaving singly on

some bleak journey   wait for me:
this   deliberate world   is
rapidly losing its edge.

Anniversary

Suppose I took out a slender ketch from
under the spokes of Palace pier tonight to
catch a seagoing fish for you

or dressed in antique goggles and wings and
flew down through sycamore leaves into the park

or luminescent through some planetary strike
put one delicate flamingo leg over the sill of your lab

Could I surprise you? or would you insist on
keeping a pattern to link every transfiguration?

Listen, I shall have to whisper it
into your heart directly: we are all
supernatural / every day
we rise new creatures / cannot be predicted

Onion

Onion on the piano under the music
yesterday I found you
had put out fine
green curves of new life

hopelessly out of the earth
the park is
delirious with March snow
and my mission is to remove your
hiding place / and all places of hiding

so that nothing can come of you
though you consume yourself wholly:
you are tender and green, but
    I must put you into the bin.

STRANGERS

Edward woke early as he always did. It was an April morning, the end of a long rainy April, and he woke with the taste of blackberries in his mouth, uncertain where he was, still lost in bracken and leaf humus. Then he looked across at his wife, asleep in her single bed, the sheets barely ruffled, the long hair like brown weeds over the coverlet. And lifted himself out of his dream. Began to dress quietly as he always did, so as not to disturb her. Looking down into the dark corridor of their bricked-up town garden, reentering his middle-aged body.

He liked to be up early. To move around the kitchen while everything could be found, before the day's clatter began. And the children. He made himself two pieces of evenly browned toast. God knows he tried to get on with the children, he liked to arrange things for them. No one's fault they were girls. Edward buttered his toast thoughtfully, moved the browning skins off his tomatoes, and was just slipping in the pepper dust when a flick of memory returned to irritate him. A silly memory. A look of—was it pity? A glance intercepted and lost as soon as it met his own.

Rainer. The boy's whole style: dress, hair, voice, made no sense to him. When Rainer had real work to do, good work. Why? Take up the manner of some pathetic Arts man, waiting to slide into show business. Edward reflected uneasily. Was it *pity* or? Opened the fridge door, looking for the mushrooms he'd bought yesterday from the market stall. And they were gone. My God, the woman had learnt nothing. She must have used them for supper, just like that.

Edward sat down. Turned off the kettle. Tried to

calm his anger. No scenes. No scenes. Anna's lips shook when they quarreled, it was those pills she took, he'd told her so a thousand times. And she *had* remembered the library books. But she'd mention it too, he thought. A minimal human achievement, but she'd have to mention it. Medals. She wanted medals for coming up to the ordinary efficiency of a second-rate machine.

It would do no good. To begin again about economizing. Christ. Anna's economies. He had to laugh, remembering the front room floor. Yes, in some terrible moment of dedication she'd hired an old machine and proposed to sand off the heavy black varnish in a day. He'd explained carefully and resignedly before leaving how the heavy roller was opened by turning two Allen keys in opposed directions, how you slid the paper in about half an inch and no more, how the paper would shatter if it caught on a nail. And she hadn't been thorough about the nails. He didn't want to be unfair, he'd tried pushing the old tank of a machine himself. It blew out shavings and black varnish with a blue explosion every time a paper jerked off. No, it was the stupidity that maddened him. Three to four feet of brown streaky floor, and they'd had to pay for the hire of the machine as well as the builders. That was Anna's way of economizing.

He went upstairs to put on the jacket of his suit. And could hear Anna stirring. He could hear her. The cough. Phlegm. Habitual, without pain. Turned to see the pale boneless face, ringed with brown about the eyes. Like a bird. Heavy-lidded. A face without expression. He hoped she was not miserable. He hoped she was not. Remembering. His own eyes looked small and pink in the mirror as he smiled at her. He watched the lines of sociable jocularity take their place around his eyes. Decided not to mention the mushrooms.

She was so small, and the funny thing was that in most of her clothes she didn't even look shapely. And

337

her face was so boneless you couldn't even decide what sort of a face she had. She was changeable as a tree. He knew all the changes of her face. On bad days it was fat and sullen as a pudding. Sometimes it sharpened with spite or. Flashed a thin-lipped grin like a boy. Not so often now, he thought sadly. That operation. Now there would be no son, ever, no male creature out of her split womb. To carry on his name. Which still meant something, whatever that boy Rainer.

He remembered: Anna, I've got a research student coming round with his thesis tonight. I don't want any comic stories about so. He cleared his throat. Put on a decent dress will you?

Remorsefully he kissed her forehead. She was a good housewife, a well-meaning woman. No one's fault she was. A bit of a fool.

Anna heard the front door go. It was like a signal. Immediately her room was invaded with noise. Round flesh, tender as butter. Her two daughters were bouncing on her bed, over her pillows, Sarah giving her cheek soft bites. Nell said:

—The kettle's on, Mum.

So Anna dressed quickly to be with them, carried along by their gaiety. After all Edward hadn't noticed the mushrooms. And Nell made chocolate, while Anna brushed at Sarah's knots, watching the shrug of that young neck scattering hair. Enjoying the promise of arrogance.

—Mummy. Nell had a serious dark eye.

—What?

—What did you do before?

Anna was puzzled: Before?

—Before you married. I don't think I want ever to get married.

—That's silly, said her mother lightly.

Didn't I marry a good decent man, she reminded herself. Laughing aloud at it.

Her daughter persisted: Well?

My God, thought Anna, it's the way her father first looked at me. What's all this?

—I was a dancer, darling, she said penitently. I used to. Give lessons.

—Did you dance on the stage? her daughter persisted.

—For a while.

—The real stage? The West End?

—Oh it was real, said Anna. Poor Nell. Who had never seen that kind of reality. Realer than. Aired clothes and the sweet smell of waxed floors and even real as. You, my lovely children. That I had to fight so hard to grow in my perverse body.

—Could I do that? asked Nell.

—You'd have to fight your father, said Anna.

—That's all right, said Nell. I'll be doing that anyway.

And the piece of your father that's in you? thought Anna, sadly. Watching Nell's phlegmatic gesture, the way she moved about the room like Edward, purposively.

—Why did you *stop*? asked Sarah. Nell had packed her bag for her, and the two of them were standing ready to leave.

—Too long. Too long a story. Anna waved them away. Yes, and no longer clear to me, she thought when they'd gone. For these white shelves, was it? No, she had loved Edward once. Had been homesick with him for a future, some magic and consecrated future when he could look around and say, my love, you have made my home, and now sit here well-loved as: Mother of all my sons.

All over now, thought Anna. Now I have nothing that is real but. Holiday. Going south. To old friends. With the children of course, or Edward couldn't have done any work. But away. Lovely. To be homeless again, to feel like a refugee through underground tunnels, struggling with children and cases, watching the dangerous claws of escalators. Even the change of landscape traveling south delighted her, the air lifting, the land softening to purple and brown. And coming down into white terraces, green tiles and pink paint, of the old seaside town. Where the air tasted like salt, like fish, a sweet seafood taste. And the junk shops, the cheap fruit shops: piled fruit, piled fish. *Plenty*. The plenty of the poor. She moved among the poor as one of them. No one would suspect her of a great house, an honored husband. And she liked that.

Away from Edward it was so easy to be happy. To kiss. Anyone. In a pub. Meaningless. So easy. So many, and one last young man with his breath faintly tinctured with hash as he bent over her. Knowing?

What? At least he did not know her husband's definitions could not taste those in her. They could not reach her here.

And Edward, when he asked sometimes, politely, what she found to do down there, was not concerned. Any reply served. The pursuit of clothes, odd jewelry, the kind of brittle nonsense he would expect her to miss. Sometimes she brought back some sea-sign which she set on a kitchen shelf, and he said: Very nice. Without looking, because his indifference was true: the *mileage* was important to him also. To take her behavior out of his territory. Locally, it was another matter: Why don't you do something useful? he pleaded. Take a degree or take up.

—Social work?

And they both knew that it was not the point that she should interest herself in these things. They were intended as a bridge, a false and hopeless bridge for her into his world. And she knew the rules for both of them, even if that failed. Nothing of her own must

intrude across that river. It was to be a total separation.
Between her frivolity and his seriousness. As absolute.
As a religious sanction.

So when she was home, she tried to keep her part
of it. Even now. Her house smelt as sweet as her body.
When the children came home from school they found
her putting out the early yellow flowers, making the
study bright for Edward and his guest. And she took
off the old black trousers and Thai shirt he hated so
much, and thought she would dress to the gaiety of
the new flowers, which was how she came to allow
the girls to make their house in the fig tree.

Even at the time she worried peripherally about the
bark, but more about their broken heads; came out
briefly to check the rope ladder they'd suspended over
the wall, and worried indecisively about the six-foot
drop to the paving. But they were behaving very sen-
sibly.

It was only when she went out to inspect the tree
that she saw that although the thick branches coming out from the bole were undamaged, everywhere
else was the betraying scatter of green and destroyed
new life.

—Quickly, quickly. Anna went pale with horror.

And they recognized the note. It meant something
that their father disapproved of was to be taken out
of sight.

—But Mummy, said Sarah. By the time Daddy gets
home it'll be dark and he won't look.

—But he will first thing in the morning, said Anna
savagely. Nell said: I don't think I care. Judiciously.
Why do you?

—Because it saves trouble, said Anna. She scooped
about at the lost branches desperately. And don't be
so bloody smart.

In preparation for the evening, not to be asleep,
Anna had come down very deliberately from her yel-

low pills, and now she was shaking with the cold. There was fear waiting in her blood, the skin lifting under her hair, she could barely control the venom in her voice as she said: You might bloody help.

And then, guiltily, to make up for that, she had to placate them with a foamy sachet for the bath. So that when she heard the key in the lock she could tell how the scent of it filled the house still. Child-talc and child-noise. At 8 P.M. Stupidity. And desperation.

—Listen, she bribed Nell, I'll bring you up some chicken on a plate if you'll just disappear now, OK? With hot chocolate, she added quickly, for Sarah.

Christ she thought. Looked at herself in the mirror. She'd overdone it, possibly, she thought. Chosen a black dress, not so much revealing flesh as the illusion of it. She could see Edward. Astonished perhaps, she couldn't read his astonishment. Perhaps he was pleased? And turned to meet his guest with an open smile.

But the shock of meeting Rainer's smile destroyed that. They had met before. He was going to say so. They had met before, and he was a piece of her south, her hidden world. The embarrassment came over her like a sea. So that she backed away from both of them, and when at last she spoke she had to cover her mouth with her hand, so that it was hard to hear what she said.

But it seemed that Edward had observed nothing. It was what he expected perhaps. Perhaps that was always her presence when the flow of her husband's world entered her walls.

—Let me get you a drink, he said protectively.

Rainer's face had blanked again; he was not stupid. She made her greeting as formal as possible, used her most measured voice, and soon the conversation moved along its appointed lines to the moment when the two men could go off to the masculine retreat of their real purpose. And she would be free to go to bed.

And yet she was not ready for that, there was something else, an irritation in her blood. So that every noise, every reply she had to make, even the cadence of a child's voice making no demand, set prickles in her blood. She hated it. The gates were down. To have the south. Her other southern self. Even by implication. Enter the walls of her home. Frightened her out of the possible retreat of sleep.

Instead of going to bed, she put on an LP. Not one she usually played when Edward was in the house; it was a strange wanton thing to do. She thought of the drums and guitars entering their male sanctuary, almost sexually. And then remembered she had a small quantity of hash from her last visit south. Went to find it. Rolled herself a cigarette reflectively. Listened to the same side twice. In timeless smoke float. Immune.

Maybe she fell asleep. Though only briefly, because the last track of a record was still playing when Edward and Rainer came back. There was an unmistakeable sweetgrass smell, everywhere, and for a moment she was afraid, meeting Rainer's amused eye. But Edward appeared to notice nothing. He looked. A little odd himself. Of course. They had been drinking the brandy.

—Can you make up a spare bed? Edward was saying. He looked anxious, she thought. But perhaps he just meant. Did the sheets match, were they ironed?

—Of course, she said. Easily. What else do I do all day long?

—Why are you still up? he focused upon her.

—I was listening.

—To this?

Edward took off the gramophone arm carefully. Plainly he felt the sapphire was defiled. She left to make up the spare room. It was cold. In timeless smoke float she dealt with it. Put on the fire. Could have slept now and there easily enough, but made herself take the staircase down. Like a good hostess.

To her surprise, Edward had already gone to bed. She was appalled. Rainer eyed her strangely.

—You've been smoking.

—Yes.

They sat down together.

—I'd better go up, she said.

—No, let's hear this first, he said.

Edward lay in bed impatiently. Damn the whole thing to hell. Why should he feel such inexpressible sadness about the boy. Because he was: beautiful and clever and young, and answered quickly, and to the point and yet. Took no fire from him. Fire. Perhaps he had no fire to give. The boy remained green-eyed and serious and sober, while Edward talked, and his hair was too long, and his mind was elsewhere the whole time. Yes, all right, Edward permitted himself to know, he'd wanted at least to be *liked* by him, that was it, that's why he'd drunk so much, he did not usually drink so much. And where had he hoped to float on that ill sea? Somewhere in his head (in his imagination he supposed) that awful cheap music went on wafting through the house. It didn't matter. It didn't matter. People got old, he thought. And the young looked at them. Like creatures from another world.

He woke with a violent pain before it was light. Stupid of him, he thought, not at least to have taken some kind of. Now he rose without looking for his glasses to go to the bathroom. But of course. No simple drug in sight. Every other kind of yellow green and. But nothing, he thought furiously, so. Healthy as an indigestion pill or. Milk of magnesia.

Now wait a minute. He'd seen some. Downstairs somewhere. He staggered for the stairs barefooted. No point waking Anna, he thought contemptuously. With the drink burning his belly he went down the stairs barefooted to the dining room.

His head was reeling a bit. Perhaps he was ill, because he could hear the same senseless track playing round and round. But then he heard, goddamn it, he *did* hear voices. Definite voices.

—And when you stop believing?

—You just come flapping down. Like

—A shot bird?

—Not so painful. More like a. Car running out of juice.

It was Anna's voice. Her giggle. Edward was acutely embarrassed. He had approached the room noiselessly and now there seemed no way to make his presence known. But it was his house. He'd bought it. With blood and work and worry while that silly bitch lay at home all day soaking up pills. It was his house, he could bloody well enter any room he chose.

So he did. Anna and Rainer were lying on the best Indian cushions with their heads on the floor. There was very little light, most of it came from the front panel of the hi-fi equipment, but both of them. Were fully dressed, he could see that, whatever might have been. So surely it couldn't be right for him to say: I'm sorry. Anna said without moving: My husband always gets up at dawn.

—Mummy. Mummy. It was Sarah's voice, as she padded, a little earlier than usual, on her morning run to the lavatory.

—Here love, said Anna. And left the room to the two men.

Edward's head banged insanely.

—I must find the Alka Seltzer, he said. I think. He felt the solidity of the teak cabinet. Ha. Yes. Here they are. After all, he laughed: Things stay where they are put.

But he found himself directing his observations to the

cabinet itself. It was most unpleasant, he found he simply couldn't meet Rainer's eye, or look in his face. Even when he said: You must have a coffee, he focused his gaze just above Rainer's hair, pretended to be searching the dial of the electric clock for his information.

He could already smell coffee. He supposed Anna was preparing breakfast. Everything seemed. Much as usual, but a bit earlier.

Apologetically, he turned off the record player.

—It's my head, he explained. And went upstairs to. Wash, he supposed. After him, following up the stairs came the unfamiliar sound of young male laughter, mixing with the excited voices of his two daughters. Mechanically, Edward prepared himself for the new day.

GEORGE DAVIS

George Davis has served as a staff writer for the
Washington Post and as a desk man for the *New
York Times* Sunday Department. He spent six years
in the Air Force and flew more than forty missions
over Vietnam during 1967 and 1968. This selection
is from his first novel, *Coming Home,* which is about
the Vietnam War and will be published by Random
House, Inc. in January 1972.

COMING HOME

ROSE

I scoot the chair forward. It is rigid under me. Its steel
legs scrape stiffly against the green marble floor. I see
Calvin, in a yellow shirt, coming down the aisle. I let
my eyes go out of focus. He is simply a blurred shape
working his way along between the rows of IBM machines, with a smaller blurred shape, Edward, in a
white shirt, coming along behind him. I cannot see the
cart, but they are separated by the length of the cart
that he is pulling and Edward pushing. The cart itself is hidden behind the machines.

I pretend not to be watching but I watch. I watch
with my eyes still out of focus, acting silly. I smile to
myself still focusing on nothing, seeing only watery
shapes as I watch them picking up the cards from the
other machines.

I put another card into my machine and watch as

it rides smoothly across to the reading station. Then I focus and begin to punch the keys slowly. I hate this place, I think.

I look at the list of numbers. Then I punch out the last number on the page. The machine hums. My bare knees are warm underneath. I turn the page and focus on the top number on the seventh page. The number is full of zeroes. I count them. Four. I punch slowly, 12-84-00003.

I hate this place but I have to stay here for at least eight months until Ben gets home. I can't let myself quit this like I quit everything else. I got to stick to something.

My eyes go out of focus again. If I had not failed Ben I would be free to sneak and give Calvin some ninnie, like I know I really want to do, instead of having to sit on it for eight months and wait to do right by Ben before allowing myself to do wrong with someone else. That would be dirty, Calvin, I say to myself.

Ben needed another kind of woman though. I was never comfortable with him.

I punch out the next number. The expression on my face begins to sour. Ben married me because he had to learn again what it means to be black after four years of Harvard. I should have helped him with that. But I was too busy wanting to be white, too busy trying to be like them. Here I was, somebody who had never known a white person personally in my life, suddenly given the chance to be around them, to have the things they had, to be married to an officer instead of to an enlisted man.

I wanted to be treated like their women are treated, not because I really wanted it but simply because their women were treated that way. So I wanted to be put on a pedestal too. I wanted Ben to do it.

Ben said I hated him because he wouldn't play husbandsy-wifesy games like the white people on television do. I wanted to be the little woman, the modern American housewife with the little apron and all, the great little housekeeper with the French Provincial furniture to dust every day while I waited for hubby. That's the Goddamn truth, I think. Ben wouldn't cooperate so when he wanted me to be the first officer's wife in the Air Force to get an Afro I went to the beauty parlor and got it straightened as slick as they could make it and dyed red, like a fool.

But then, as soon as they took him to the 'Nam, what did I do bigger than shit but go right out and get the biggest, bushiest damn Afro you ever saw. I could do it after he was gone, but while he was here I couldn't have the thing sitting up there on my head saying every time he looked at it that he was right and I was wrong. Oh no, I couldn't give him that. Shit. I feel like spitting in my own face.

CALVIN

There's no such thing. I think, as we come down the aisle picking up the IBM cards. I don't really give a fuck what they say. All you can have is something that hangs together for you. That's all. I slide my feet each time because I only get one step in as I move from one machine to the other. I pick up the cards on the left. Edward does the ones on the right.

Then I look up and think: She wants to pretend that she hasn't been looking at me. I saw her looking when I came off the elevator. Sooner or later it's got to happen—with her old man gone off to the war too. I just want to be around when it do happen. She is small behind her machine with her jet black Afro teased up high on her head.

Of course she's gon' pretend that she doesn't want to talk to me either, but she's jive. She might be scared.

349

She knows I can talk a hole in her drawers with her old man gone.

Edward pushes the cart tight against me. I keep my hands behind me holding it away from me. Slow down man, God damn, I think, you must think these white people are paying you piecework.

I knew she was looking. My mind was off arguing something else, true, but you can tell when someone is looking at you—especially a bitch. So when I got off the elevator I started down the aisle cool enough with one shoulder low and a kink in the flow of my hips as I slid my foot along from one machine to the other. And I had my pants jacked up high so the "reaper" could ride my leg so she or any of the other bitches could see it if they were interested. Which they were. I laugh.

"Hey, It's me again," I say without looking at her. I pick up the cards from the machine ahead of hers. Then I look at her. She is punching keys. "Hey," I say.

She smiles and finishes out the number.

"Damn, you looking good. If I ever commit rape I want you to be my first victim."

She finishes the number. "Oh, Calvin, you say the sweetest things." Her voice is full of sauce.

"Hey, one minute." I help little Edward get the cart turned around with his helpless Uncle Tom self. He starts picking up the cards on both sides as he goes back up the aisle faster than the both of us came down. I turn around and try to hit on my man's wife.

ROSE

"Why don't you let me take you to the party tonight?" he says.

I finger my wedding ring. Then I slide it up and down on my finger like I am tempted to take it off.

350

"That's okay, I'm married too," he says. He leans on the machine.

"Calvin, you know I ain't going nowhere with you."

"Shit, don't say never."

"I didn't say never."

"Yeah, I noticed that. You used to say never." He mocks me, " 'I ain't never going nowhere with you.' Getting rough, ain't it, baby."

I laugh.

He says something else. I watch his straight even teeth while he is talking. His features are round. His skin is very smooth and black, and he looks nice in his open-collared shirt. "You're letting them waste your life," he says.

I have to admit that I've often wondered how he'd be, but I've never wondered it while he was standing up in my face trying to look cute.

"You let 'em waste your life and they'll do it." His lips come down over his white even teeth.

I bite my lip and smile. He is an easy man to be with. Ben was hard to understand, but I can't blame it on Ben totally. I was confused. I didn't give poor Ben a chance. I was too busy trying to be a socialite. I have to laugh about it now. He used to say, "All you want to do is sit around the officer's club and sip tea with a bunch of empty-headed women—with the girls," he used to say.

And I'd say: "Everybody didn't have a chance to go to Harvard like some of us."

"Now you know that's not what I'm talking about."

"You want me to stay around the house all day."

"I just don't want you sitting around sipping tea and munching crumpets all day with your long white gloves on and a silly pillbox hat sitting on top of your fried head, grinning and saying shit like, 'Oh, you don't say. . . . How perfectly darling. . . . Oh, isn't that abso-

351

lutely *love*-ly.' Shit." He walked around the living room
with his wrist limp imitating a woman.

"You look like a faggot anyway. You don't have to
pretend," I said. He should have gone up side my head,
but he didn't and every week I was back over there
sitting on the ball of my ass which my girdle kept so
tight that I forgot there was a hole in it.

Calvin keeps on talking. I could drive poor Calvin
crazy like his wife already done. "Look, I ain't got
that much time. Let me take you to the party?"

"See me before you go home," I say.

"I heard that before," he says and continues talking.

I made Ben bring me long white gloves from Spain,
and a wig from Formosa. The wig is right there now
on the styrofoam dummy on the dresser which shows
that I ain't that deep in the faith or I would throw
the thing away or sell it. I made him buy me a ball
gown and take me to the commander's New Year's Eve
Ball, where he didn't want to go because the commander hated black people. I forced him to wear his
military formal which he hated. And there we stood
all night like two rigid smiling fools. I should spit in
my face.

Calvin says, "You see what I mean?"

"Yeah," I say.

"Shit, you don't see nothing. I don't want to keep it.
I just want to use it for a while." He laughs. Then he
looks at me like he knows something about me, but
there is nothing to know unless he knows that Ben
started running around about a month or so before he
left. I hate for a man to look at me like that. His thick
lips are pinched at the corners. He tilts his head to the
side. He is cute. There is a lot of mahogany in his com-
plexion. His eyes are very clear for a man who drinks
a lot. I wonder if he thinks I'm going to go out with
him just to get even with Ben. "You just need to get
out more. Shit, I bet you dance like people were doing

when Ben—is that his name, Benjamin—left." He laughs.

"That don't mean I have to go anywhere with you."

"If you go out by yourself crime-in-the-streets might get you, and since I know crime-in-the-streets, I'm gon' tell him to wait for you outside your house. Anyway why waste taxi fare?"

"My husband left me a car."

"Excuse me." He laughs. "I know one thing he didn't leave you." He laughs and claps his fool hands. "Jesus."

I look around to see if anyone is looking at us. "Why don't you do some work?"

"Why don't you let me take you to the thing?"

"Where?"

"You know damn well where. To the party."

"Oh, to the party." I act surprised. I want to get rid of him now.

"Yeah, to the goddamn party."

I laugh this time. "You're not getting mad, are you? Is Momma's little baby getting mad?" I stroke his long fingers hanging over the machine, then I pout playfully. "Yeah, Momma's little baby's steaming. I didn't want to hurt 'um's feelings. But 'um does look cute when 'um's feelings hurt. 'Um's eyes get so pretty."

"Don't be simple, woman," he says.

"Aw, you know you got pretty eyes, nigger. Calvin, your eyelashes are naturally curly." I look close. "Unless you curl your eyelashes. You don't curl your eyelashes, do you Calvin?" I laugh way back in my throat.

"Fuck you." He rushes off.

CALVIN

Simple bitch, simple bitch, simple bitch. If I ever get you alone, I say to myself as I catch Edward. I bet I get her. I bet I get her.

EDWARD

I see him coming and say to myself: Don't come rushing back up here after I done everything. I'm glad she turned you down. I hurry and get the cards from the last two machines. He-he-he-he-he. He can make the whole next round by himself while I sit in the basement and give myself a shoeshine.

ROSE

I get up and get more cards from the front desk. Then I come back and scoot my chair in to the machine. I hate this place. I watch the clock jump ahead. Then I punch out one number.

The day is hot outside, I remember. I almost wish I wasn't too lazy to go bike riding. I could borrow Raymond's bike and Marcellus could ride with me. Friday. I've got the knit pants I can wear. We could ride out in Dupont Park. Calvin brags too much. If I was smart I'd find an older man who doesn't talk so much. I watch the clock. It doesn't look like it has jumped since I stopped watching it before. I might go to the party.

I stare straight ahead for a while. I'm sorry I hurt Calvin's feelings. But he does the same thing to me. I don't owe him anything. This morning he said "You're looking uglier than usual for some reason today, Rose." And I like a little fool went into the ladies' room to look at myself in the mirror, and he was waiting when I came out. He said "Girl, don't pay no attention to me. You were looking good." And little Edward said "Great God A-mighty," like he always does with his dirty little self whenever you walk past him with a tight skirt on.

And then Calvin said, "Can I take you to the party tonight?" And I said: "I'm a married woman." And he said, "If you don't tell, I won't."

I watch the hands of the clock jump ahead. I'm certainly not going to give him any sympathy pussy. He used to score on me all the time. One day he told me, "You're almost the finest woman in D.C. except for one thing."

And I like a fool ask him "What?"

And he laughed, leaned close to me and said, "Your hinnie is a little too big for your legs," and he tucked his bottom lip in under his top teeth and stood there, smiling.

And Edward sang:

"Kildee legs and bony thighs
Great big head and baboon eyes."

CALVIN

"The party is pretty good. I told you. Nobody here knows you or your husband. Quit peeping," I say.

"I ain't peeping. I'm glad no one lives in the basement or they'd have a headache by now," she says above the stomping and laughing and booming of the stereo. The speakers look like they're about fourteen inches apiece. Everyone begins to clap in rhythm and stomp like sanctified people in church.

"Just as well get us some too," I say and start to dance. She joins the clapping. By the time the thing gets good the music is over. We lean back against the wall. The large room is crowded.

Nearly all night her mind has been somewhere else. Maybe she feels guilty, I think. I decide not to test it. I can see in her eyes that she is thinking about something else. I'm tired of talking to her. She dances nice

355

and she looks good. Luscious. Music starts again. She moves nicely to the beat. I look around while we dance. Most of the girls here are from Howard. I don't know too many of the guys. Maybe they're from Howard too since they dance like they're from out of town— New York or Philly. Even if she hadn't come I could have done all right, I think. I look at my reflection in the window. I would have done all right, but I hate to mess with college girls. Too much confusion.

I look back at Rose. She has a nice little step. Small beads of sweat break out on her face again. I do the D.C. bop. I lean back and dance widelegged, swinging my arms like I have a big apple hat in my hand. She smiles at me and starts into the little bit of the bop that she has learned since coming to D.C. I fake to the right and spin her left. Then I fake left, spin her halfway right and jerk her back to the left. She keeps on around twice holding her arms in close to her body on the crowded dance floor. The guy should move the sofa, I think. Make everybody get up. We lean away from each other and wideleg for a while. Then I drop her hand and we do the Philly Dog like the girl at work from Detroit does it.

Her small face is intense while she dances. The momma don't play, I think. Her eyes are not focused on anything. It's getting worse, I think. I'd better take her on out before she tightens up. The music ends and we go back to the wall near the blue lamp. "I told you the thing's going to be nice," I say.

"Yeah."

"You don't want to say it but you know it."

"You got too many women, Calvin."

"I'm versatile."

"You better versatile on home to your wife."

"Aw-aw."

"I better go on home soon myself."

"Aw-aw."

"You can get messed up messing with someone else's husband."

"Shit, everybody's somebody's husband."

"You full of stuff, Calvin."

"No I'm serious. Whatever don't already belong to somebody, you don't want. Hey, lemme talk to you for a while."

"Okay, I'm listening."

I frown. "Not here. Too loud. Let's dance one more time and fall over to my boy's house."

"Where?"

"Northeast."

"Calvin?"

"Shit, all I'm gon' do is talk. The options are yours. I ain't gon' touch you 'less you act like you want to be touched."

"The least you could do is get me a drink before we go."

"Okay."

I go to the kitchen. The kitchen is crowded with people eating ham and potato salad. I'm a little hungry too, but I don't want to take a chance on messing up so I hurry and get her a cup of wine punch. I dip my cup into the tub full of ice and red liquid. Someone pokes me in the ribs. I see that Rose has followed me. I guess she doesn't want to get too far from the decision she has made, poor thing. I laugh. We go back to the living room where the dancing is.

ROSE

The wine makes me think about it less. I feel funny too, as if everybody here knows that I am married. I watch the Howard girls. Some of them have gone already. I feel much older than they are, but actually I'm not. Twenty. I should have gotten pregnant be-

357

fore Ben left. You can go crazy living in a house by yourself full of the things that remind you how you and your man didn't get along. The furniture, my clothes, the wig, the green shoes, my leather purse—all remind me of battles we had.

I don't want to live in that place by myself. I should go home and stay with Momma and them.

I slowdance with a stocky black man who smells like tobacco. His sport coat is wool. It hurts my face. His hair smells good. Maybe I can't have babies. We never used birth control. I hate to go home by myself.

Calvin is no good. I should date someone like the guy I am dancing with. I could get away from him any time I wanted to. If I go with Calvin I will be convicting myself of something. Ben always said I gravitated toward a clothes-wearing shit-talking nigger, rather than one who was trying to do something. Gravitate. Ben. I smile. "Just so the nigger can talk shit, you don't care," he used to say. I never loved Ben.

Even though I know about me, I won't try to change me. I wonder how Calvin's sweat tastes. I like Ben. From far away, I like Ben. The music stops. Calvin has been dancing with a yellow somebody. He picks our wine cups up off the floor behind the lamp table. I drink. Then we go to the bedroom to get our coats. I've got to get the oil changed in the car, I think as we sort through the coats. Ben said to change it in February and here it is April. All I do is get in and ride, like he said. I'd ride it until it falls down and then get out and leave it alongside the road. We come back into the living room.

With our coats on and flung back we finish the last dance. His thing bulges in his pants. I don't pull away from it. Tall as he is it hits me belly-high. The music stops. We go outside. I button my coat and we go down the stone stairway. Oh Lord, I think. His hand is warm against my back like he is leading me to slaughter.

The place on my belly where I was dancing against his thing still itches. I know he thinks he got me. I guess he has but I hate for him to know though.

We go down the walk. His hand is firm against me guiding me toward his car. If I could feel a moment of indecision in him I could regain control but he is firm for a young dude. Resolute, Ben would say. He probably won't even try to talk for fear of giving me something to pick at. He'll just start kissing.

A tall guy comes up the walk towards us. There is something familiar about him. His face causes a small explosion in my mind.

"Yeah," he says and stops.

Then I remember he is the guy from Baltimore who went to Thailand before Ben. He taps his finger on my shoulder several times while he struggles to remember. "Nellis Air Force Base. Nellis Air Force Base," he says. "You're my man's wife. Yeah. I'm James Childress. I just left your husband about five days ago. In Thailand."

"Yes. How's Ben?" I say. "How's he doing?"

"I got back Thursday. Yesterday. I'll be damn. Ben is fine. I'll be damn."

"How is he doing? How did you find this place?"

"Accident. Let me stop lying. I been looking all over D.C. for you." He rubs his chin. I don't know whether he is joking or not. He laughs. "You look very good for a lady in waiting," he says.

We walk back toward the concrete front porch. He is not handsome but there is something rugged and forceful about him. "I got a lot to tell you about Thailand," he says.

"I'm listening."

Calvin drops his hands to his sides. "Ain't this a motherfucking shame," he says.

TARJEI VESAAS

The late Tarjei Vesaas was one of Scandinavia's lead-
ing writers. His novel, *The Ice Palace*, won the 1963
Nordic Council Literary Prize. Before his death in
March 1971 Mr. Vesaas had written 25 novels, plays,
books of poetry, and short stories. This excerpt is from
A Boat in the Evening to be published by William
Morrow and Co., Inc. in early 1972.

THE BOAT IN THE EVENING

Spring in Winter

The air was full of wet snowflakes, but that didn't matter. Everything was just as it should be; it was a beautiful evening.

A cluster of houses stood there, not large enough to
be called a town. The houses had been laid out one
by one, without any overall plan, and for this reason
there were many unexpected alleys and corners.

Over this a snowstorm was sweeping. At the narrow
corners the mild snowfall met the strong light from
the outdoor lamps, and seemed to turn it whiter than
white.

And the whiteness poured down into the corners in-
cessantly. The snow near the lamps was trackless. People were indoors.

But not all of them. Out of doors someone was happy on account of the beautiful evening. A short girl was standing close to the wall in the shadow. Or half-shadow, for the mingled snow and lamplight were so strong that the shadows were weakened.

The girl must have been standing there for quite a while; her footprints had been wiped out. She might have tumbled straight out of the night sky.

The girl stood motionless. You could almost believe she was here simply to be snowed under in this lonely place—but she must have had other reasons for coming to stand here glittering.

Snowed under? No, I can't get snowed under, she thought with a bubble of joy. That dark, hard man of iron over there on his block of stone—he can be snowed under, he probably will be snowed under. I can only get warmer and warmer.

The snow won't settle on me, she thought, but if it does, that's all right.

In the meantime the wet flakes fell thickly and heavily onto her shoulders and onto the boyish cap she was wearing on the back of her head, and wherever it found the slightest basis for piling itself up. She already had small drifts of it on her here and there.

Of course the snow is settling on me, she thought when she noticed this. Why shouldn't it? I mustn't move, she thought. I want it like this. Not to be snowed under, but I'll look different, and that's what I want. Everything's different this evening.

He shall see me like this, different, when he comes to meet me.

She stood as motionless as the dark man of iron. He was lonely and deserted. The girl was bubbling inside with joy.

I'll stand like this till he comes. She thought: He's no man of iron; he's a live boy. "Is it you?" he'll say. "Or is all this just snow?" he'll say.

Warmer and warmer.

What does the snow matter then?

It was the first time they were going to meet like this, by agreement. It felt important. It was more important than the evening and the snow.

She thought:

What shall I find out?

What is he like? I don't know much about him. I've only seen him a couple of times.

There was music in her and she said:

But I know enough. I've seen enough.

It could snow as much as it liked; she was thinking about the coming meeting.

What will he do?

She was really thinking only this one thing. What will he do?

He'll say "Good evening" and take my hand.

Yes, yes, but what will he do?

He could do many things.

Will his hands come close after a while perhaps? They do that, I know. Someone has done that already, but I'm not going to think about it, because it wasn't as it ought to have been.

Tonight it will be right.

I wonder how much *will* be right this evening?

This was a dangerous train of thought. She completely forgot her plan about the snow that was going to transform her and make her beautiful. Her thoughts were suddenly as wild as the snowstorm and just as difficult to check. She did not check them until she had taken the measure of all she knew, and it proved to be more than she had expected.

She looked about her and thought: Good thing no one can see what you're thinking.

She shut it away.

Meanwhile it went on snowing, building her up into towers and spires. She carried it well. She was short and lightly built, and seventeen.

He's no older either, she thought. It won't be long now before I shall find out something, whatever it may be. It's almost time. I *wanted* to be first and stand waiting for a long time.

There he is!

Through the whirling snow she caught sight of something coming towards her, seeing it only as something black.

It is, and here I am with all this snow on me!

It was a man or a boy, and he was approaching quickly. But she started in surprise: It was not the boy she was waiting for. It was someone else, from her own neighborhood. Someone she knew slightly. The boy she was waiting for didn't even live here. What does this mean? That he's passing purely by chance, of course. Don't move a muscle because of him.

But he stopped right in front of her and gazed at her as she stood in her heavy robes, her eyes glittering deep in the snow.

"What on earth . . . ?" he began, but did not finish it. Sudden astonishment. He stood there and simply looked at her. She couldn't help it, she looked back at him with that charm she was capable of putting into it; it happened automatically before she had time to feel ashamed. Her eyes were dancing inside the wet snow. It was true that the shadow was not real shadow, after all.

He came close. Suddenly she felt afraid and whispered, "What is it?"

He put out his hands as if to touch the snow piled on her, but withdrew the hand again. It seemed an unconscious gesture.

She whispered, "What is it?"

No answer. He looked at her, thunderstruck. Walked round her, his eyes fixed on her all the time. She did not revolve with him, but whispered into the air after him, "What is it?"

Now he seemed to remember. He gazed into her face. But still he gave no answer to her question. She had stopped glittering at him, even though it was tempting to make use of what she possessed so plentifully.

Suddenly he began talking, fumbling for words.

"Yes, there is something—you mustn't be frightened, you see."

She felt a shaft of ice pass through her. The certainty of what this meant, this thing he had not said, came to her by some mysterious path.

"Isn't he coming?"

He simply looked at her.

She questioned him harshly the second time, and about worse things, knowing it already.

"Has he gone?"

The boy scarcely nodded. This one was a young boy too. His eyes were bewitched now. He simply nodded.

She did not start trembling so that the snow fell off her. She just stood. It was because of his eyes. But she felt as if the snow slid off like an avalanche. There seemed to be a roaring as when an avalanche falls. A cold wind blowing. No, she noticed then that not a flake had fallen off.

"Did he get you to come here and tell me this?"

He would not discuss it. Had probably said enough by nodding. Stand steady, said a voice inside her.

The messenger said something quite different.

"Don't move. You have no idea what you look like."

He didn't manage to say what he wanted. He had taken on himself too powerful a message.

But she knew in her innermost being what she looked

365

like. He could think what he liked. Nor was she in complete control of herself: sudden tears welled up in her eyes, quickly and briefly. Then it was as if the weather turned milder, and no more came. The young man stood watching.

"That's good," he said when her tears stopped just as suddenly as they had come.

She did not understand. She only asked, "Did he say why?"

He did not answer her. Instead he said something that made her start in surprise.

"I'll unpack you."

Again she heard her thoughts. Without waiting for her permission he did as he wished. He took off the worn pair of gloves he was wearing, and used his bare hands to lift off the snow crown that had built up on the boyish cap.

"Won't be fun any more now," he said. "Think it's stopped snowing."

Yes, it had stopped. She had not noticed before. It was silent and the air was mild. He shook her cap free of snow and put it on again. She was the short girl once more. He unpacked her out of the snow piled on her shoulders. She was confused by his manner of doing all this.

"Unpack you," he said. Over and over again. Fistful by fistful. He took his time.

He unpacked her out of the little snowdrift on her breast. She saw that his fingers were uncertain. And so cold, she thought.

What will he do?

She held her breath, but all he did was go on unpacking her. Bit by bit she turned into an ordinary girl.

"That's that," he said, and had finished at last. But he did not go.

What will he do now?

Again she held her breath. She saw he was trying to

say something, and he was so strange to look at in everything he did that evening. He said unexpectedly, "You cried."

She had no answer to make. No use denying it.

"I said you cried."

"Maybe I had reason to."

He said, "Maybe. I don't know."

She snapped, "No, you certainly don't know everything!"

"*I'm* not sorry about it," he said, ignoring the interruption. "But that's another matter," he added.

"Why are you standing like that?" she asked.

"Can't I look at you? I feel as if I've never seen you before. It's so strange," he added. He sounded quite helpless.

She replied, "Yes, I suppose it is."

Then he said something: "My fingers are cold from unpacking you out of the snowdrifts all this time."

Something in her responded. "Are they?"

There was more to be said. Both of them knew it. So he said it.

"Maybe I should warm you."

"No," she said quickly.

"All right," he said.

All she said was, "That's good."

He stood looking at her. Everything seemed to be standing on its head. And it was so incredibly mild.

"The snow's quite wet," she said, confused.

"Oh yes," he answered, almost as an aside.

But would he go now? She had been a little abrupt with him. So he would probably go.

She stammered, "Are you going?"

He muttered something and there was an embarrassed silence. He mustn't go. She stammered again, "What about those cold fingers of yours?"

He brightened a little and asked, "What about them?"

"Nothing."

"If they really are so cold," she said again.

"Oh no. They're not so cold really. They've been colder."

"Yes, I expect they have."

Everything was standing on its head.

"Why don't you feel them?" he asked.

It was incredibly mild. She let the hands come. The hands, cold as ice, held her close. They made her burning hot. Neither of them could feel cold now.

He said softly: "Awfully good to hold in your hands."

"Yes," she replied, in scarcely a whisper.

TED HUGHES

Ted Hughes is the author of several books of poetry
including *Crow*, an extraordinary cycle of poems and
songs, which Harper & Row published last year. The
following is an interview between Mr. Hughes and
Egbert Faas, which appeared in *London Magazine*,
in which Hughes discusses his poetry.

AN INTERVIEW

TED HUGHES AND CROW

*The following interview took place on 10 May 1970
in the Hampstead flat of the poet's sister where I had
first met Ted Hughes early this year. What was then
planned as a short half-hour talk grew into a discussion
of several hours at the end of which we agreed to meet
again and tape our conversation.*

*Ted Hughes later asked me to delete many brilliant
and interesting passages of the original tape recording,
mainly, I assume, to avoid sending his critics, as Eliot
did, "off on a wild goose chase after Tarot cards and
the Holy Grail."*

Egbert Faas

Critics have often described your poetry as the "poetry
of violence." Obviously such a label overlooks the wide

philosophical issues even of your earliest work, which according to your own words is inspired by the "war between vitality and death . . . and celebrates the exploits of the warriors on either side." But how does such poetry relate to our customary system of social and humanitarian values and to what degree can it be considered as a criticism of these values? . . . Probably this is two questions in one.

Hughes: The role of this word "violence" in modern criticism is very tricky and not always easy to follow. I wonder if it's used in other countries. Do American critics use it? It's hard to imagine how the distinction can be made, outside recent English poetry.

One common use of it I fancy occurs where the reviewer type of critic is thinking of his audience . . . his English audience. When my aunt calls my verse "horrible and violent" I know what she means. Because I know what style of life and outlook she is defending. And I know she is representative of huge numbers of people in England. What she has is an idea of what poetry ought to be . . . a very vague idea, since it's based on an almost total ignorance of what poetry has been written. She has an instinct for a kind of poetry that will confirm the values of her way of life. She finds it in the milder parts of Wordsworth if she needs supporting evidence. In a sense, critics who find my poetry violent are in her world, and they are safeguarding her way of life. So to define their use of the word *violence* any further, you have to work out just why her way of life should find the behavior of a hawk "horrible" or any reference to violent death "disgusting," just as she finds any reference to extreme vehemence of life "frightening somehow." It's a futile quarrel really. It's the same one that Shakespeare found the fable for in his *Venus and Adonis,* Shakespeare spent his life trying to prove that Adonis was right, the rational skeptic, the man of puritan good order. It put him through the tragedies before he decided that the quarrel could not be kept up honestly. Since then the difficult task of any poet in English has been to locate the force which Shakespeare called Venus in his first poems and Sycorax in his last.

Poetry only records these movements in the general life . . . it doesn't instigate them. The presence of the great goddess of the primeval world, which Catholic countries have managed to retain in the figure of Mary, is precisely what England seems to have lacked, since the Civil War . . . where negotiations were finally broken off. Is Mary violent? Yet Venus in Shakespeare's poem if one reads between the lines eventually murdered Adonis . . . she murdered him because he rejected her. He was so desensitized, stupefied, and brutalized by his rational skepticism, he didn't know what to make of her. He thought she was an ethical peril. He was a sort of modern critic in the larval phase . . . a modern English critic. A typical modern Englishman. What he calls violence is a very particular thing. In ordinary criticism it seems to be confused a lot with another type of violence which is the ordinary violence of our psychotic democracy . . . our materialist, inorganic democracy which is trying to stand up with a bookish theory instead of a skeleton. Every society has its dream that has to be dreamed, and if we go by what appears on TV the perpetual tortures and executions there, and the spectacle of the whole population, not just a few neurotic intellectuals but the whole mass of the people, slumped every night in front of their sets . . . in attitudes of total disengagement, a sort of anesthetized unconcern . . . watching their dream reeled off in front of them, if that's the dream of our society, then we haven't created a society but a hell. The stuff of pulp fiction supports the idea. We are dreaming a perpetual massacre. And when that leaks up with its characteristic whiff of emptiness and meaninglessness, that smell of psychosis which is very easy to detect, when it leaks up into what ought to be morally responsible art . . . then the critics pounce, and convert it to evidence in a sociological study. And of course it does belong to a sociological study.

On the other hand it's very hard to see where that type of violence becomes something else . . . a greater kind of violence, the violence of the great works. If one were to answer that exam question: Who are the poets of violence? you wouldn't get far if you began with Thom Gunn . . . and not merely because his subject is far more surely gentleness. No, you'd have to begin with Homer, Aeschylus, Sophocles, Euripides, etc., author of Job, the various epics, the Tains, the Beowulfs, Dante, Shakespeare, Blake. When is violence "violence" and when is it great poetry? Can the critic distinguish? I would say that most critics cannot distinguish. The critic whose outlook is based on a rational skepticism is simply incapable of seeing Venus from any point of view but that of Adonis. He cannot distinguish between fears for his own mental security and the actions of the universe redressing a disturbed balance. Or trying to. In other words, he is incapable of judging poetry . . . because poetry is nothing if not that, the record of just how the forces of the universe try to redress some balance disturbed by human error. What he can do is judge works and deeds of rational skepticism within a closed society that agrees on the terms used. He can tell you why a poem is bad as a work of rational skepticism, but he cannot tell why it is good as a poem. A poem might be good as both, but it need not be. Violence that begins in an unhappy home can go one way to produce a meaningless little nightmare of murder, etc. for TV, or it can go the other way and produce those moments in Beethoven. *You probably know that there has been a whole con-*

troversy between Rawson and Hainworth as to whether
or not you celebrate violence for its own sake. . . .

Hughes: I think I've probably already answered that.
The poem of mine usually cited for violence is the one
about the hawk roosting, this drowsy hawk sitting in a
wood and talking to itself. That bird is accused of being
a fascist . . . the symbol of some horrible totalitarian
genocidal dictator. Actually what I had in mind was
that in this hawk Nature is thinking. Simply Nature.
It's not so simple maybe because Nature is no longer
so simple. I intended some Creator like the Jehovah
in Job but more feminine. When Christianity kicked the
devil out of Job what they actually kicked out was Nature . . . and Nature became the devil. He doesn't
sound like Isis, mother of the gods, which he is. He
sounds like Hitler's familiar spirit. There is a line in
the poem almost verbatim from Job.

As in the case of "Hawk Roosting" your two poems
about jaguars are often interpreted as celebrations of
violence.

Hughes: I prefer to think of them as first, descriptions
of a jaguar, second . . . invocations of the Goddess,
third . . . invocations of a jaguarlike body of elemental
force, demonic force.

It is my belief that symbols of this sort work. And
the more concrete and electrically charged and fully
operational the symbol, the more powerfully it works
on any mind that meets it. The way it works depends
on that mind . . . on the nature of that mind. I'm not
at all sure how much direction, how much of a desirable aim and moral trajectory you can fix onto a symbol by associated paraphernalia. A jaguar after all can
be received in several different aspects . . . he is a
beautiful, powerful nature spirit, he is a homicidal ma-
niac, he is a supercharged piece of cosmic machinery,
he is a symbol of man's baser nature shoved down into
the id and growing cannibal murderous with depriva-

tion, he is an ancient symbol of Dionysus since he is a leopard raised to the ninth power, he is a precise historical symbol to the bloody-minded Aztecs and so on. Or he is simply a demon . . . a lump of ectoplasm. A lump of astral energy.

The symbol opens all these things . . . it is the reader's own nature that selects. The tradition is that energy of this sort once invoked will destroy an impure nature and serve a pure one. In a perfectly cultured society one imagines that jaguarlike elementals would be invoked only by self-disciplinarians of a very advanced grade. I am not one and I'm sure few readers are, so maybe in our corrupt condition we have to regard poems about jaguars as ethically dangerous. Poems about jaguars, that is, which do have real summoning force. Lots of people might consider I'm overrating the powers of those two poems, but I'm speaking from my own evidence. I wrote another jaguarish poem called "Gog." That actually started as a description of the German assault through the Ardennes and it turned into the dragon in Revelations. It alarmed me so much I wrote a poem about the Red Cross Knight just to set against it with the idea of keeping it under control . . . keeping its effects under control.

What you say about "Gog" and "The Knight" reminds me of a similar problem Blake may have had to go through with "Tiger, tiger burning bright."

Hughes: Blake's great poem "Tiger, tiger" is an example, I think, of a symbol of this potentially dangerous type which arrives with its own control—it is yoked with the Lamb, and both draw the Creator. Yeats's poem about the Second Coming is very close—and the control there is in the direction given to the symbol in the last line—"towards Bethlehem." Not so much a control as a warning, an ironic pointer—but fixing the symbol in context.

Behind Blake's poem is the upsurge that produced

the French Revolution, the explosion against the oppressive crust of the monarchies. Behind Yeats's poem is the upsurge that is still producing our modern chaos —the explosion against civilization itself, the oppressive deadness of civilization, the spiritless materialism of it, the stupidity of it. Both poets reach the same way for control—but the symbol itself is unqualified, it is an eruption, from the deeper resources, of enraged energy —energy that for some reason or other has become enraged.

From what I gather, the solution to this whole problem of violence, as you see it, seems to lie in some form of new mythology.

Hughes: Any form of violence—any form of vehement activity—invokes the bigger energy, the elemental power circuit of the universe. Once the contact has been made—it becomes difficult to control. Something from beyond ordinary human activity enters. When the wise men know how to create rituals and dogma, the energy can be contained. When the old rituals and dogma have lost credit and disintegrated, and no new ones have been formed, the energy cannot be contained, and so its effect is destructive—and that is the position with us. And that is why force of any kind frightens our rationalist, humanist style of outlook. In the old world God and divine power were invoked at any cost—life seemed worthless without them. In the present world we dare not invoke them—we wouldn't know how to use them or stop them destroying us. We have settled for the minimum practical energy and illumination—anything bigger introduces problems, the demons get hold of it. That is the psychological stupidity, the ineptitude, of the rigidly rationalist outlook —it's a form of hubris, and we're paying the traditional price. If you refuse the energy, you are living a kind of death. If you accept the energy, it destroys you. What is the alternative? To accept the energy, and find methods of turning it to good, of keeping it under control—rituals, the machinery of religion. The old method is the only one.

You not only find yourself in opposition to some of your critics but also to most of the New Lines *poets who write very much from the same point of view, dealing almost exclusively with life in our civilization. And although Robert Conquest included four of your poems in* New Lines II *he did so only after having rejected the poetry of violence in the introduction.*

Hughes: I haven't read that introduction so I'm not sure what he'd mean by the poetry of violence. One of the things those poets had in common I think was the postwar mood of having had enough . . . enough rhetoric, enough overweening push of any kind, enough of the dark gods, enough of the id, enough of the Angelic powers and the heroic efforts to make new worlds. They'd seen it all turn into death camps and atomic bombs. All they wanted was to get back into civvies and get home to the wife and kids and for the rest of their lives not a thing was going to interfere with a nice cigarette and a nice view of the park. The second war after all was a colossal negative revelation. In a sense it meant they recoiled to some essential English strengths. But it set them dead against negotiation with anything outside the coziest arrangement of society. They wanted it cozy. It was an heroic position. They were like eskimos in their igloo, with a difference. They'd had enough sleeping out. Now I came a bit later. I hadn't had enough. I was all for opening negotiations with whatever happened to be out there. It's just as with the hawk. Where I conjured up a jaguar, they smelled a stormtrooper. Where I saw elementals and forces of Nature they saw motorcyclists with machine guns on the handlebars. At least that was a tendency.

From the very beginning of your poetic career you have

been considered an outsider. And although this has changed in recent years mainly through your already far-ranging influence on other poets you still don't fall into what Robert Conquest would consider the mainstream of the English poetic tradition. Now what is your attitude towards this tradition which you once referred to as "the terrible, suffocating, maternal octopus of ancient English poetic tradition"?

Hughes: I imagine I wouldn't have said that if I hadn't burdened myself with a good deal of it. I should think my idea of the mainstream is pretty close to Robert Conquest's. What I meant by the octopus was the terrific magnetic power of the tradition to grip poets and hold them. Helped by our infatuation with our English past in general. The archetypes are always there waiting . . . swashbuckling Elizabethan, earthy bawdy Merrie Englander, devastatingly witty Restoration blade and so on. And some of the great poets are such powerful magnetic fields they remake us in their own image before we're aware. Shakespeare in particular of course.

As you suggested in our previous interview you try to escape this influence by drawing on your own native dialect and its medieval literature. From Sir Gawain and the Green Knight, *for example, you derived the title and motto of* Wodwo.

Hughes: I grew up in West Yorkshire. They have a very distinctive dialect there. Whatever other speech you grow into, presumably your dialect stays alive in a sort of inner freedom, a separate little self. It makes some things more difficult . . . since it's your childhood self there inside the dialect and that is possibly your real self or the core of it. Some things it makes easier. Without it, I doubt if I would ever have written verse. And in the case of the West Yorkshire dialect, of course, it connects you directly and in your most intimate self to Middle English poetry.

The main poets who are mentioned in the criticism of

377

*your poetry are Hopkins, Donne, Dylan Thomas, and
D. H. Lawrence. Would you agree that these poets
exerted the greatest influence on your work? Also what
is your relation to Yeats and Blake whose work and
development seems to show an increasing resemblance
to your own poetry and especially to your development
from a poet of nature to a "sophisticated philosopher"
and a "primitive, gnomic spellmaker"?*

Hughes: Well, in the way of influences I imagine everything goes into the stew. But to be specific about those
names. Donne . . . I once learned as many of his poems
as I could and I greatly admired his satires and epistles.
More than his lyrics even. As for Thomas, *Deaths and
Entrances* was a holy book with me for quite a time
when it first came out. Lawrence I read entire in my
teens . . . except for all but a few of the poems. His
writings colored a whole period of my life. Blake I
connect inwardly to Beethoven, and if I could dig to
the bottom of my strata maybe their names and works
would be the deepest traces. Yeats spellbound me for
about six years. I got to him not so much through his
verse as through his other interests, folklore, and magic
in particular. Then that strange atmosphere laid hold
of me. I fancy if there is a jury of critics sitting over
what I write, and I imagine every writer has something
of the sort, then Yeats is the judge. There are all sorts
of things I could well do but because of him and prin-
ciples I absorbed from him I cannot. They are prin-
ciples that I've found confirmed in other sources . . .
but he stamped them into me. But these are just the
names you mentioned. There are others. One poet I
have read more than any of these is Chaucer. And the
poet I read more than all other literature put together
is Shakespeare. More than all other fiction or drama or
poetry that is.

In one of your essays you speak of Shakespeare's utility

general-purpose style. I think it is in one of your essays on Keith Douglas.

Hughes: Maybe that's an ideal notion, and yet maybe not. It's connected to the dream of an ideal vernacular. I suppose Shakespeare does have it. I remember the point in Lear where I suddenly recognized this. It was very early in my reading, we were going through Lear in school and Lear as you know is the most extraordinary jumble of styles. I can't remember what I thought of Shakespeare before that but at one particular mutilated and mistaken-looking phrase I suddenly recognized what Shakespearean language was . . . it was not super-difficult language at all . . . it was super-easy. It wasn't a super-processed super-removed super-arcane language like Milton . . . it was super-crude. It was backyard improvisation. It was dialect taken to the limit. That was it . . . it was inspired dialect. The whole crush and cramming throwaway expressiveness of it was right at the heart of it dialect. So immediately I felt he was much closer to me than to all those scholars and commentators at the bottom of the page who I assumed hadn't grown up in some dialect. It enabled me to see all sorts of virtues in him. I saw all his knotted-up complexities and piled-up obscurities suddenly as nothing of the sort . . . they were just the result of his taking shortcuts through walls and ceilings and floors. He goes direct from center to center but you never see him on the stairs or the corridors. It's a sort of inspired idleness. Wherever he turns his attention, his whole body rematerializes at that point. It's as if he were too idle to be anything but utterly direct, and utterly simple. And too idle to stop everything happening at the speed of light. So those knots of complexity are traffic jams of what are really utterly simple confrontations. His poetic virtue is hitting the nail on the head and he eventually became so expert that by hitting one nail he made fifty others jump in of their own accord. Wherever a nail exists he can hit it on the head.

When did you first get interested in poetry?

Hughes: When I was about fifteen. My first subjects were Zulus and the Wild West. I had sagas of involved warfare among African tribes, for some reason. All in imitation of Kipling.

From what you're saying, I gather that the influence of Hopkins, Thomas, and Lawrence is not really as great as often claimed.

Hughes: I read Lawrence and Thomas at an impressionable age. I also read Hopkins very closely. But there are superficial influences that show and deep influences that maybe are not so visible. It's a mystery how a writer's imagination is influenced and altered. Up to the age of twenty-five I read no contemporary poetry whatsoever except Eliot, Thomas, and some Auden. Then I read a Penguin of American poets that came out in about 1955 and that started me writing. After writing nothing for about six years. The poems that set me off were odd pieces by Shapiro, Lowell, Merwin, Wilbur, and Crowe Ransom. Crowe Ransom was the one who gave me a model I felt I could use. He helped me get my words into focus. That put me into production. But this whole business of influences is mysterious. Sometimes it's just a few words that open up a whole prospect. They may occur anywhere. Then again the influences that really count are most likely not literary at all. Maybe it would be best of all to have no influences. Impossible of course. But what good are they as a rule? You spend a lifetime learning how to write verse when it's been clear from your earliest days that the greatest poetry in English is in the prose of the Bible. And after all the campaigns to make it new you're stuck with the fact that some of the Scots ballads still cut a deeper groove than anything written in the last forty years. Influences just seem to make it more and more unlikely that a poet will write what he alone could write.

In fact there is an increasing use of mythological and biblical material in your poetry, in particular since Wodwo. T. S. Eliot once described the use of myth in James Joyce's Ulysses (and indirectly in his own Waste Land) as a means of "manipulating a continuous parallel between contemporaneity and antiquity . . . [and as] a way of controlling, or ordering, or giving a shape and a significance to the immense panorama of futility and anarchy which is contemporary history." How does your own use of mythological and biblical material differ from this?

Hughes: He speaks specifically of contemporary history which was his own red herring I imagine. Somewhere else he speaks of the *Waste Land* as the chart of his own condition, and of history, if at all, just by extension and parallel.

But you speak about the disintegration of Western civilization as well. Might not T. S. Eliot have attempted something similar?

Hughes: I can't believe that he took the disintegration of Western civilization as a theme which he then found imagery and a general plan for. His sickness told him the cause. Surely that was it. He cleaned his wounds and found all the shrapnel. Every writer if he develops at all develops either outwards into society and history, using wider and more material of that sort, or he develops inwards into imagination and beyond that into spirit, using perhaps no more external material than before and maybe even less but deepening it and making it operate in the many different inner dimensions until it opens up perhaps the religious or holy basis of the whole thing. Or he can develop both ways simultaneously. Developing inwardly, of course, means organizing the inner world or at least searching out the patterns there and that is a mythology. It may be an original mythology. Or you may uncover the Cross—as Eliot did. The ideal aspect of Yeats's development is that he managed to develop his poetry both outwardly into history and the common imagery of everyday life at the same time as he developed it inwardly in a sort of close parallel . . . so that he could speak of both simultaneously. His mythology is history, pretty well, and his history is as he said "the story of a soul."

So, when you use biblical and mythological material, these really represent, as it were, the aim in themselves, and are not merely a kind of device as in Eliot to give order, as he says, to something else.

Hughes: You choose a subject because it serves, because you need it. We go on writing poems because one poem never gets the whole account right. There is always something missed. At the end of the ritual up comes a goblin. Anyway within a week the whole thing has changed, one needs a fresh bulletin. And works go dead, fishing has to be abandoned, the shoal has moved on. While we struggle with a fragmentary Orestes some complete Bacchae moves past too deep down to hear. We get news of it later . . . too late. In the end, one's poems are ragged dirty undated letters from remote battles and weddings and one thing and another.

May we for a moment come back to The Waste Land *and its difference from* Wodwo *the main theme of which you described to me as a "descent into destruction of some sort." Even in* Wodwo, *anticipating* Crow, *you seem to go beyond portraying the disintegration of our Western civilization.*

Hughes: What Eliot and Joyce and I suppose Beckett are portraying is the state of belonging spiritually to the last phase of Christian civilization, they suffer its disintegration. But there are now quite a few writers about who do not seem to belong spiritually to the Christian civilization at all. In their world Christianity is just another provisional myth of man's relationship with the creator and the world of spirit. Their world is a continuation or a re-emergence of the pre-Christian world . . . it is the world of the little pagan religions and cults, the primitive religions from which of course Christianity itself grew.

Which writers are you referring to? Are you thinking of Schopenhauer and Nietzsche, whose thought seems to show a striking resemblance to yours?

Hughes: The only philosophy I have ever really read was Schopenhauer. He impressed me all right. You see very well where Nietzsche got his Dionysus. It was a genuine vision of something on its way back to the surface. The rough beast in Yeats's poems. Each nation sees it through different spectacles.

Like Schopenhauer you had to look towards the east in quest of a new philosophy. When did you first read the Tibetan Book of the Dead?

Hughes: I can't say I ever quested deliberately for a philosophy. Whatever scrappy knowledge of Indian and Chinese philosophy and religious writings I have I picked up on the way . . . tied up with the mythology and the folklore which was what I was mainly interested in. And it's the sort of thing you absorb out of pure curiosity. The *Bardo Thodol,* that's the *Tibetan Book of the Dead,* was a special case. In 1960 I had met the Chinese composer Chou Wen-chung in the States, and he invited me to do a libretto of this thing. He had the most wonderful plans for the musical results. Gigantic orchestra, massed choirs, projected illuminated mandalas, soul-dancers and the rest.

Did you ever write this libretto?

Hughes: Yes, I rewrote it a good deal. I don't think I ever came near what was needed. I got to know the *Bardo Thodol* pretty well. Unfortunately the hoped-for cash evaporated, we lost contact for about nine years, and now of course we've lost the whole idea to the psychedelics. We had no idea we were riding the

zeitgeist so closely. We had one or two other schemes
. . . and maybe we'll do them some day.

The Bardo Thodol *must have brought you a confirmation of many ideas which are already latent in your earliest work, even in* The Hawk in the Rain. *How far and in which way can one speak of its influence on* Crow? *An expression like "womb door" seems to be lifted straight out of the* Tibetan Book of the Dead *and besides such obvious direct parallels one could easily point to several more general metaphorical, thematic, and philosophical resemblances.*

Hughes: From one point of view, the *Bardo Thodol* is basically a shamanistic flight and return. Tibetan Buddhism was enormously influenced by Tibetan primitive shamanism. And in fact the special weirdness and power of all things Tibetan in occult and magical circles springs direct from the shamanism, not the Buddhism.

What exactly is Shamanism?

Hughes: Basically, it's the whole procedure and practice of becoming and performing as a witch-doctor, a medicine man, among primitive peoples. The individual is summoned by certain dreams. The same dreams all over the world. A spirit summons him . . . usually an animal or a woman. If he refuses, he dies . . . or somebody near him dies. If he accepts, he then prepares himself for the job . . . it may take years. Usually he apprentices himself to some other Shaman, but the spirit may well teach him direct. Once fully fledged he can enter trance at will and go to the spirit world . . . he goes to get something badly needed, a cure, an answer, some sort of divine intervention in the community's affairs. Now this flight to the spirit world he experiences as a dream . . . and that dream is the basis of the hero story. It is the same basic outline pretty well all over the world, same events, same figures, same situations. It is the skeleton of thousands of folktales and myths. And of many narrative poems. The *Odyssey,* the *Divine Comedy, Faust,* etc. Most narrative poems recount only those other dreams . . . the dream of the call. Poets usually refuse the call. How are they to accept it? How can a poet become a medicine man and fly to the source and come back and heal or pronounce oracles? Everything among us is against it. The American healer and prophet Edgar Cayce is an example of one man who dreamed the dreams and accepted the task, who was not a poet. He described the dreams and the flight. And of course he returned with the goods.

In comparison with Wodwo *which, appropriate to its theme, has a kind of open form, your new volume has a much denser and more coherent structure. First of all, the poems seem to interconnect on the basis of fairly coherent "apocryphal" narrative, as you have called it, in which you turn the biblical account of the creation, of the fall of man and the crucifixion, etc. upside down. This narrative is quite easy to reconstruct from the poems themselves. But last time you told me a long story mainly concerning* Crow *himself which is only partly reflected in the sequence.*

Hughes: The story is not really relevant to the poems as they stand. Maybe I'll finish the story some day and publish it separately. I think the poems have a life a little aside from it. The story brought me to the poems, and it was of course the story of Crow, created by God's nightmare's attempt to improve on man.

Parts of this story already appear in "Logos." You told me in our last conversation that the imagery in Crow *forced itself upon you and that writing the poems had been like putting yourself through a process. Do you feel that this process has come to a kind of completion or do you think that you will enlarge further upon your new mythological system?*

Hughes: In a way I think I projected too far into the

future. I'd like to get the rest of it. But maybe it will
all take a different form.

One of the unifying devices in Crow, *it seems to me,
is the recurrence of particular themes. Especially complex is your symbolic use of the notions of Laughter,
Smiling, and Grinning. To each of these notions you
also devoted one entire poem, in which Laughter,
Smile, and Grin appear as vividly realized personifica-
tions or allegories. Now would you agree that these three
notions stand for an acceptance of suffering and evil
and that they also express your attitude towards the
absurd, which, however, is radically different from
Beckett's?*

Hughes: I'm not quite sure what they signify.

*Another recurrent motif is Crow eating in the face of
adversity, in the face of suffering, violence, etc., or I
remember Crow sitting under the leaves "weeping till
he began to laugh," weeping being another recurrent
motif which here fuses with the notion of laughter.*

Hughes: Most of them appeared as I wrote them. They
were usually something of a shock to write. Mostly they
wrote themselves quite rapidly, the story was a sort of
machine that assembled them, and several of them that
seem ordinary enough now arrived with a sense of having done something . . . tabu. It's easy enough to give
interpretations I think and draw possibilities out of them
but whether they'd be the real explanations I don't
know.

*So in your poem about Laughter you don't seem to have
had Samuel Beckett and his notion of the absurd in
mind?*

Hughes: No.

*You have referred to Beckett's notion of the absurd in
your article on Vasko Popa, where you describe Vasko
Popa's world as absurd but different from Beckett's
because Vasko Popa, as you say, has the "simple animal courage of accepting the odds."*

Hughes: Popa, and several other writers one can think of, have in a way cut their losses and cut the whole hopelessness of that civilization off, have somehow managed to invest their hopes in something deeper than what you lose if civilization disappears completely and in a way it's obviously a pervasive and deep feeling that civilization has now disappeared completely. If it's still here it's still here by grace of pure inertia and chance and if the whole thing has essentially vanished one had better have one's spirit invested in something that will not vanish. And this is a shifting of your foundation to completely new Holy Ground, a new divinity, one that won't be under the rubble when the churches collapse.

I just remember that in Crow *the first and second creation seem to be separated by a nuclear blast which you describe or hint at for example in "Crow Alights," the following poem and "Notes for a Little Play." Perhaps this is pinning it down too much chronologically. But there seems to be this notion of a nuclear blast separating the two worlds.*

Hughes: Yes, a complete abolition of everything that's been up to this point and Crow is what manages to drag himself out of it in fairly good morale.

Do you think that what you said about Vasco Popa applies to Francis Bacon?

Hughes: Yes, and I like Francis Bacon very much. He's very much in both worlds. A complicated case. Because in a way like Eliot and Beckett he's suffering the disintegration, isn't he? Yet one doesn't at all have a feeling of desolation, emptiness, or hopelessness.

You seem to use less and less formal devices such as rhyme, meter, and stanza which to some extent occur in your earlier poetry. Do you feel that these devices are generally inadequate in modern poetry or that they just don't suit what you personally want to say?

Hughes: I use them here and there. I think it's true that formal patterning of the actual movement of verse somehow includes a mathematical and a musically deeper world than free verse can easily hope to enter. It's a mystery why it should do so. But it only works of course if the language is totally alive and pure and if the writer has a perfectly pure grasp of his real feeling . . . and the very sound of meter calls up the ghosts of the past and it is difficult to sing one's own tune against that choir. It is easier to speak a language that raises no ghosts.

Which poems in Crow *do you like best?*

Hughes: The first idea of *Crow* was really an idea of a style. In folktales the prince going on the adventure comes to the stable full of beautiful horses and he needs a horse for the next stage and the king's daughter advises him to take none of the beautiful horses that he'll be offered but to choose the dirty, scabby little foal. You see, I throw out the eagles and choose the Crow. The idea was originally just to write his songs, the songs that a Crow would sing. In other words, songs with no music whatsoever, in a super-simple and a super-ugly language which would in a way shed everything except just what he wanted to say without any other consideration and that's the basis of the style of the whole thing. I get near it in a few poems. There I really begin to get what I was after.

FREDERICK BARTHELME

Frederick Barthelme is presently living in Houston. He has written two novels, *Rangoon* and *War and War*. *Ten Bears*, from which the following excerpt comes, will be published by Doubleday and Co., Inc.

PEOPLE WERE THINKING

Panda was thinking: *He stretches his eyelids at me, his ill-mannered bird's eyes waver in a separate glance for the pair of points of light marking the opposite ends of a very smoothly drawn path fluttered with leaves between the rich swollen curve of my breasts.*

People in the street were thinking: *What does he have that we haven't got? What makes him so special? Who does he think he is? What's got into him? What makes him think he can get away with it? Just how far is he going to push it? Who is he kidding? What is he hiding?*

Bodo was thinking: *What do I have that they haven't got? What makes me so special? Who do I think I am? What's got into me?*

The president of the United States was thinking: *Maybe, if I can get a berth on the tennis team. . . .*

Bobby Dylan was thinking: *Emm . . . sure is a nice day. Hey Bertha—*

Bobby Darin was thinking: *Hey Bertha—*

The governor of Texas was thinking: *Hey Bertha—*

The pope was thinking: *My father, who art in heaven. . . .*

Walter Cronkite was thinking: *I wish I were an apple, ahangin' on a tree. . . .*

T. S. Eliot was thinking: *Curds and whey. Would curds and whey be better? Teas and cakes? Or is it cake and teas? Ices? Where do the ices come in? I guess it don't matter, them things are more like biscuits anyway.*

Plato was thinking: *If I am unhappy, then it is fair to say that I am blue. If my thought process is unique, then it is fair to say that I am special. At this moment then, I am a blue Plato special.*

Cynthia Plastercaster was thinking: *God! Remember Jimi! What a fuckin' dong! Rubberhole mother dog! God! Remember the jelly! And Frank's works? Jesus daddywhip Gog! Bloodsuck cunt-throb marbled flick asshole plunk! She-fuckin-it! Oh man oh man! Whew! Shit! Shit shit shit.*

Rod Steiger was thinking: *What's wrong with my new hairstyle?*

Paulie was thinking: *Golly guys, gee fellas.*

John was thinking: *Motherfuckersonofabitchcuntlickingpissant!*

George was thinking: Mea culpa, mea culpa, mea, mea mea culpa.

Ringo was thinking: *Maureen? Maureen? Zak? Where are y'all? Maureen? Zik? Zak?*

A high government official was thinking: *I am blue and I am white. I have sixteen tiny legs. I have three arms in front and two in back. I crawl on my belly and get awful smelly. I sleep in bed with mommy. Who am I?*

Bodo was still thinking.

I long to intuit myself as other than the Christ but alas, I am lost. If I am the Christ as I suspect then the civilization has been sourly deceived, for I am but a rude and fuzzy image of that myth so long handled by so many peoples, a squat remembrance of that man

of miracles, that patient ghost on the water, that hir-
tellous embodiment of Elysium.

Still, I do my best under the circumstances—oh! them
holy and extenuatin' circumstances. What would I do
without 'em? I *do* do my best, everything I can think
of here as we go along, each new thing gaining rele-
vance and authority from the before and the after,
each new thing a part of the whole I'm trying to push
out here so that you might read it and weep, so that
you might love me. And I is tired already. It is only
ten A.M. and I is exhausted. Nevertheless, driven by
raw desire, I prod each new day with Olympian thrusts
and Athenian pokes. I have some questions for my
Panda when she comes home from wherever she's been.
I ask if anyone touched her, where, why, and for what
duration did the touch obtain (in the case that a contact did occur then she must make a Four-B pencil
drawing on linen at the scale of one inch equals one
foot showing the approximate location of the contact,
the placement of the various limbs and body parts in
the context of the contact, dimensions, pressure, and
stress calculations including those pressures and stresses
intended by the party initiating the action as sexual
or erotic advances, the duration of especially these last
pressures and stresses, the index of response covering
type, intensity, etc. on her part and the part of the
party of the second part, and finally, she is to fill out
the space at the bottom right corner of the sheet where
I have been considerate enough to leave room for her
personal comments and notations concerning questions
and area of questioning left unexplored theretofore). I
then ask the ostensive or manifestly demonstrative purpose of her involvement, the actual purpose in her estimation, the degree and—by way of duplicating some of
the information on the drawing so that she is tested
as to the consistency of her story—the intensity of pleasure or pleasures taken by her, the genre of such pleas-

ure or pleasures as were taken, an estimation of the class status, social conscience, and financial responsibility of the party of the second part, or *parties* of the second part if indeed that is the case and a true thing where this contact is concerned, the attribution of attributable responsibilities, a short description of the environ wherein the contact occurred except in such cases where environ played a direct and considerable part in the contact itself, and in these cases a lengthy and detailed description of environ and its relation to the contact is asked, with special attention to be given temperature and wind speed. What I am asking her for, in short, is a full description of the composition of the contact, a description which, as I have it ordered in my mind, throws open the contact's undercarriage to the closest possible scrutiny and allows me, in the shortest space of time, to see just what has gone on. Needless to say, Panda is not very happy with this situation. She thinks that she deserves to be, as she puts it, "trusted." Where they get such notions I'll never know.

A bunch of things happen, can it be said otherwise? She wants to change her name. She wants to be called Wichita Woman. What can I say? She handed me a Viva towel with this intelligence on it in blood. Okay, I said. Relax. Do whatever you want, I said.

So I called her Wichita Woman. She liked it. She even thought of going down and having it changed legally, but interest dwindled somewhere along the line and she never got around to it. On one occasion when she stayed home from work it was in her mind to impose her new name on each and every article and object that she could rightly call her own. It happened that I chose the same day to call in sick, so we had the whole day together, there in the bedroom, she working on her possessions and I on a new novel tentatively entitled *Chaucer Takes a Bath*, more about which later. Well, it happened that during that day she smiled at me a lot and I noticed for the first time—somehow I had missed them—these enormous teeth of hers. Really big teeth, I mean *really big!* And they were shaped okay, they weren't bent or hooked or anything like that, but they were quite large, you know? Big as billboards! Sitting right there in her mouth as if nothing had happened! "Why didn't you have them cut off?" I asked. "Surely you knew they were overlarge? Surely you noticed? And where was your mother? Surely *she* noticed? Of what, my dim-witted Wichita Woman, could you and she have been thinking?" When I finished she sat very still for a minute and I knew that I had said too much or been too forceful or something. I knew that I had opened something or other and that something was going to come out and that whatever it was it wasn't pleasant. In that split of a second as we sat there silently I wished that I had been a bit more casual, and I wished, seeing the raindrops of sorrow fall on her face and ripple the radiance of this special day, seeing the glow go, replaced with rotten memories of childhood, with pictures of rashes and perspiration and the foul breath of an empty stomach, then I wished that whatever it was that had been the case had not been the case, that Panda did not have this thing in her history that gave her so much pain, and that now that I knew she had it there I wished that we could get through it quickly so that the new pain to her would be minimal.

"My mother," she said slowly, "was a bitch. I hated her when I was a child. I hated what she was and I loved what I wanted her to be. I hated her when she fucked up my image, and she did that repeatedly. I was a child. She drank. She slept with a thousand men. I would come home from school and find her on the couch with some fuck she'd picked up, some toad with the filth of a night or two in his pockets and the manners of a clown in a hospital. She was always wearing a slip, that was her idea of decorum—or maybe it wasn't. God knows—but inevitably it was wound up round her hips when I arrived. There were bottles on the floor and glasses, clothes and magazines, bitten legs of chicken and crumbs of cake left there from the last time and picked up again as if only a minute had gone by, not a day or a week. And there were new men at night, a different kind of men, cheaper or less cheap— I can't remember. I sat there in our room trying to do math, a sad ugly little girl wanting, in the numbers, to salvage some sense of quality, wanting to feel something in common with the pretty little girls in my class, maybe wanting to better them in arithmetic if I couldn't claim a better home life. And I couldn't. Boy, how I couldn't. I would ask mother for help with these stupid problems and nine times out of ten she was so drunk that she could hardly remember the numbers much less add or subtract them. So I sat there and some dim pecker of a truck driver would ring up and come over, or just come over unannounced, and the two of them would get into mother's bed, behind the sheet she had tacked to the ceiling so that I wouldn't see what went on there, and then they would go after one another with low moans and groans and cautious whispers. A symphony of cautious whispers with a wizard at the baton. That was my mother, the wizard. At intermission mother would come out from behind the screen and waltz to the bath and then the kitchen. She might get a couple of bottles of beer from the icebox and then, on her way back to the bed, she would say 'Hello Luv, everything all right?' in as straight a voice as she could muster considering that she had inside her right at that point enough sperm and alcohol to open the first combination brewery and artificial insemination clinic on the Continent. Of course I said yes, everything was all right, even though it most assuredly was not. And when I realized that she wasn't going to stop it, when I realized that it was going to be this way for her for the rest of her days, and for me too if I stayed, then I left and went to live an extraordinarily clean and wholesome life with my father in New Berlin, New York. That life was ultra-structured, and though nobody cared much about me and I had to pay for my keep with a plague of small chores, it was better by far than the other.

"That was my big mistake. Leaving her has turned out to be the only thing I regret in my life. When I began to understand mother's problem I began to hate myself for having left her to suffer it alone. There had been no alternatives at the time, I know that, but still I have felt and do feel guilty. It doesn't make sense, I know, but I still weep and wail my contrition once a year on the date of her death. I still think that when she needed me I wasn't there—couldn't have been there, the possibility precluded by my being me. Perhaps that fact, that I couldn't, was not capable of being with her, that what now seems a right thing was prevented then by the very fact which would have made it appropriate, my being me, her daughter, flesh of her flesh and all that, perhaps this is the most offensive part of the whole thing. Perhaps this is why I cry every year, because in the end, on a massive human race scale, kind of in every case and each example everything is so entirely unlikely—nothing connects.

"And so," she said sighing and wiping her cheeks clean of the melted eyeliner, and with a little self-conscious laugh that said Well, there it is! "the story of my life, the short version. It is a cartoon, dear flat-footed Bodo, of a good heart."

I really don't remember how we got through the afternoon, quietly I guess. Her interest in Wichita Woman diminished considerably, I recall, and the day became one of those that you wish would hurry up and get done with so that you could go to sleep and start again. And in the end that is exactly what happened.